HOME IS WHERE THE ART IS

ABOUT THE AUTHOR

Doris Banowsky Arrington, Ed.D., ATR-BC, is a licensed clinical psychologist and professor and chair of the Art Therapy Psychology Department at the Notre Dame de Namur University of California. This department awards master's degrees in both art therapy and marital and family therapy. Dr. Arrington has authored or supervised 35 funded art therapy grants. She has produced and edited 25 videos of the life histories of presidents and pioneers in art therapy for the American Art Therapy Association, Inc. (AATA) in addition to authoring six manuals and a number of articles and chapters on an art therapy approach to family therapy. Dr. Arrington, a member of the editorial board of The Arts in Psychotherapy, is the recipient of the Honorary Life Member award from the Northern California Art Therapy Association, the Distinguished Service Award from AATA, and the Outstanding Educator Award from the University of San Francisco. Currently, she is a member of a medical team that works in Kiev, Ukraine serving children and advising state and private shelters and orphanages. Her clinical and research areas of interest include family influences on basic visual constructs and symbolic schemas in both Western and Eastern cultures. Dr. Arrington is married with three sons and seven grandchildren.

HOME IS WHERE THE ART IS

An Art Therapy Approach to Family Therapy

By

DORIS BANOWSKY ARRINGTON, Ed.D., ATR-BC

Art Therapy Psychology Department
Notre Dame University of California
Belmont, California

Charles C Thomas
PUBLISHER • LTD.
SPRINGFIELD • ILLINOIS • U.S.A.

Published and Distributed Throughout the World by

CHARLES C THOMAS • PUBLISHER, LTD.
2600 South First Street
Springfield, Illinois 62704

©2001 by CHARLES C THOMAS • PUBLISHER, LTD.

ISBN 0-398-07160-8 (hard)
ISBN 0-398-07161-6 (paper)

Library of Congress Catalog Card Number: 00-066658

Printed in the United States of America
SR-R-3

Library of Congress Cataloging-in-Publication Data

Arrington, Doris Banowsky.
    Home is where the art is : an art therapy approach to family therapy / by Doris Banowsky
Arrington.
        p. cm.
    Includes bibliographical references and index.
    ISBN 0-398-07160-8 – ISBN 0-398-07161-6 (pbk.)
    1. Art therapy. 2. Family psychotherapy. I. Title.

RC489.A7 A73 2001
616.89′1656–dc21

00-066658

This book is dedicated to my family of origin, who fostered both creativity and courage; to my nuclear family, who created an environment of love and support; and my extended family with whom I continue to share ultimate concerns.

Special thanks goes to Amanda, Chris, Connor, Courtney, Rett, Ryan, and Wesley.

PREFACE

Family is never far away from therapy. When you work with children you work with family issues. When you work with adults you work with relationship issues. Image is never far away from either child or adult. My son, Chris, a school psychologist and an art therapist, reminds me often, "You can't work with kids without using art and most hurting adults have a little kid in there somewhere."

My original training was as an artist and art educator, and later as an art therapist. Still later, my training as a psychologist was in Jungian depth psychology and family therapy. This book, entitled *Home Is Where the Art Is—An Art Therapy Approach to Family Therapy,* reflects my three decades of clinical practice with children and their families, and adults and their families. During two of those decades, I have taught family art therapy and directed an art therapy psychology program that awards master's degrees in art therapy and marital and family therapy. With family therapists currently licensed in 50 states, more and more families or family members are being treated from a family systems approach. Communication, clearly not always verbal, is a major component in the success or failure of family relationships, not only in the nuclear family, but also over many generations. Therapists, using whatever means necessary to help family members communicate and repair, often turn to art. Written for students and professionals this book integrates the two approaches, art therapy and family systems.

- Art, in any age and in any country, is humanity's first model for sharing experiences and communicating meaning.
- Art therapy is a therapeutic treatment that incorporates the process of the client creating or selecting images, reflecting on the art, and interacting with a trained professional for assessment, communication, stress reduction, and intervention. The art process, the art product, and reflection on both are used to identify inner and outer attitudes, behaviors, dreams, experiences, feelings, and thoughts. It is often the treatment of choice for the young, the old, and all those in between who are unable to put their inner feelings in words.

- Family therapy, regardless of ethnicity or culture, is a systemic model of relationships. Its goal is to investigate the family system, repair areas that keep it from working, reinforce areas that do work, and reduce stress between members in the system or between a member and the system.
- Family art therapy combines "thinking systems" and "seeing systems," the two concepts of family therapy and art therapy.

Although much has been written on art therapy and much, much more literature exists on family therapy, few integrate the two theoretical approaches (Arrington, 1991; Kwiatkowska, 1975, 1978; Landgarten, 1981, 1987; Riley & Malchodi, 1994). Perhaps this is because a healing agent that introduces art making with its patterns and enactments as a modality for solving issues in, between, and about relationship is, in itself, a cognitive, behavioral, and intuitive paradox. If this is the case, then mental health professionals, of whatever theoretical orientation, might find it interesting to explore additional methods of applying cognitive behavioral paradoxical strategies in the therapeutic "process of reality construction, maintenance and change" (Sluzki, 1998, p. 417). In the case of introducing art, image-making, and creating for communication and relaxation, the brief, spontaneous, and even fun strategies enrich family therapy. They represent an unobtrusive offer to relate to and communicate with others (Gunter, 2000).

The structure of the book reflects my personal approach to art. My art media are painting and combining found objects. The structure of this book is also painterly, combining found objects. The overall theme of family can quickly be seen within it, but this theme is overlaid with art, archetypal patterns and meanings, and symbolic enactments. It is also interfaced with personality development, and in this "era of the brain," with neurobiological research.

The introduction begins with a brief epitome of Randy and his Dad and Stepmother. It continues by addressing the questions of what is art and art therapy. Chapter 1, "Family Art Therapy," looks at the marriage of art and family therapy, the clients, the goals, and art in family art therapy. It looks at the significance of how relaxation and "flow" are part and parcel of the creative process. It explores an integrative theoretical approach that incorporates three key perspectives of family art therapy: the historical, the interactional, and the existential perspectives. These three theoretical perspectives are expanded in a family art-based assessment with Sandy S. and her family.

Chapter 2 begins with the question: What is a family? It continues with a discussion of basic family functions and reparation of family problems, and looks at why marriages fail. Once again, we meet Randy, as his symbolic search for home leads through multiple divorces and remarriages. The chapter briefly addresses early development of family therapy and family art therapy. Another question, why integrate art and family therapy, is answered with an illustration of an attempted family art-based assessment with Gary and his family. The chapter concludes with a search for information about Anne, an individual who is also a family member.

Chapter 3 introduces the reader to the "Cycle of Love" and the family influences in personality development, seen in personality theorists and theories (e.g., Freud, Jung, attachment and object relations, Erikson, and Piaget). Stories about Michelle, Elizabeth, Tucker and Carl provide theoretical examples.

Since more and more family therapy practice includes violence associated with the unfilled basic human needs of nourishment and nurturing, Chapter 4, "The Cycle of Violence," begins with a discussion of violence and its effect on early childhood environments. The chapter explores broken trust in families where there is a lack of nourishment and nurturing. It includes stories about the homeless Chad and Bethanne, the shifted and reshifted Randy, and Nancy's horrific family experience.

Chapter 5 continues the theme of violence within families: Cathy and Sam experiencing painful failure as parents, and Andre, Barry and Clay, children witnessing domestic violence. The chapter ends with Anne revealing psychological violence in her life experiences.

Chapter 6, "The Cycle of Healing," includes a discussion of resilience illustrated by a variety of stories from an integration of family and art therapy. Stories about Sharri, Mary, Humberto, Jenny, Sallie, Ron, and Neal and Michael, Nancy, Anne and Randy complete the cycle of healing.

Appendix A is filled with the practical "how to's" of family art therapy, from general instructions on the gathering of materials, the basics of preparation, and clean up to where to go for information on professional ethics. Eight family art-based assessments are described.

Appendix B includes "how to" interventions. It begins with the "Life Cycle Log" and wordtapping and includes other techniques and interventions used with individuals in families, families, and family subsystems. "My Lifetime" was initiated by art therapist Jayne Rhyne (*Gestalt Art Therapy*, 1973). "The Value Garden" is an extension of a value clarification technique that I learned as a teacher (Simon, Howe & Kirschenbaum, 1972). The "Genogram" is a broadly used family therapy technique initiated by Bowen (1976). The rest of the techniques come from my own clinical and teaching experiences with input from clients, friends, peers, and students. I have included specific credits in the technique instructions.

Appendix C includes key terms and concepts of a select group of family therapy theorists. These include Satir, Bowen, Minuchin, Haley and Gottman.

INTRODUCTION

Just as in writing, when letters form words, and words form sentences that convey meaning, in visual art, color, lines, forms, movement, space, tones, and textures become part of a syntax, a visual syntax that represents preverbal and repressed memories encoded in early childhood. "This content is more likely to appear in symbolic images than it is in verbal form," says Lusebrink (1990, p. 127). Hence, words do not get in the way; instead, "images seem to shudder with life-giving energy" Gadon (1989, p. 324). For some, such as Andrew Wyeth, a renowned twentieth-century American painter, just doing art is healing; for others, a sponsor, an officient, a therapist is needed to help them focus on their special needs, culture, and experiences (Kwiatkowski, 1978).

Remembering his pain after the death of his father, Wyeth writes:

> I think in my life the real turning point—when the emotion thing really became the most important—was the death of my father. The first tempera I did after that is called "Winter 1946." It's a boy running, almost tumbling down a hill across a strong winter light, with his hand flung wide and a black shadow racing behind him, and bits of snow, and my feeling of being disconnected from everything. It was me, at a loss—that hand drifting in the air was my free soul, groping. Over on the other side of that hill was where my father was killed, and I was sick I'd never painted him. The hill finally became a portrait of him. I spent the whole winter on the painting—it was just the one way I could free this horrible feeling that was in me—and yet there was a great excitement. For the first time in my life, I was painting with a real reason to do it (cited in Corn, 1973, p. 58). (See Figure 1, Winter 1946 by Andrew Wyeth.)

WHAT IS ART?

Picasso asks, "What is not art?" Art is a Latin word defined as skill in performance, acquired by experience, study, or observation. With a describable

Figure 1. Winter 1946, by Andrew Wyeth.

form and achieved with competence, it is thought of an as embellishment of ordinary living that reflects emotion, intellect, and spirit (Webster's New World Dictionary, 1966).

Pre-scientific, universal, and intrinsic, visual art has pumped life and meaning through the veins of humanity, communicating, commemorating, exploring, obscuring, and transforming. It is and has always been accessible to all ages in all cultures, interfacing with the human soul, in the worship of the powerful and almighty creator, awesome parents, and fearful creatures. Then and now, the arts identify symbols of clan, gods, kin, nature, and trades. They peak interest, raise concerns, and identify subjects of adoration.

People of all ages and cultures use art as a language and a healing balm for psychological and physical pain. Art and image descend into the uncon-scious, stirring memories, empowering spiritual values, and healing loss. They engage the mind, body, and spirit of men, women, and children, opening each of us to "the life of soul" (Jung, 1966/1972, pp. 38–40). At no stage in the development of civilization has humanity been able to exist without art expression in the form of image and ceremony, or its outward form of social and conventional behavior.

Art engages human speakers who adapt natural things to their own use and hidden meanings: human speakers who develop skills and aesthetic tastes to create images and myths that interface with dance, drama, and rhythm. It is those images and myths that reflect not only the attitudes of the times in which we live, but instill in us courage to defeat our enemies, courage to motivate others and ourselves for success in other tasks of life, and courage to repair broken hearts and minds. One has only to remember the funeral processions of Princess Diana and Mother Teresa, watched by billions, to comprehend how archetypal rituals, with mysterious meanings, arouse, inform, heal, and sustain countries, communities, families, and individuals.

Why Therapy? Why Art Therapy?

No one comes to psychotherapy because he or she is feeling good. People come with symptoms, deeply immersed in psychic and somatic pain. They come because there has been an act or fact of losing, especially unintentional parting with someone or something of value. They come because they have lost human and spiritual connection, personal identity, opportunity, support, and soul (Gilligan, 1995).

The R. family sat in the counseling office that was complete with toys, a family of anatomically correct dolls, sand tray figures, Smurfs®, games, and a variety of art materials. From the outside, the small family unit appeared like any other small nuclear family. Randy, age five and a half, slumped in his chair, eyes clued to Dad. Dad, glum, looked from wife to son, to therapist, and then back again. Stepmother, eyes wide open, mouth pulled tight, sat looking like a deer caught in the headlights. She was ready to bolt.

Through an intake interview (a variety of written and oral questions), a genogram (a three-generational family tree [Bowen, 1978]; Appendix B-C), and a Family Art-based Assessment (Appendix A), I sought to discover the cast of characters in this family (Satir, 1972) and an answer to my internalized question, what had brought them to this place at this time? Dad, but mostly Stepmother, contributed information. Three months earlier, Randy had come to live with them. During that time the family life had become more and more painful. Randy's behavior had become unacceptable and punishment was not helping. Acting out at school, he fought and cursed other children, but when he was at home, and his Dad was away, he isolated himself in his room. A recent call from school that focused on Randy's behavior precipitated Stepmother calling for a counseling appointment.

While I talked with the adults, I sensed the tension that settled on and around the small boy whose feet dangled above the floor. Seeking to release the tension and engage Randy in the assessment process, I asked if he would

Figure 2. *Let's go home,* by Randy.

like to look around the room. While his parents and I continued talking, he slid out of his chair and walked from one group of toys to another. Picking up a puppet, he looked at it and then put it down. He buried a male figure in the sand tray and then he settled in front of the art table. Engaging him, I said simply, "Randy, would you like to draw?"

Randy picked up a red crayon and drew a house with windows and a door (Figure 2). He drew a small flower on the left side of the house and a large one with encapsulated (enclosed) roots on the right. In place of the sun, he put a smiling face. Like other children throughout the world whose moms, dads, brothers, sisters, and grannies (their significant attachments) have vanished from their daily lives, Randy was confused and grieving. I wondered what he was thinking. As I look back, I wonder if it wasn't "Why am I always wrong? I didn't do anything. Although I love Dad, I didn't ask him to bring me here." I am sure Randy was thinking about his home. But where was home? Where was his mom? Where was his brother? Was his brother safe with his stepfather? Why wasn't he at his grandmother's? She had a big house and he liked living with her. Finished with the painting, he turned and quietly said, "I want to go home."

What is home? For most people, home is a place of safety where one lives with loved ones called family. It is a comfortable dwelling place in one's native land. It is a place where one's heart feels warm and safe. Home is a place where one belongs.

In order for Randy, his dad, and his stepmother to communicate, to blend, to merge, to become a family that could live together in a home where each felt he or she belonged, they needed to be heard and treated fairly, with affection and concern. But young children are powerless. Adults around them provide the environment or the voice with which they both can participate. Often this requires professional help outside of the family. For families in all cultures, with children like Randy, family therapy from an art therapy approach is often the treatment of choice.

ACKNOWLEDGMENTS

This book could not have been written without the innovative art therapy work with families begun fifty years ago by Hanna Kwiatkowska. Trained in art, art therapy, and psychology, Ms. Kwiatkowska in the 1950s worked at the National Institute of Mental Health. During that time she identified the power art had in transforming families and family members and authored *Family Therapy and Evaluation through Art,* published in 1978 by Charles C Thomas. In the late 1970s, Ms Kwiatkowska came to Northern California to lecture about her work. The Art Therapy Program at the College of Notre Dame was just beginning and I was fortunate enough to talk to her about Family Art Therapy and its future. I am sure she could never have for seen how her approach would take hold and grow. For over 20 years, family art therapy has been used and broadened, not only at the College of Notre Dame, but also in colleges and universities throughout the United States.

I am grateful to my professional family at the California Notre Dame University (CNDU) and in the American Art Therapy Association; Drs. Frances Anderson and Carolee Stabno, who scaled tall buildings, red penciled chapters and performed other miracles; Dr. Valerie Appleton, Barbara Danielsen, Cay Drachnik, Elizabeth Ratcliffe, and Dr. Betty Jo Troeger, who over the twenty years that I have taught Family Art Therapy throughout the United States have helped me formulate this book; and Dr. Vince Fitzgerald, CND, who encouraged me from the beginning to write from the perspective of real people and their lives not just about the theory that helped improve their quality of life. While writing this book, colleague and friend Dr. Judy Rubin asked me if I liked what I was writing. As I now finish this book, it is pretty obvious that what I liked most was reporting on the stories of families and individuals in them that were influenced for healing in some way by the art they created.

Thanks go to members of my office staff, Dolores Kopesec, Loren Breithoff, and Jonathan Johnson, who consistently attended to projects and pressures while providing unlimited personal support. Jonathan's positive attitude and professional skills as a graphic designer and "high techer" were indispensable. Over the years graduate students at CNDU, Florida State University, Illinois State University and others across the country to whom I have taught family art therapy have been wonderful and generous with their contributions.

I am grateful to my co-family art therapy faculty members at CNDU, Drs. Arnell Etherington and Richard Carolan, who contributed both to this Family Art Therapy approach and to the environment that has made teaching at CNDU truly a privilege and a pleasure and to Sr. Roseanne Murphy who continues to be our art therapy guardian angel. Nancy Gallenti's wise and loving words kept me close to my thesis that creating art and image exercises the brain relaxes the mind and, after reflection, heals the soul. Dr. Peter Yorgin, one of my Ukrainian team-mates, and his beautiful wife Lisa, scanned, adjusted and cropped over one hundred photographs. Over and over, friends and family have generously given time, energy, and support.

I sincerely thank the following authors, publishers, and agents for permission to reprint their copyrighted materials: Frances Anderson; Foster W. Cline; Helen Landgarten; William Smith; Rachael Cherry, Elsevier Science Ltd. and *The Arts in Psychotherapy;* Open Court Publishing Company, a division of Carus Publishing Co., Peru, Illinois; *From The Inward Journey* by Margaret Fringe Keyes, 1983; John Gottman; Judith Rubin; Taylor & Frances; Charles C Thomas Publishers; John Wiley & Sons; Andrew Wyeth; and the North Carolina Museum of Art.

I deeply appreciate and honor the clients who have shared their struggles and images, and the following family members who wanted to share their story and art. These include Randy, Nancy, and Anne, Cathy and Sam, Sharri, Mary, Humberto, Jenny, Sallie, Ron, Michelle, Tucker, Carl, Mandy, Michael, Chris, JR, Walker, Sandi and her family, Beverly Stone and her case of Gary and his family, William Smith and his case of Neal, Michael and their mom, and Rachael Cherry, who works with children from violent homes.

I particularly want to thank Marsha Calhoun, who was always there when I needed help crossing my t's and dotting my i's.

It is an honor for this book to be published by Charles C Thomas, a publisher involved from the beginning in the establishment of the field of art therapy and family art therapy. I am grateful to Michael Thomas at Charles C Thomas Publisher for his belief and support in this book and in me. His warm and immediate responses were always a welcome relief.

Throughout the writing process, my husband, Bob, worked to keep a balance in our nuclear family by continually filling my time with family and family events. Thank you.

CONTENTS

ILLUSTRATIONS

TABLES

GENOGRAMS

The vignettes and stories used in this book are based on actual families and individuals in families with whom I have worked, supervised their treatment, or hold in the highest regard for the way they have lived their lives. These stories illustrate theoretical and clinical issues of family art therapy and sometimes to make the point, several cases are integrated. Except where an adult has requested, all names and circumstances have been changed to protect confidentiality. This is true of the illustrations as well. Some have been redrawn from lighter drawings, in hopes of allowing the reader to concentrate on the basics of visual language rather than the diversity of artistic complexity.

SPIRIT

As a woman in the roles of family art therapist, artist, administrator, psychologist, professor, wife, mother, grandmother, and lifelong family member, I have heuristically found that those ultimate concerns that guide and motivate my life, that help me to be with myself and others, relate to what I call SPIRIT. SPIRIT is acquired from both nature and nurturance, my genetic gifts and the nurturance that was provided or not provided in my early and ongoing environments filled with significant others known as family.

- The S in SPIRIT stands for *security,* the security I received or did not receive from my family of origin. The security I have or have not mastered in my abilities and skills. The security I have or do not have to live and to risk in love, work, and being.
- The P in SPIRIT stands for *purpose,* my individual and collective purpose in living; what I want to do with my life; my motivation at this time, in this place.
- The first I in SPIRIT represents personal *identity.* We ask ourselves, What is my identity? Does my history, my profession, or my family define me? Am I known because of where I come from or because I am intelligent, creative, wealthy, strange, caring? One radio commentator is known as "her son's mom." What are you known as?
- The R in SPIRIT stands for *relationships.* Relationships, primary and extended, form the center of SPIRIT: my center. As an individual, I am always in relationship, whether at work or in love. I am also in relationship with my image of and belief in a Supreme Being or higher force. I form and am formed by my relationships.
- The second I in SPIRIT stands for *images.* Every day I choose images to represent me: images of clothing, housing, and transportation, images that construct and display my faith, my gratifications, and my dreams. The images I consciously or unconsciously choose communicate my inner thoughts and feelings. The images in agencies, associations, and

institutions with which I choose to associate define my purpose, form my identity, and expand my relationships.
- Finally, the T in SPIRIT stands for how, over *time* and through experiences, as I age and become more experienced, sophisticated, foolish, or wise, my security, purpose, identity, relationships, and images are all *tempered* in one direction or another, positively or negatively. We have all heard the story of the person who found the barn half full of manure and whined, feeling cheated and victimized, while the next person immediately started looking for the pony.

Human beings live along an innate and learned SPIRIT-filled continuum. A work in process, it ranges from negative to positive, always forming, adapting, defining and responding to experience and relationships. With age, choices fall between the two extremes, bitter or better, and we are wise to query: What direction am I going?

HOME IS WHERE THE ART IS

Chapter 1

FAMILY ART THERAPY

F AMILY IS THE FRAMEWORK for human structure. Art and image are the canvas for its expression. "Family art therapy as the primary mode of treatment is certainly the most challenging and rewarding application of art techniques with families. However, it also demands a solid background in family therapy and extensive psychotherapeutic experience in addition to art therapy training," Hanna Kwiatkowska (1978, p. 137).

If someone wanted to know more about herself, she would focus on her internal thoughts and feelings and her external behavior. If she wanted to understand why she related to other people as she did, those with whom she lived and worked, she would focus on how her personality was shaped in the family and in the environment in which she was born and raised. It might help if she knew how her parents were raised, and how their parents were raised, and then their parents. Family, an ever-expanding circle of individuals in influential relationships, is the center of human development.

Therapy requires knowing both how and who to treat. It involves verbal and non-verbal language, needed both to acquire and process theoretical knowledge, and to gather information necessary for treatment. This book begins by looking at the "degree of fit and congruence" between family therapy and art therapy (Liddle, 1982). Family functions and dysfunctions will be explored as well as human language, encoding, and expression using words and images.

THE MARRIAGE OF ART AND FAMILY THERAPY

Family dynamics, communication and functions are the core component of family therapy (Connell, Mitten, & Whitaker, 1993). They shape and

3

reshape the past, present, and future of families and individuals in families. Image is the core component of art therapy. It is born of the creative process, shaped and reshaped for expression, communication, and meditation. When the two disciplines, family therapy and art therapy, are integrated into family art therapy, they do so sharing theoretical frameworks of personality development, family systems, and the art therapy process and product of non-verbal communication and reflection.

Nichols and Everett (1986) propose an integrative family systems theory that is a "good fit" for incorporating art therapy. It is a model integrating major theories of family systems, including among others those of Bowen (1978), Minuchin (1974), Haley (1973), and Satir (1972), in historical, interactional, and existential perspectives. Nichols and Everett's model refers to a system's origins, and functions developmentally. They propose that the *historical* perspective "views the individual or the family developmentally in relation to what has happened in the past to some member or members or directly to the family as a whole. The therapist is looking for a review of historical situations and data that create an emotional milieu that helps to connect the current context of the family with it living history." (p. 83)

Interactionally, the Nichols and Everett integrative model is "concerned with what a system looks like and how it behaves" (p. 117). It is both reciprocal and continual with its environment and in its informational feedback processes.

The Nichols and Everett *existential* perspective involves "being adequately responsive and sufficiently differentiated from the family at the same time so as to be able to carry out related tasks of being empathic with family members while consciously playing roles and conducting tasks appropriate to the therapeutic needs of the clients" (p. 84). This includes helping family members become responsible for their own lives, purposes, and potential.

Because major theories of family systems have been discussed thoroughly by their original authors as mentioned above, and in other texts (Becvar & Becvar, 1993; Goldenberg & Goldenberg, 1998), this book will provide only a brief overview of the theories and the interconnective patterns, concepts, goals, and terms shared between those theorists (Appendix C). In addition, a brief review of Gottman's (1998) theory of cognitive behavioral family therapy emphasizing the importance of repairing family relationships will be included, with a recommendation to consult the original source.

Humans and their family structures are works in process. Therefore, when a therapist works with a child, the therapist works with family issues. When he or she works with an adult, relational issues are interdependent with the ultimate concerns of love and work. Be they growth-oriented or problem-focused, the client's troublesome behaviors, concerns, and tensions have roots in family issues of attachment, communication, development, homeostasis and structure. These troublesome behaviors and tensions break, hurt, and destroy individuals and families. They may manifest in one or all of the following: negative behaviors toward family members and significant others; lack of responsibility; violent and self-serving behavior and; chemical abuse as well as normal and extraordinary life problems. Families and their influences, often identifiable in the client's art product are never, as some therapists may fear (Tomm, 1984), invisible. In cases of human emotional trauma, such as abandonment or physical or verbal abuse, basic trust within the human family is broken, and, like anything else that is broken, it must be repaired or replaced or eventually it will be discarded. When an individual suffers physical trauma, such as bodily injury due to accident or illness, the psyche is also wounded and must be repaired if the person is to continue to grow and develop. Further, when a family member suffers physical or psychological trauma, the entire family is psychically wounded.

The Client

Condensing and simplifying to make the point, the family's world view and interactional patterns regulate the behavior of its members. Therefore, family therapists treat individuals in a family or whole families from a systems perspective. That perspective includes professional knowledge of family structure, boundaries, interpsychic processes, and the influence of the therapist. Family art therapy treats similar clients from the same systemic model, with similar knowledge, but in addition it includes information gained in the clients' non-verbal communication, and seen in both their creative process and product. Family art therapists treat individuals within the family, subsystems of the family, or the whole family who are willing to use art media and image for communication, problem-solving, relaxation, self-soothing, self-observation, and reparation.

The Goals

Family art therapy goals are to provide time, materials, and a safe environment where therapeutic art procedures (spontaneous image-making, selecting of art media and materials, and when appropriate, verbal reflecting in response to questions specifically designed for this particular family or these individuals within their family and their culture) facilitate favorable personality changes and patterns. In such an environment, clients use the universal language of art and image for expression, in the process of relaxing, remembering, and recounting stressful or distressing experiences. The therapist, with the assignment of guiding and empowering, acts as a sponsor observing the clients' processes and, through questions and observations, paces their reflections. She brings into awareness interactions, or the lack of interactions, among family members, and between family members and the art materials, the therapist, and the therapy itself. The therapist assists the clients' reflection through her expert knowledge of creative expression, archetypal themes, and personal symbols that help or hinder each family member from finding acceptance, forgiveness regarding their past experiences, meaning in their present behaviors, and hope in their dreams of the future. Through visual expression of feelings and experiences, family art therapy facilitates not just surface changes, but second order changes, changes that affect both conscious and unconscious behavior.

THE ART IN FAMILY ART THERAPY

The art in family art therapy, both product and process, is a vehicle for communication. The experience of making art and the image itself allow all individuals in the creative process to be both "seen and heard," building trust in the therapy, the therapist, and in the participants' own sense of self. Spontaneous or directed art-making, with limited censorship, allows the communication of inner thoughts and feelings. Whether the art is symbolic or abstract, it is expression. From the beginning of time, as shown by the discovery of the Earth Mother of Willendorf and the Lascaux cave drawings, art-making has provided an ancient and universal language (Arrien, 1992, 1993; Arrington, Eslinger & Virshup, 1975; Ault, 1989; Campbell, 1972; Cirlot, 1962; Cornell, 1994; Gadon, 1989; Hammer, 1958/1967; Koplewicz & Goodman, 1999; Kris & Kurz, 1979; McMurray, 1988; Politsky, 1994; Shlain, 1998). The language is motivated by *play, desire* to soothe or to enrich the individual's environment, or *need* to communicate inner experiences and sacred feelings (Arrington, 1998; Bloomington, 1998; Dissanayke, 1992).

Images reflect collective and individual social experience, as well as inner realities and fantasies. The creative process and the art product link individual to family, family to culture, and culture to ageless humanity and collective divinity. Over the life span of humankind, themes and images have given insight into this symbolic and creative language. Since the beginning of time, humans have explored, focused, and depicted symbols of creation and the center of their world. They have created portable and wearable art with magic powers in the forms of treasures, totems, and sacred animals. They have created images of monsters as negative powers, and gods and goddesses as authority figures, benefactors, and heroes and heroines. They have depicted symbols of love relationships and sacred marriages, and they have honored hope, as demonstrated in their fascination with the inner or divine child. Humans have portrayed symbols of their need for assistance in savior figures, and their need for glory and honor in sacred kingships and vulnerable princesses. Both in the present and the past, humankind has created symbols of inter- and intra-duality, reconciliation, revelation, and transformation (Moon, 1991). Because creative expression narrows the attention span, it involves "some degree of dissociation and resultant cortical inhibition, similar to that which occurs in prayer and meditation" (Kroger, 1963/1977, p. 93). Therefore, it relaxes both the body and the mind.

Whereas the creative process itself is natural and ordinary, active and activating, it is also unique, engaging individuals, alone or even in large gatherings, in a state of self-forgetfulness or self-study. Through the process of selecting symbols and spontaneously expressing them, all individuals, consciously and unconsciously, communicate their inner feelings and attitudes. The images selected or created flow "through us like children" says McNiff (1992, p. 38), allowing observation and documentation of the creator and the creation in a step-by-step process.

Images express ultimate concerns: feelings of security or insecurity, individual and collective purposes, identities and relationships that, over time, have been tempered by experience. These creative products, two and three-dimensional visual constructs, provide concrete material for assessment, diagnosis, communication, and treatment (see Appendixes A and B).

Directed art, used therapeutically, imposes paradoxical and projective experiences on participants. These art therapy experiences and the images created provide structure for working alone and/or with others. Focusing cortical energy, they relax the creator, thus eliciting strong feelings or unconscious material that demonstrates both his or her weaknesses and strengths (Ulman, 1975). Through projective art processes, the expression, comprehension, and transmission of information within the family system is maximized, while allowing the therapist to remain "responsive and sufficiently differentiated" (Nichols & Everett, 1986, p. 86).

RELAXATION. Relaxation refers to reducing any physical stress that, in the long term, may block blood circulation, affect the immune system, and cause coronary disease or viral infections (Alder, Underwood, & Kolb, 1999) and in the short term may cause actual physical discomfort (Gottman, 1998). Relaxation also refers to the use of techniques that "fill stress management seminars, therapy sessions and the many books on the topic" (Sapolsky, 1998, p. 325). These techniques teach self-reliance, build self-esteem, and reduce dependency. Of significance to those interested in health and healing, creative expression and choice of media and subject promote physiological soothing, moving participants to their own appropriate and empowering outlets of self-soothing. Relaxation techniques that use images move clients either slowly or quickly, but directly, into deep experiences of "hope giving" (Sapolsky, 1998, p. 328), controlling the uncontrollable (p. 331) and what Sapolsky refers to as "John Henryism, having an internal lotus of control against incredibly negative odds" (p. 332). Art experiences bend and shape those who create while allowing those creators to operate at peak efficiency, to "zone out." Making, or even just looking at art allows individuals and groups "to flow," to be refreshed, and to be replenished (Arrington, 1998b; Csikszentmihalyi, 1990, 1999). Art and creative expression change how one sees the world and in a very real sense, they provide survival resources to the next generation (Bateson, 1991).

Used as a starting point for communication, the art process in family art therapy addresses life's issues and challenges, while the product provides a blueprint of family structure, subsets, boundaries, and an ongoing instrument of assessment. For example, an initial beginning for family art therapy is the introduction of an art directive. That directive, a family art-based assessment or protocol, could be as simple as "Draw whatever comes to mind," "Paint whatever you want," "Draw your lifeline," "Draw your marriage line integrating both positive and negative feelings and experiences," "Select your family from these pictures," "Make a picture of how it felt to grow up in your family," or "Draw how you present yourself to the world on the outside, and then how you think or feel on the inside." These and other directives open past, present and future perspectives for both visual and verbal expansions by all participating family members.

Today, in the diverse culture of Western society, ethnic sensitivity requires that family art therapists also engage clients by using cultural healing practices that are specific to their clients' ethnicity. Culturally-based art therapy might involve asking clients to draw a mandala incorporating both the positive and negative aspects of the relationship (Jung, 1964; Kellogg, 1978), asking clients to make a *retablo* (a drawing that includes a miracle experience, a hero identified, or a wish for something in the present or future) (Acton, 1998), asking clients to work together to build fish kites (Tolin, 1994), or even asking them to build a space animal with their children.

THREE KEY PERSPECTIVES OF FAMILY ART THERAPY

To facilitate working with a variety of issues and family constellations, family art therapy, building on the work of Nichols & Everett (1986), integrates three similar perspectives (Arrington, 1991) that include the interconnection and interdependence of a variety of personality and family theories with art as communication, assessment, diagnosis, and treatment.

The Historical Perspective relates to personal history as it reflects on current concerns. This perspective includes knowledge and understanding of the following elements:

- Creativity and archetypal symbols and themes (Arieti, 1976; Arnheim, 1954/1974, 1969; Cane, 1951; Cirlot, 1962; Jung, 1933/1955; 1954/1974; Moon, 1991; Scarre 1993).
- Art development (basic visual constructs) and significant understanding of ethnic, idiosyncratic, and regressive qualities in the artistic expression (Altschuler & Hattwick, 1947/1967; Anderson, 1992; Arrington, 1986; Drachnik, 1995; Furth, 1988; Kellogg, 1969-1970; Lowenfeld, 1957; Lusebrink, 1990; Troeger, 1992; Ulhin, 1972).
- Personality development theorists (Bowlby 1969/1982; Brazelton, 1990; Bronfenbrenner, 1979; Erikson, 1963; Freud, 1905; Jung, 1954/1974; Mahler, Pine & Bergman, 1975; Piaget & Inhelder, 1969).
- Art therapy theorists (Keyes, 1983; Kramer, 1958; Kwiatkowska, 1975, 1978; Landgarten, 1981; Naumburg, 1966; Rhyne, 1973; Rubin, 1978; 1987; Ulman, 1975; Wadeson,1980).
- Family therapy theorists (Bowen, 1978; Gottman, 1994, 1996, 1998; Haley, 1973/1976/1984; Knudson-Martin, 1994; Minuchin, 1974; Palazzoli, Boscolo, Cecchin & Prata, 1978; Papp, 1983; Satir, 1964/1967, 1972; Tomm, 1984).

The Interactional Perspective consists of:

- Creative participation and relaxation (Arrington, 1985; Brown & Smith 1992; Campbell, 1972; DeLue, 1994; Kellogg, 1978; Kramer, 1987; Progroff, 1980; Rhyne, 1973).
- Observing client behavior and images as they relate to family of origin and present family concerns (Arrington, 1992; Buehlman, Gottman & Katz, 1992; Burns & Kaufman, 1972; Landgarten, 1981, 1987; Keyes, 1983; Kwiatkowska, 1975, 1978; Wilcoxon, 1987).
- Identifying issues with the therapist (Connell, Mitten & Whitaker 1993; Gottman, 1993; Haley, 1973; Jung, 1963; Minuchin, 1974; Rhyne, 1973; Satir, 1964/1972).
- Identifying client interaction with time, space, materials, process and product (Betensky, 1973; Kwiatkowska, 1976; Lusebrink, 1990).

The Existential Perspective consists of verbal and graphic expression as it relates to:

- Ultimate concerns of the client(s) (Frankl, 1984; Hillman, 1996; Jung, 1954/1974; Moore, 1992; Seppa, 1997; Simpkinson & Simpkinson 1993; Simpkinson, Simpkinson & Solari, 1995).

• Reflections by the therapist (Arrington, 1991, 1998; Bridges, 1980; Callagan & Rawls, 1993; Gilligan, 1995; McNiff, 1998; Moon, 1994).

The following story of the Smith family uses a modified family art-based assessment (FABA) integrating the three perspectives to assess family development. (For a comprehensive review of this case, see Chapter 5 of *Art for All the Children,* Second Edition, by Frances Anderson.)

FAMILY PORTRAITS AND MURALS

The Smith Family–A Family Art-Based Assessment

The original call was from mother, who reported that Sandy, her five-year-old daughter, and the family had been referred to a female family art therapist by Sandy's male psychiatrist. Mother noted that school records indicated that there was a two-year discrepancy between Sandy's age and scholastic ability and she was not improving.

Treatment began with the whole family in a formal verbal interview, construction of a genogram (a family tree; see Appendix B, Intervention C), and a family art-based assessment (FABA; see Appendix A-3). In gathering family historical information and identifying family behavior patterns, the therapist's initial approach was similar to that of a constructionist model. In this model, the therapist takes a "non-expert, not-knowing" position, one of a respectful listener who does not understand too quickly and encourages family members to tell their stories (Christensen Russell, Miller, & Peterson, 1998, p. 18). After this joining process, the therapist, by pacing questions and stories, facilitates a safe and fair environment that encourages individual and family remembering, retelling, dreaming, and hoping (Satir, 1972).

The family genogram indicated that Dad, an only child, was 15 years older than Mom. Raised by his widowed mother, he had three children from a previous marriage and two children in this union. Currently, he cared for Sandy and her brother while Mom worked. In addition to receiving funds from his father's trust, he led hunting and fishing trips. Mom, from a large family, held a highly responsible job in a local technology firm.

FROM THE HISTORICAL PERSPECTIVE–FAMILY HISTORY

Modifying Rubin's (1978) family art-based assessment (FABA, Appendix A-3), the family art therapist used a free picture, a family portrait by each of

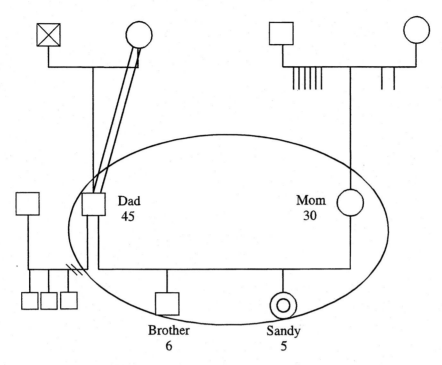

Genogram 1. Smith Family. (Bowen, 1978; Carter & McGoldrich, 1980).

the four family members, and a mural that members of the family completed together. Art materials provided included 12 by 24 inch white paper, markers, chalks, oil pastels, and crayons.

First Art Task: Draw Whatever Comes to Mind

The first task in the FABA was nondirective, *Draw a free picture.* Nondirective tasks reduce tension and relax participants, allowing them to be in control and draw whatever they want (Schmidt, 1998).

Researching the question, to what extent does art used in therapy act as a relaxant, Baker (1986) found that when art was carried out prior to written language assignments, it served as a relaxant. As a relaxant, it allowed the improvement of cognitive abilities of learning disabled children in both written language and reading. Through monitoring heart rates and skin temperature, DeLue (1994), supported by Folken (1998), found the creation of mandalas to be significantly more physiologically relaxing for elementary school children than participating in puzzles. Cohen (1994) measured the number of angles found in the drawing of mandalas to determine signs of tension, anger, or pain. She found that adolescents in psychiatric residential care who engaged in the creation of mandalas experienced a reduction in anxiety and agitation. Schmidt (1998) working with adults in a partial hospitalization program, found that non-directed art tasks in groups reduced stress levels significantly more than directed art or written tasks.

Dad began with a lime green marker and drew two hills with a flowing stream between the hills (Figure 3). Across the base of the hills he drew a small, brown, continuous fence with seven fir trees on the left-hand side. He filled in the hills with a light green crayon and labeled his drawing, *The Hills*.

Mom used crayons to draw a rainbow low on the page with seven birds above (Figure 4). Under the rainbow, Mom placed a transparent boat heading to the left and a small fir tree. A brown ground line extended partially across the water. She labeled her picture *Fishing under the Rainbow*.

Brother encapsulated his picture (contained it within a frame). He used a black marker to draw the frame around the picture and inside the frame, he identified with Dad and drew four sharply pointed mountains (Figure 5). He filled one half of one of the mountains in with black. The other mountains he colored with blue chalk. He placed two clouds over the mountains, with three lightning bolts coming down to the mountains. He completed his picture with small green grass marks across the bottom of the picture representing grass. Using a brown marker, he wrote his title, *The Mountein plase,* on one of the mountaintops.

Sandy, using oil pastels and markers, followed Mom's lead, drawing a picture she called the *Rainbow House* (Figure 6). Mom wrote the title on the paper. The rainbow house was a square with four round, encapsulated heads floating on the right side. Sandy used a black marker to give the impression of writing around the edges.

Second Art Task: Family Portrait

Exploring the comfort level of this family in relation to each other, the second picture the participants were asked to draw was a *family portrait*. Because family portraits include family relationships that encourage recalling family experiences, they often build tension. This tension is reflected in the art by omissions, encapsulations, erasures, corrections, or past memory inclusions.

In chronological order, Dad used a brown marker to draw Mom's head (Figure 7). He used dark blue for Sandy's head, green for Brother's head, and black with red ears for his own head. All heads floated, and went from large to small beginning with Mom to Sandy, to Brother, and then Dad.

Using crayons, Mom encapsulated the family in a transparent green house with a chimney and smoke (Figure 8). Outside, on the left, she used a black marker to draw a small doghouse. Then she changed to crayon to draw two dogs, a brown one and a black one, and a large red flower. On the right

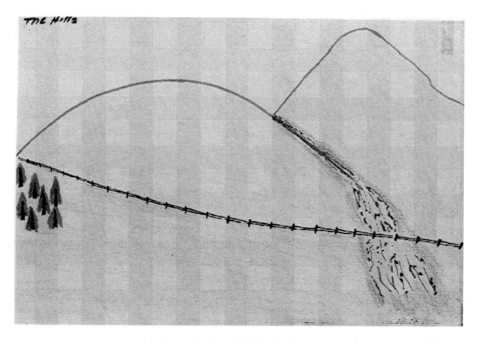

Figure 3. *The Hills* by Dad.

Figure 4. *Fishing under the Rainbow* by Mom.

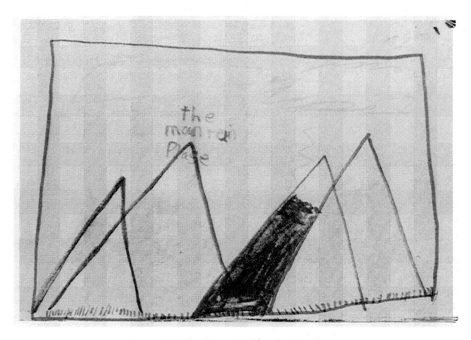

Figure 5. *The Mountein Plase* by Brother.

Figure 6. *Rainbow House* by Sandy.

side she drew two large red flowers. Inside the house she drew a fire in the fireplace, and a TV. She placed herself encapsulated on the couch and Dad smiling in his recliner. She used red dashes to represent steps to the second floor where Sandy and Brother were both encapsulated in what Mom referred to as their beds. Her figures were drawn at the developmental level of a latency-aged child.

Starting on the left-hand side of the paper, Brother used a brown crayon to draw Sandy, fully dressed, with hands, fingers, and eyelashes (Figure 9). Next he drew a stick figure of himself, perhaps one-third the size of his sister. He put himself between his sister and his Dad, who was drawn twice as large as his sister. His dad had no face or feet, and a circle represented his large stomach. Brother colored in Dad's genital area in the shape of a small square.

Using pastels, Sandy drew four heads with legs, one without a face, and a large pink flower encapsulated under a pink and blue mountain (Figure 10). She wrote her name across the top and covered it with black crayon.

Third Art Task: Joint Mural

For their third art task, the family was asked to create a *Joint Mural* on a 3-by-5 foot piece of butcher paper (Figure 11). Joint murals give a family art therapist an opportunity to observe coalitions and how family members work together.

Without prior discussion, this family began drawing. Mother began with a face, eyes, eyelashes, a nose and mouth, and pink cheeks. She looked up and saw that Dad was drawing geometric shapes. She stopped and began drawing her own shapes, a triangle protruding into a circle. Dad in the mean-time drew a box in perspective, a triangle, and then two more boxes. Broth-er had started with a house on the same side with Dad. Then Brother moved to the end and drew a racecar on large wheels. Sandy, sitting next to her mother, drew a large circle and encapsulated seven small circles. At the bot-tom she drew a smiling face. Next to her mother's art, Sandy drew a large phallic candle shape. Than she moved over toward the corner of the paper, where she created a cascading waterfall splashing onto the racecar that Broth-er was drawing.

When asked to name the mural, Mother looked around and quickly announced, "We can call it the *Smith Family Creation.*" No other family mem-ber commented or disagreed.

Creativity, Archetypal Symbols, and Themes

Early humans recorded their very existence through observing and cre-ating decorative art, musical sounds and rich ceremonial life. They adapted

Figure 7. *Family Portrait* by Dad.

Figure 8. *Family Portrait* by Mom.

Figure 9. *Family Portrait* by Brother.

Figure 10. *Family Portrait* by Sandy.

Figure 11. *The Smith Family Creation* by members of the Smith Family.

natural things to their own use and enjoyment developing collective and aesthetic tastes. They created sacred sites with images and myths that reflected their ultimate concerns. Their faith and religions were born from humanity's "fundamental passion to express inner life" (Gadon, 1989, p. 3). Art interfaced and continues to interface with dance, drama, and rhythm to create a language for communicating the height and depth of life's mysteries. That language is contained in major archetypal themes embedded in the symbol systems of all cultures (Cirlot, 1962; Cooper, 1978; Fontana, 1993; Jung, 1964; Walker, 1988). Archetypal themes often bring up questions that shed a new or different light on finding meaning in the art. In order to understand the influences that art expression, images, and symbols may have in family therapy, it is important for the therapist to recognize archetypal symbols and themes, and the meanings they have for their clients.

Anthropologist Angie Arrien (1993) researched the origins of over 1,200 different symbols to learn about the consistency of meaning given to each symbol by the different societies in which it is found. She identified five basic shapes that appear in the art of all cultures: circle, square, triangle, cross, and spiral (p. 12). "Each shape shares a universal meaning, i.e., the circle symbolizes wholeness; the square, stability; the triangle, goals, and dreams; the cross, relationships; and the spiral, growth" (p. 12). These symbols have been and continue to be incorporated in images of humans and beasts. These and other images have always been part of culture, religious rituals, and sacred sites.

In Sandy's family, the male members' symbols and themes were mountains, the triangular-shaped mountain that symbolizes inner loftiness of spirit, and the center of the world where creation by mother earth began (Arrington, 1986). Were Dad and Brother limited to their own perspectives of life, distanced by negative thoughts about mother figures (Dad's fence that cut across two breast-like mountains and Brother's sharp and cold mountains)? Had the two males perceived either of their mother figures as being instrumental in cutting off their goals and dreams?

Female themes in this family were rainbows. The rainbow is often seen as the bridge between heaven and earth representing a covenant of faith (Arrington, 1986). Because rainbows encapsulate pictures or portions of pictures in which they appear, they can be seen as protection from the environment, and reflect isolation and fear. "Hardin found that 8.5% of molested children, regardless of age, spontaneously added rainbows to their human figure drawings. Females did this more than males" (Peterson & Hardin, 1997, p. 134). Did Mother and Sandy need protection in their home?

Major Theories of Personality Development

Early in the twentieth century, Margaret Naumburg (1966), trained in both Freudian and Jungian theory, came to believe that the analytic process of art-making brought unconscious material into awareness. She worked originally with children and later with adults and groups. Building on the work of Freud and Jung, Naumburg explored the inner personal meaning of symbols. She believed that the unconscious was made conscious through art expression. Explaining the process of dynamically-oriented art therapy, Naumburg noted that it was based on the recognition that a person's fundamental thoughts and feelings are derived from the unconscious and often reach expression in images rather than in words. Wilson (1987), supporting Naumburg and Beres (1965), found that images developed in a "hierarchy of perceptual experiences" (p. 48), along with personality, served both adaptation and communication (p. 57). In the case of young Sandy, we see her developmental art ability was at the three-year-old level whereas her chronological age was six. An art therapist would note this discrepancy and look for significant trauma while exploring Sandy's life experiences when she was three.

Theories of Change and Healing as Seen in Both Art Therapy and Family Therapy

The process of therapeutically facilitating the making of art and image by children, adults, or family units provides timely information that is not otherwise accessible (Anderson, 1992; Appleton, 1989; Arnheim, 1969; Arrington, 1986; Drachnik, 1995; Gantt & Tabone, 1998; Goleman, 1995; Hammer 1958/1967; Hays & Lyons, 1981; Howowitz, 1970; Jung, 1964; Kaiser, 1996; Kaplan, 1997; Kellogg, 1978; Kwiatkowska, 1975, 1978; Levick, 1983; Lowenfeld, 1957; Lusebrink, 1990; McKim, 1980; Miller, 1990; Naumburg, 1966; Peterson & Hardin, 1997; Rhyne, 1973; Rosal, 1992, 1996; Rubin, 1978; Troeger, 1992; Ulhin, 1972; Wadeson, 1980).

Research defines the efficacy of the gestalt isomorphic principle that art expression can be an external expression of an internal or feeling state. The isomorphic principle substantiates the parallel process of the structure and content of an art piece and the affective and cognitive processes of the individual who created it (Brudenell, 1989; Drachnik, 1995; Shagman, 1996; Ulhin, 1972).

Dad's free picture, *The Hills* (Figure 3), was drawn with seven trees and two large mounds that possibly represent the seven members of his nuclear family and his mother. Free-flowing nourishment flows in a stream between the mounds. The fence across the bottom of the mountains is unusual. It looks like a stitched wound. As the therapist reviewed the family portraits, she was concerned about Dad's self-esteem. His head is the smallest and in his drawing of Sandy, she is represented as a teenager. Does the art reveal a break in his relationship with his mother? Is there an issue between Dad and Sandy? Dad gives more power to Mom and Sandy, whom he drew first and second and larger, than he does to Brother and himself.

Mom's free picture, *Fishing under the Rainbow* (Figure 4), has a small boat with its antenna up, returning to the past (going left rather than right and the future). The boat looks small and isolated. Mom's family portrait is a transparent house. The therapist wondered what Mom wanted to reveal about this house. All figures are compartmentalized and encapsulated, some twice, providing boundaries and protection from their environment. Individual figures are underlined, making them more important than others. This combination of visual syntax, far outside of the normal range of drawings, is indicative of a need for protection (Peterson & Hardin, 1997, p. 61). Mom's art, drawn at the level of a latency-aged child, communicates a desire to tell someone about something that happened when she was a child. It also indicates a need for protection, but protection from whom?

Brother's free picture, *The Mountein Plase* (Figure 5), has excessively sharp mountains with cold-looking snow. By drawing mountains like his father did, Brother established a gender coalition with his Dad. He colored one of his four mountains black. As questioned earlier, does this represent a negative picture of his mother? He colored Dad's genital area. What was his purpose for sexualizing Dad? The three figures are not grounded, but floating. Reviewed together, all of these cues suggest the need for further investigation (Peterson & Hardin, 1997).

Sandy's picture, messy, overlaid with color, and developmentally delayed, is also encapsulated. Did Sandy need protection in her environment? She established a gender coalition by naming her drawing *The Rainbow House,* (Figure 6). Her family portrait is peculiar because of the regressed figures (Figure 10). Her ego-self axis, as defined by Allan and Bertoia (1992), is out of alignment, indicating that Sandy's needs are not being met. Sandy's art indicates that she is having trouble holding her world together. From the family mural (Figure 11), it would appear that each family member is disconnected and the children have needs that are not addressed.

A second kinetic family drawing (K-F-D) drawn by Sandy during the following week was even more disturbing (Figure 12). In it, the family members are encapsulated and compartmentalized in boxes. All figures are distorted and regressed. The brother's head is in the right box. The girl's head is in the left box and the parents' heads are in the right box. The boxes are floating and the art media is smeared. The peculiar quality of the drawing and the distorted figures provide visual clues that further investigation is needed. Sandy has no sense of her own physical development. Her art, however, is a vehicle for communication and provides a way she and the therapist can join.

Knowledge of Art Development (Basic Visual Constructs)

The last content area under the historical perspective is having knowledge of art development (basic visual constructs) and the significance and differences of ethnic, idiosyncratic, and regressive qualities in artistic product.

Viktor Lowenfeld (1957), an internationally renowned scholar in art education, built on the work of pioneers in art education and art therapy (Alschuler & Hattwick, 1947/1967; Arnheim, 1954/1974; Bender, 1938; Cane, 1951; Goodenough, 1926; Naumburg, 1950; Prinzhorn, 1972; Read, 1958; and Schaefer-Simmern, 1948). He researched stages of artistic development and their significance, and concluded that creative activity assists in mastering difficult situations and in providing emotional outlets for the many frustrations encountered in growing and developing.

As the Smith family's art therapist reviewed Dad's drawing of heads in his family portrait, she saw that Dad had drawn at an adult level (Figure 7). However, because he drew only heads, he appeared out of touch with, or in denial of, his body. This possible denial was further evidenced in Dad's extreme physical obesity. Reviewing Mom's figures in her family portrait, the stick figures appeared to have been drawn by someone in a latency developmental stage (Figure 8). In Brother's figure drawings in his family portrait, Sandy and Dad, who were drawn in an age-appropriate manner, appeared more important than the minimally drawn stick figure he indicated was him. Brother did not include his mother in his family portrait.

Figure 12. *My Family* by Sandy, age 6.

As the therapist reviewed six-year old Sandy's body concept in her art, she noted that Sandy was drawing in a three-and-a-half to four-year-old age range (Figure 10). Anderson (1992) notes that "a child must have a concept before she can draw representationally" (p. 26). A child who has a distorted and confused concept will draw distorted and confused pictures.

Hardin's (Peterson & Hardin, 1997) researched data on the screening inventory for children's human figure drawings (HFD) indicates seven serious indicators of sexually abused children. These include explicit drawing of genitals, concealment of genitals, omission of the genital regions and the central part of the figure, encapsulation of the drawing, fruit trees added, and drawing of the sex opposite that of the artist. In addition, indicators from the research of Jolles (1964/1992), Koppitz (1968), and Osler and Gould (1987) include tiny figures, distortion or poor integration of body parts, hands cut off, omission of peripheral parts of figures, belly button added or emphasized, big hands, transparency, and jagged teeth. Mailloux (1998) examined graphic indicators of sexual abuse in the HFDs of latency-age children. She found six statistically significant indicators that occurred more often with the sexually abused children. These included (1) figures drawn on the bottom edge of the paper, (2) light line pressure, (4) small figure size, (5) large arms and hands, and (6) body distortions.

Comparing kinetic family drawings (Burns & Kaufman, 1972) of children who have been identified as sexually abused to KFDs of a control group, Powell (1997) found that children who had been sexually abused scored considerably higher and showed more sexual abuse indicators than the control group. Powell's study found that several of Burns and Kaufman's (1972) indicators were valid as sexual abuse indicators for his population of children. These included compartmentalization, encapsulation, and bird's-eye views (looking from a distance). Bird's-eye view drawings occurred only in the identified group and highest scores were in the girls' drawings. Powell suggests that this could possibly be linked to dissociation experiences. Dissociation, a common defense mechanism the brain uses to separate itself from a traumatic event, is often described by sexual abuse victims as being above a situation or looking through a tunnel where everything looks small. Research in art therapy indicates that through the use of art, client denial and defensiveness are reduced, thereby enhancing communication and promoting relaxation. These are significant benefits for using art with family members. Through research, art as therapy has been identified as the treatment of choice for both children and victims of post-traumatic stress disorder (PTSD) (Goleman, 1995, p. 211). Research is continuing to affirm this concept (Chapman, 1998).

FROM THE INTERACTIONAL PERSPECTIVE

Facilitating Client Participation

The interactional perspective of the family art therapy model relates to pioneer Edith Kramer's (1958, 1974, 1987) therapeutic value of the art processes. Working mainly with children, Kramer stressed the importance of the therapeutic value of the art process, and described the art therapist's task as one of integrating the client's manual, intellectual, imaginative, and emotional faculties.

This perspective also relates to Eleanor Ulman's (1975) theoretical view of art as motivation for inner healing and organization (p. 14), and to Kwiatkowska's (1975) theoretical view of the importance of the art process in exploring culture, experiences, and needs in relationships. The artwork is concrete evidence of the family's interactional performance.

Client Behavior as it Relates to Family of Origin or Present Family Concerns

Reviewing archetypal symbols as they appeared in their art, the family art therapist noted that both Sandy's Dad and Mom appeared to continue to be influenced by their families of origin, if only unconsciously. Dad's free picture, *The Hills* (Figure 3), indicated a wounded relationship with his mother.

Both of Mom's individual art tasks referred to the past (Figure 4). *Fishing under the Rainbow,* with the boat facing left, was a return to her past. Her family portrait (Figure 8), drawn at the skill level of a latency-age child, was reflective of latency-age memory.

The FABA provided direct observation of the family working together and how they felt about being in that family. Dad's interactions with the family were cognitive. He was in denial (Levick, 1983) of body issues. When Mom retreated to take care of her animals rather than staying with the family, she may have been interacting with her family in the way that she had learned in her family of origin.

The interview was held in the family home, which was neat and clean. All family members appeared to understand and interact appropriately with the therapist and in the art tasks. Relaxed and cooperative, they drew voluntarily, taking the directives seriously. Mom and the children were more open than Dad to reflecting on the process. The children, ages five and six, were age-appropriately active and verbally expressive, but verbally negative to each other. The children argued, bickered, and whined over space, materials, and attention from parents throughout the interview session. Sandy was excessively verbal.

FROM THE EXISTENTIAL PERSPECTIVE

Ultimate Concerns of the Client

In family art therapy, the existential perspective consists of facilitating both verbal and graphic expression as they relate to ultimate concerns and the human spirit of each of the clients. Because of its developmental role in the formation and functions of persons, Nichols and Everett (1986) see the family as an integrative and existential system. Existential philosophy is described as dealing with the ultimate concerns of existence. Existentialism refers to the ontological context of existing or being-in-the-world. It is dedicated to liberating humanity from its denial of inescapable anxieties, fears, and shallow routines through validating the ultimate concerns of freedom, meaning, isolation, and death (Moon, 1994).

All humans who have not been deeply scarred have what Simpkinson and Simpkinson, (1993) and Simpkinson, Simpkinson and Solari (1995) refer to as ultimate concerns. Ultimate concerns have to do with such questions as, Why am I here? What is my meaning? What is my purpose? What do I contribute to the human community? What do life and death mean to me? What motivates me? When no one else is around, what do I think about? What is the dumbest thing that I ever did? I had a reason for doing it, fear, ignorance, entitlement, love; what was it? What would I give up my life for, or more importantly, what would I live for? Alice Miller (1990) found that her spontaneous paintings helped her discover her early family history and the meaning of her life, freeing her of compulsive behaviors caused by her upbringing and training. The meaning of life, for Jung, was the realization of the self, the self that flows from the concept of the inner experience of divinity (Acton, 1998).

"To survive in these struggles calls for focused awareness in the passionate and active engagement with life as it is" (Moon, 1994, p. 7). The therapist recognizes and values this engagement with life, the struggle and suffering, the physical and emotional experience, and the expression. In times of crisis, individuals and their spouses, children, and all extended family members (parents, brothers, sisters, grandparents, aunts, uncles, and close friends) have the freedom to choose how they will accept life, just as they have the freedom to choose its subsequent process of acceptance, change, reparation, or resistance. Gilligan (1995) challenges therapists, saying that "our job as therapists is to sponsor the development" of the human soul: our own, our clients,' and those with whom we come in contact daily.

In the case of the Smith family and Sandy, the therapist assisted by providing a safe environment where together, the family could focus in new and varied ways, cultivate their senses through touching, smelling, and seeing, while creating images that helped them relax and remember. This kinetic process of creating literally allows blood and oxygen to flow into blocked areas of the spinal cord and the brain, stimulating and repairing neurons stunted by trauma and time. Because the creation is a substantive product, it not only can be explored but it can be revisited again and again. Unconsciously, Sandy and members of her family created images, nurtured by therapy, that probed abandoned or untraveled cortical territories. Eventually those images overflowed with meaning that facilitated dreams, hope and knowledge of our interdependence on our understanding of a higher being.

Whereas humans long for this Holy Grail (Johnson, 1974), this sense of a significant purpose in both meaningful and menial tasks is often difficult to grasp or even to see. When misfortune that we have not caused comes, it is hard to see the good or even the meaning in it. When Nathan, age 10, is shot in the face by a neighbor boy, do we know the meaning? When parents are too young, too self-centered, or too ill to care for their children, do we know the meaning? When a mom and her teenage daughter are car-jacked and murdered, do we know the meaning? When children are used and abused, when latency-age children are exposed to drugs and alcohol by adults who should care, where is the meaning? When rape, murder, and "ethnic cleansing" sweep through entire countries, what is the meaning? Even when we do not see or understand the meaning, humans still live behaviorally with the experience. Frankl (1984) believed that each of us is responsible for how we live our lives in both the good and the bad times.

In order to understand the client's active engagement with life, the symptom, its emotional and physical manifestation, and its expression, the therapist seeks to comprehend the emotional life of the family and its members. This is influential while the family member lives physically within the walls of the family home, but it continues long after the family member moves away. The family's influence continues to work between and within family members for generations yet to come. In addition, the therapist, always aware of the importance of his or her own emotional experience and reactions (Nichols & Everett, 1986) as they relate to the client, uses them as a barometer to question, provide art tasks, or otherwise motivate both thinking and feeling.

From birth, family members draw close and then push away from significant others. Family members long to belong, yet find that belonging has its own form of restraints. These struggles show up in metaphors of connecting ribbons, drawn strings, tight ropes, and heavy chains. Clarifying our responsibilities and ultimate values is our life's task. It is precisely the journey of the SPIRIT that motivates what Jungians refer to as the hero's journey (Simpkinson & Simpkinson, 1993).

REFLECTIONS OF THE THERAPIST

The parents in the Smith family cared deeply for their children and wanted them to grow and develop to their full potential. But because of intergenerational transmissions, Mom and Dad had been stymied in their own developmental potential. Not quite sure what was best for their children, they sought guidance and worked to incorporate that guidance into their lives.

Current attachment models expand their "psychoanalytic perspective focusing on the infant and parental interactions, to a systemic perspective focusing on the young child or adolescent parental interactions" (Erdman & Caffery, 1997/1998, p. 12). Research on intergenerational transmissions of attachment patterns (Byng-Hall; 1990) indicates that "attachment patterns adults learned in their own families significantly influence the development of their attachment pattern with their own children" (p. 12). Parents of abused or neglected children have often been abused or neglected when they were children.

During the following year, Sandy, feeling heard, revealed that she had been molested by a babysitter when she was only three. As a three-year-old, Sandy had told her parents that she did not like the babysitter or want to go to the babysitter. They had not acknowledged her feelings, further damaging Sandy's sense of self and basic trust.

Sandy's cycle of love had not only been broken, but broken again and again as her parents took her to preschool and her molester. Helping Sandy rebuild a trust relationship with her parents was paramount to her being able to trust herself. "I told him to stop but he wouldn't do it," Sandy told the therapist and then her mother and father. Pieces of the puzzle now begin to fit together, i.e., Sandy's behavior problems, her low self-esteem, and her developmentally delayed artistic development.

At three to four years of age, Sandy had not liked her body being violated. As she got older, the memory of the experience faded, but the memory of the feelings became even more distasteful. A friend of the family—someone that the family had trusted to take care of her—had betrayed Sandy. When she told her parents that she did not want to go to preschool because Uncle George was "yucky," they dismissed her. The molestation had gone on for several months and Sandy's preverbal reality had become menacing. As her need for safety increased, her trust decreased. Her family failed to protect her. Sandy found it much safer to retreat into a world of her own rather than to live in a world that was as unsavory as hers had become. She needed to be able to trust her parents to protect her. Sandy was quickly losing her right and her ability to grow into a productive adult. It was important that she have a chance to communicate through talking, drawing, and playing out every memory or fantasy when she felt safe to do so.

Although Dad had a fractured relationship with his mother and was modeling this behavior to his son, this was not the family art therapy issue. In the reality of the managed care arena, family therapy and family art therapy are both brief therapy models focused on restoring family hierarchy and homeostasis. This was true in Sandy's case. The focus was on establishing a protective home life for the children. Six-year-old Sandy and her family needed a "sponsor" who could intervene and restore Sandy's sense of trust in her parents and herself (Guilligan, 1995).

Torras De Bea, as cited by Schneider, Ostroff, and Legow (1990), believes that "the child partly receives its body schema (ideal body image) from the mother and father and from the sensorimotor experiences with all their relational and affective components" (p. 135). With the molestation occurring between two and three years of age, Sandy had not as yet established an ego. She had never developed a positive sense of self. Her body image expressed in her art represented the maturity of a three-year-old with emotional disturbance. Over the next two years, both Sandy and her mother learned ways to self-soothe, to reduce anxiety, and to build a trusting relationship. While Mom grew, Dad, with a slight improvement in his interactive behavior, maintained his attitude of entitlement. Brother continued to take his lead from Dad.

Mom, reaching for her own potential, revealed, as her original artwork had, that in her latency years she had also been molested. She addressed its negative impact on her sense of self, her development, and her mothering. Through the art produced in family therapy, Sandy's entire family found alternative ways to communicate and address fear, anger, and distrust. Alice Miller (1990) writes that by the time she grasped the fact that she had been abused as a child, and had used art as therapy to validate her memories and experiences, she realized that her own parents had undergone similar experiences in their childhoods and had learned to regard that abuse as having been for their own good . . . for when we no longer need to confront the child's suffering blindly, we suddenly realize that it up to us adults, depending on how we treat our children, either to turn them into future monsters or to allow them to grow up into feeling and hence responsible, human beings (pp. 8–9).

Chapter 2

FAMILY AS HUMAN STRUCTURE

Keeping up to date with family rules is one of the characteristics
of a nurturing family. (Virginia Satir, 1972, p. 98)

WHAT IS A FAMILY?

THE AMERICAN FAMILY as we have known it, always vulnerable to cultural, social, and economic change, is becoming an endangered species. Today, while the structure of the family is being reshaped and recreated, American culture is becoming exceedingly complex with multiple social sets. Although traditional families with mothers and fathers who are married to each other and produce children are still the norm, there are almost twelve million single-parent families in America and "alternative configurations are increasingly common" (Vo, 1999, p. 4). In the past, families descended from a common progenitor and were connected through blood, lineage, and DNA. Currently, although "the ingredients to make a baby haven't changed (then and now one needs an egg, a sperm and a womb)—medical advances have made it possible to create babies without having sex" (Vo, 1999, p. 1). In our expanding multicultural society, the question, "What is a family?" grows broader and deeper.

Today, as in the past, the family—nuclear, blended, or extended—is a framework for human structure. It consists of those members present, in body or spirit, when we are "hatched, matched and dispatched" (Anderson, 1999, personal communication). It is a natural social system that surrounds children from birth to death as they grow and develop. Families are composed of dyads: parent/child, mother/father, husband/wife, mother/son, and father/daughter. "Family roles," says Satir (1972), "always mean pairs and share reciprocity. You cannot take the role of a wife without a husband, nor father without a son or daughter, and so on" (p. 146).

Entering into a family and exiting a family are both significant and ritualistic. Entrance is through birth, adoption, or marriage (Goldenberg & Goldenberg, 1996). Once one is in a family, whether it is a family of princes and princesses or paupers, one is in community, living with formal or informal roles and rules, but always in the tension of opposites: isolation versus intimacy, individuality versus togetherness. Family is a place where one can be supported or abandoned, isolated or smothered, nurtured or negated. Exiting attempts, such as divorce, separation, or death, separate the body, but the spiritual presence (or absence) is generally notable throughout life's course.

BASIC FAMILY FUNCTIONS

Primitive or sophisticated, families nurture and educate their young through love and control or discipline about surviving in the world, as it is known. In their own way, and to the best of their ability, families provide food, shelter, love, affection, and ways of maintaining physical health for their members. They protect their children from emotional harm and provide moral and ethical guidance (Forward & Buch, 1989). Basic family functions include establishing and maintaining the family as a unit (Rosenblatt & Horwitz, 1996; Zilback 1986). These functions provide roles and rules for both belonging and separating (Minuchin, 1974). Miller (1990) says that these basic functions are present in all families and their manifestations range from the nurturing imparting of socialization skills to extreme child abuse. Healthy child development begins when the child is totally dependent on primary caretakers, and moves toward independence (Pipher, 1996).

In the mid-fifties, Parson and Bales (1955) identified two irreducible and interactive long-range functions: the socialization of the young, and the stabilization of adult personalities. These functions have not really changed. Families mentor, model, and support behaviors and attitudes, creating behaviors and expression of their own ultimate concerns. Families provide environments that both foster and limit human potential. Because of commitments, early bonding influences, and experiences, family members are irreplaceable, influencing each other for life and often extending their influence into future generations.

Overt and covert family dynamics played out on the family stage encode family members in both an historical and a developmental context. These early and continuing events and relationships significantly influence human affect, behavior, and cognition. Therefore, primary boundaries must be flexible enough to provide initial protection from the outside world, while permitting increasing attachment of the child "to values and relationships outside the immediate family" (Nichols & Everett, 1986, p. 103).

Family Reparation

Families, specifically and in general throughout their life span, are like the waves breaking on a sandy beach, covering each other, blending and then receding, exposing what is left, rhythmically pushing and pulling. In this process, families polish, smooth, undercut, and wash away. Every family in daily life together messes up, and every marriage has a dark or shadow side. When this shadow side emerges in behavior or mood, tension builds, as in a minor or mighty storm, sweeping in alien objects and spreading change and destruction. This shadow side emerges just as quickly from lack of discussion of deep and intense feelings, resulting in one family member's using guilt or power as an insidious means of control. Recent research has found that that what matters most in keeping families together is the ability to repair things when they go wrong.

The process of change or acceptance is essential to family reparation. In the reparation process, Christensen et al. (1998) identified three necessary clusters: *Affect,* which refers to the personal feelings of all concerned; *communication,* which implies connecting with family members' "new discoveries of fact, perspective or understanding" (p. 182) and, *cognition,* which refers to a way of acquiring new information and "thinking about previously known facts" (p. 182).

These clusters are only effective when preconditions of "safety, fairness, normalization, hope and pacing" can be provided (p. 184). Reparation occurs quickly or slowly through acceptance, change, forgiveness, and the grace of a new perspective.

Why Do Marriages Fail?

Because of the epidemic proportions of divorce in the United States (50% of those recently married, 60% of those who have remarried), serious questions continue to arise about why marriages fail and which couples divorce and why (Blaisure & Geasler, 2000). Gottman (1994, 1996), of the Seattle Marital & Family Institute, and associates (Gottman & Levenson, 1985, 1992; Gottman & Katz, 1989) have researched these questions for the past 20 years. Using physiological tests, interviews, and video cameras, Gottman and his team have predicted "with 90% accuracy" which couples would divorce in the first seven years of marriage, or between 16 and 20 years of marriage, and why (1998, p. 15). The research team discovered two reasons couples divorce. In the early years, couples divorce because they engage in negative interaction when they fight, i.e., criticism, defensiveness, contempt, and stonewalling, which results in distancing and isolation. Couples who divorce in the later years do so because, although they may not have fought during their early years of marriage, they lacked positive affection, communication, and interactions. "Both aspects appear to be somewhat independent and both seem to be essential. . . . Lasting effects in marital therapy are most likely when interventions are designed with two prongs: one to increase everyday positive affect (not just in the resolution of conflict), and one to reduce negative affect during conflict resolution" (Gottman, 1998, p. 15).

In working with married or committed couples, Gottman (1998) found that happy or unhappy, all deal with the same tasks. It is not the case that Gottman's identified predictors of divorce never occur in marriages that are stable and happy; they just occur less often. Significantly, couples who repair or make sincere attempts to repair negative interactions have fewer divorces than those couples who do not.

Reviewing evidence of gender-sensitive reaction to "negative affect in marriage and close relationships," Gottman & Levenson (1988, p. 33) found differences and similarities. Gottman's research teams discovered that "predictions of marital outcome involved the physiological soothing of the male by either" the male himself or his female companion. Psychological soothing included "de-escalation by the husband, humor by the wife, validation by the husband, and affection by the husband." When such soothing events occurred, the heart rate of the husband decreased significantly, actually reducing physical discomfort. This physiological decrease was significantly higher in couples who were stable and happy compared to other couples studied.

If criticism, defensiveness, contempt, and stonewalling (traits that Gottman [1998] calls the four horsemen of the apocalypse) are destructive to adult relationships, would they not be equally destructive to children with young minds and tender bodies? Knowing how to repair anything is a natural talent or a learned skill. If emotional repairing were not part of a family's behavioral repertoire, if these skills were not modeled or taught, it is unlikely that young family members would have those interpersonal repairing skills. Therefore, in educating youngsters for long-term relationships, those skills must be sought and acquired outside of their family of origin.

Findings from Hetherington, Bridges, and Insbella (1998) indicate that divorce occurs more often in second and third marriages than in first marriages among remarried wives who have custody of the children from their first marriages than among remarried husbands who do not. Children, it would appear, are the pivotal point here. They both live in dysfunctional homes or unstable environments and acquire the dysfunctional and narcissistic survival skills that they observe. These behaviors–lack of trust, looking out for number one, taking care of self above all others–are rarely conducive in later life to living in relationship with others.

The following story is transgenerational. Although it is a continuation of Randy's story, it is systems oriented, including both second and third generation interaction and role modeling. It demonstrates how basic trust, broken and rebroken, requires super-human glue and professional skill to repair it.

RANDY R. SEARCHES FOR HOME

Randy R. was two-and-a-half years old and Charlie, his brother, was six months old when Dad moved out of the home. Much earlier, both parents had stopped trying to repair breaks in their relationship. When Dad moved, Mom, a woman raised with wealth, returned to her family of origin, where servants could care for the physical needs of her children and she could "get on with her life." Eventually Dad took a job out of state, leaving the children with their mother.

Randy, from age two to three, in the height of Mahler et al.'s (1975) object constancy, rapprochement phase and Erikson's (1963) autonomy stage, had free reign at grandmother's large and comfortable home. He followed the maid, buddied with the butler, and was mentored by an uncle who had a mouth like a drunken sailor. Randy was greeted at the end of each day by the return of a sweet-smelling grandmother who gave him a hug and a dollar bill for being a good boy regardless of his behavior. Randy and his brother were repeating mother's permissive childhood, playing in her playhouse, riding the family's ponies, and making their own messy ice cream sundaes in the kitchen. Whereas two-year-old Randy had not bonded with either of his absent parents, by age three he had bonded with his indulgent grandmother.

Mom soon remarried and life rapidly changed again. Randy, his brother Charlie, and Mom moved from Grandmother's house into the new stepfather's house until a new and larger home was completed. There, with pool table, soda fountain, swimming pool, cabana, and glass cases in sterile garages for golf trophies and collectibles, Grandmother would visit several times a week, bringing more and bigger goodies. Often Mom would drop the boys off at Grandmother's home, where they either followed the maid or had the run of the house with the maid following behind them. From a distance it appeared to be a child's dream, but viewed closer it was a nightmare in the making. The children, with a growing need for a connected, nurturing adult who would provide stable love and discipline, replicated all they saw: an environment fraught with human need and unrequited love. Their behavior was unruly and vulgar, frothing with bigoted language modeled by adult family members. Basic family functions of emotional protection and moral guidelines were lacking. It was in this period that Randy, as a teenager would report that while his grandmother was away, the maid frequently sexually molested he and Charlie. Later, much later, mother would vaguely remember that a babysitter had sexually abused neighborhood children. She was unsure if her little boys had been involved, but, 'not to worry," the boys were young, and they would get over it.

Stepfather, 20 years older than Mom, had never had children and soon wearied of the boys' obnoxious deportment. Little Charlie, now three, anxious and insecurely attached, found it difficult to potty train, often soiling his training pants. According to Randy, Stepfather would spank Charlie and then leave him under cold water in the shower to punish him. Charlie, frightened and hurting, cried and cried. Each evening the scene was repeated. When Mom became pregnant and took to her bed, the boys were left to Stepfather's beatings and merciless discipline. When Stepfather punished Charlie, Randy, in survival mode, declared war on Stepfather in hopes of driving him away. Over the next several months Randy, filled with rage and crying for help, threw away Stepfather's mail, messed up his home office, hid his shaver, and stood on the open dryer door. But when Randy did the naughtiest of naughties, used one of Stepfather's golf trophies for a hammer, Stepfather took after him with vengeance. In order to save her marriage, Mom, with little planning, packed up Randy and sent him and a cardboard box of broken toys and outgrown clothes, to live with Dad and his Dad's new wife.

Randy's cycle of love had been diminishing for some time. Now, as his emotional needs changed, his hope for relief dissolved. Randy, angry and confused, was rejected and sent far away.

Divorce and Living Alternatives

Divorce, a developing event, "disrupts family relationships and propels family members, particularly children, into numerous adjustments" (Baisure & Geasler, 2000, p. 2). It begins with the first unrepaired break in a couple's relationship and continues for the rest of a child's life. It begins with one spouse not being there, in heart, mind, or body, and couples fighting, or just interacting negatively. As mentioned earlier, since the 1960s, there has been a rapid increase in divorce. More than half of all marriages in the United States each year end in divorce. A variety of states in America, reeling from the world title of the country with the highest divorce rate, "called for a roll back of no-fault divorce laws and even for premarital waiting periods" (Kirn, 1997, p. 48). Fifty-percent of those questioned in a Time/CNN poll (Kirn, 1997) believed it should be harder than it was currently to get a divorce. Sixty-

Figure 13. *Me,* by Randy, age 5.

four percent of those questioned in the same poll believed couples should be educated about marriage before they could get a marriage license.

Children in all ethnic groups from divorced or multiple divorced families, in comparison with children from two-parent, non-divorced families, are at risk for a plethora of physical and emotional adjustment problems. These problems flood schools, clinics, communities, and state agencies. The stresses associated with divorce and remarriage affect everyone in the family and often exacerbate existing problems in children. Divorce does not necessarily make children ill; it simply puts them at greater risk for disease (Hetherington et al.,1998). "When compared to children from intact homes, children with divorced parents are twice as likely (20–25% vs. 10%) to exhibit emotional and behavioral problems (e.g., depression, delinquency, pregnancy). . . . Children's adjustment to divorce is associated in varying degrees with parental conflict," parenting skills, parental involvement in their lives, and life stresses (Blaisure & Geasler, 2000, p. 2). Research indicates that sons do worse with divorce than daughters and daughters do worse with remarriages than sons.

Research also indicates, however, that the sons of African-American women appear to benefit from stepfathers in their homes (Hetherington et al., 1998).

In American society, as in many other Westernized countries, marriage is more of an option than a permanent institution. One of the alternatives to marriage, or remarriage, is cohabitation. Cohabitation has its down side in that it exposes children to far more family transitions and constellations. Many children are born out of wedlock to adolescent mothers. As a result, these children are raised for longer periods of time in single-parent households that may include permanent and/or revolving extended family members (Hetherington et al., 1998).

In reaction to crime and welfare dependency as a result of family breakups and single mothers, Great Britain conducted the most comprehensive study ever into the state of modern marriage. Three-quarters of the people interviewed believed in marriage and 64 percent believed it should be forever. The British study found that 81 percent believed it is wrong to ever have an extramarital affair and twice as many unmarried men than women wanted to marry in the future (Appleyard & Carrol, 1998).

Research in both England and the United States has found that children in all ethnic groups from divorced, multiple divorced, or single-parent families, in comparison with two parent, non-divorced families, suffer from a cycle of negative events (Hetherington et al., 1998). This cycle of negative events "begins with marital conflict, followed by dissolution of the current family structure and culminates with the formation of separate households" (p. 403). Throughout their lives in relationships and in their sense of self, these children often continue to experience moves from home that result in loss of familiarity, transitional objects, support systems, friends, and community. This cycle of negative events is much more stressful than the actual divorce, because it results in broken attachments and acculturated stress. As children from broken homes mature, their cycles of negative events (the brokenness) that their families experience continue to resurface. They resurface at recitals, sports events, baptisms, bar mitzvahs, scout ceremonies, graduations, marriages, holidays, and with future-in-laws. It is not surprising that child-related issues are often the motivation for families entering therapy.

FAMILY THERAPY

Family therapy, holistic and inclusive, is a different way of thinking about therapy, not just a different way of doing therapy. It relates to both "knowledge and language" (Anderson, 1999, p. 2) of the function, structure, and process of nuclear and extended families, attitudinally, behaviorally, and cognitively. It grew out of a need to extend beyond traditional individual approaches of psychotherapy and include a "focus on the local context of the individual or the interpersonal relationship system, namely the family" (p. 2).

Accepting family therapy, however, does not mean rejecting individual therapy. Instead, family systems theory works as a vehicle for individuals to access and integrate information as it relates to themselves, their significant others, and the environments in which these relationships were formed and exist. "Individuals cannot be separated from their relationships" (Anderson, 1992, p. 3). The family therapist works with clients to set goals that customize therapy (knowledge and language) to the family unit and family culture, thus empowering family members to review, reflect, and when possible, repair relationships.

Occurring within the dynamics of relationship, family therapy interfaces with individual and family developmental stages. Not all family therapists agree that seeing individuals alone is family therapy (Minuchin, 1998). But the integrated model of family art therapy, where art and image become a vehicle for language of personal and perceived family information, the issue of who is seen in therapy, individual or family, is one of "congruence and fit." The following brief history of family therapy is included to focus specifically on the early integration, and "congruence and fit" of art therapy with family therapy.

Early Development of Family Therapy

In the 1940s, Nathan Ackerman began his clinical practice at the Menninger Clinic in Topeka, Kansas. Ackerman saw the family as a social and emotional unit. He, and later his clinical staff, began seeing mothers and their children together rather than separately. Later, working with rural clients, his staff saw whole families in their homes. After World War II, Ackerman moved to New York City, where he continued working with families in therapy.

Whereas Ackerman was known as the grandfather of family therapy, George Bateson, on the Western side of the continent, became known as the father of family therapy. Bateson was interested in systems theory and communication styles, making significant connections with fellow researchers Jay Haley, John Weakman, and Don Jackson. Together they undertook research that focused on broad levels of communication: communication with otters, guide dogs in training, humor, popular movies, and schizophrenics. The Bateson Group's focus in schizophrenia was in addressing "communication as an interpersonal, relational phenomenon, rather than an intrapsychic disorder" (Becvar & Becvar, 1989, p. 23). For its time, the message that therapy might focus on relational issues rather than on intrapsychic ones was revolutionary.

In additional studies on communication, Jackson and associates Watzlawick and Beavin, (Watzlawick, Beavin, & Jackson, p. 63) found that when relationships were the central issue of communication, verbal language was all but meaningless. Instead, body language, tone, gesture and reflection, all forms of meta-communication, actually defined the intent of the sender.

Soon after World War II, another young psychoanalyst named Murray Bowen began his career at the Menninger Clinic. Bowen's interests were also family-based. He studied mother-child symbiosis as it related to schizophrenia. "Bowen left Kansas in 1954 and went to the National Institute of Mental Health (NIMH) where he instituted and directed the classic study in which whole families of schizophrenic patients were hospitalized for observation and research" (Becvar & Becvar, 1989, p. 25). Lyman Wynne had joined NIMH two years earlier. When Bowen left NIMH, Wynne succeeded him as head of Family Studies. During Wynne's 29-year tenure at NIMH, he worked with many family therapy notables and contributed much to the research on family and schizophrenic behavior. One of his contributions applicable to family art therapy was his establishment of an inter-modal family therapy team. This team included art therapist Hanna Kwiatkowska, an internationally known sculptress and former student of art therapy pioneer, Margaret Naumburg (Kwiatkowska, 1978).

Early Development of Family Art Therapy

From 1958 to 1973, Kwiatkowska was associated with the NIMH, where she introduced art therapy, headed the art therapy unit and pioneered the development of family art therapy. Kwiatkowska's work culminated in a book, *Family Therapy and Evaluation through Art* (1978). Today—largely through Ms. Kwiatkowska's influence—family art therapy is widely practiced and accepted (Drachnik, 1975).

Early in her work at NIMH, Kwiatkowska (1978) came to believe that her basic task was to help people in relationships "get in touch with their special culture, experience and needs" (p. 17) through the spontaneous self-expression of art. Initially she worked with individual patients, supporting their art process and reflections. As parents and family members visited the patients, following them from activity to activity, Kwiatkowska encouraged the family members to participate in the art directives rather than just watch. She found the art productions and interactions often produced unexpected assessment materials. She began "including the whole family in the art therapy program" (p. 150). Having the entire family working together in art often resulted in family members being less guarded than they were in verbal therapy sessions. For example, she found that family dependency issues became more apparent in the art process, and anger and hostility were expressed with less guilt in the product. In addition, she found that family members were able to perceive themselves and other family members in a more accurate way. At first, families using art presented with great resistance. As Kwiatkowska experimented with different structural approaches to the sessions and different family constellations, six standardized procedures evolved for evaluation purposes. "These procedures assisted the resistant member of the family to tolerate the difficulties of the group situation" (p. 117). Working with the family on spontaneous or directed art processes provided Kwiatkowska and her team the opportunity to experience the emotional climate of the family along with their reaction to the experience. Kwiatkowska called her art-based assessment the Family Art Evaluation (FAE) (see Appendix A-1). Since the 1970s, the term *family art therapy* has become closely linked with Kwiatkowska and her work.

AN ATTEMPTED FAMILY ART-BASED ASSESSMENT WITH GARY AND HIS FAMILY

The following story of Gary (Arrington, 1991) is an example of the use of Kwiatkowska's Family Art Evaluation (FAE, see Appendix A-1) and how, even when incomplete, it is useful in assessment, communication, and treatment (Portions of this story were presented at the 1989 American Art Therapy Association conference in San Francisco. I would like to thank Beverly Stone, who worked with Gary in her practicum placement).

While some marriages are made in heaven, most marriages are made between human beings here on earth and have periods of distress or even total failure. Marriages are made by people who on occasion need help. Sometimes they seek it, sometimes others seek it for them, and sometimes no one seeks it, resulting in everyone—spouses, children, in-laws, out-laws, friends and relatives—suffering, sometimes for generations.

Gary, an 18-year-old, was the only son of an unmarried African-American couple who lived together part-time in a low income, high-crime area. Mom had nine children by her first husband, who had been murdered during a robbery. She met Gary's dad the following year. Gary, a diagnosed paranoid schizophrenic, had a history of verbal assaultiveness toward his parents resulting from his belief that they might harm him. After numerous hospitalizations in a psychiatric hospital, Gary was readmitted after he physically assaulted his Mom. Unable to be stabilized, he was transferred to a long-term facility. The two therapists working with the family felt that art therapy would provide a means of assessing the family dynamics and provide necessary information.

The family art therapist introduced the art-based assessment tasks and the other therapist acted as a participant/observer. The therapist requested the

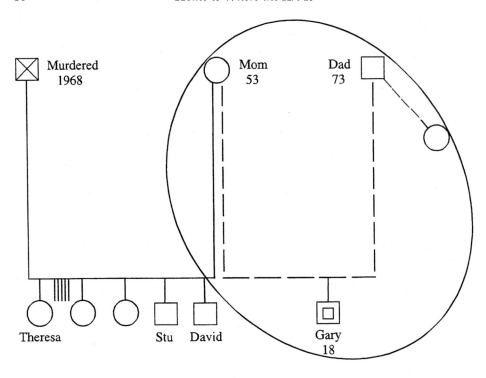

Genogram 2. Gary's Family

family "to draw whatever comes to mind" (a free picture), and surprisingly, everyone cooperated, but only after Mom said, "We will do the best we can." The three drew individual pictures.

The first drawing often is an introduction of the self, or may present the family problem (Kwiatkowska, 1978). Mom's drawing, (Figure 14) was a fraying, childlike, primitive, and concrete representation of a person that she labeled Sallie. This appeared to be an accurate portrayal of Mom's rather primitive and concrete thought processes, often expressed in a disconnected manner. She also drew "a tree" that looked like a feather.

Gary's first drawing was both primitive and confusing (Figure 15). It included five concentric circles, indicating maternal dependency, and the name "Mickey Mantel." When Mom told Gary to draw a tree, he drew an archetypal cross-lined configuration (just as the author has observed in a rock drawing done in Jordan, approximately 7000 BC). Mom scolded him, saying that he had not drawn a tree, and told him to copy hers. He drew a second, unrecognizable configuration.

Dad's drawing was disturbing in a number of ways (Figure 16). Drawn in black crayon, the picture shows a sad horse with its head bent so low that it

Figure 14. *Free picture* by Mom.

Figure 15. *Free picture* by Gary.

Figure 16. *Free picture* by Dad.

appears decapitated. It faces a can with four sticks. It appears to be struggling to move forward. Dad actually resembled the horse in the picture, bent over, depressed, and struggling to move forward. In the anal area of the horse there is a peculiar phallic symbol inside the body.

For the second art assessment task, Mom, Dad, and Gary were asked to draw a picture of their family. Mom stopped, asking in a hostile tone, "Why do you want to know about our family?" The therapist explained that by working with the family through art, Gary might be better helped. Mom explained that she was recovering from eye surgery and that her doctor had told her she was "not to do this type of thing." She continued, noting that neither she nor Dad had any problems, and even her minister had told her that there were certain things in families that were personal and that she didn't have to tell anyone about them. With Mom's refusal, Dad no longer participated. Gary, however, had already begun to draw his family portrait, and the therapist encouraged him to complete it (Figure 17).

Gary completed it only after Mom told him who he should draw next and how to draw that person. Gary voluntarily drew a third picture (Figure 18). The four remaining art tasks, however, were not assigned because of the high level of resistance from Mom. The interactional family patterns that appeared while family members were doing the tasks were carefully observed.

Gary's second drawing followed the family art therapist's instruction. It showed eight people, in two groups of three figures on the top row and two people on the bottom row. What were most noticeable in this drawing were the fairly clear role definitions. Gary's stepsiblings and parental subsystems are grouped together, and yet there is little differentiation as to personal characteristics, sex roles, or body types among family members.

While Mom talked, Gary voluntarily continued drawing on his own. His third drawing is simple and looks like a cigar with a face, with cross-hatching on the body of the cigar. Gary called it his "dog that needs a haircut." Mom, oblivious to Gary's drawing, did not interfere or make suggestions.

In observing the process of the family during the art tasks, it was clear that the family system was closed and constricted. Airing "dirty laundry" to "outsiders," or two white therapists, may well have been too conflictual. Hampson, Beavers, and Hulgus (1990, p. 308) note that "blacks who appear mute in the therapy room may talk endlessly on their home turf" with trusted friends and ministers. Was this true in Gary's case? His family had only participated in therapy when required to do so in response to Gary's issues.

In this place, at this time, Mom was clearly in the position of power. No one drew until she began and gave the okay. She was deeply enmeshed with Gary and Dad; neither spoke to the therapists during the session. The therapists hypothesized that this enmeshment carried over to the other family

Figure 17. *My family* by Gary.

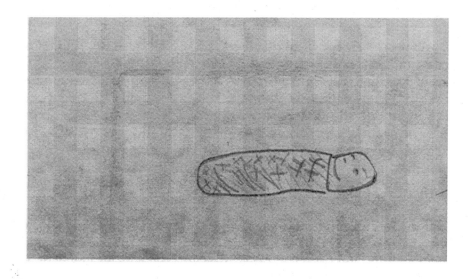

Figure 18. *Dog that needs a haircut* by Gary.

members as well. Mom, vigilant in protecting her family, expended considerable energy in maintaining family secrets. This was illustrated by her drawing a figure and naming it Sallie (not explaining why she did not use her own name), and her refusal to complete a family drawing. Gary completed his family drawing only under her strict scrutiny and supervision.

Using an Art-Based Assessment Evaluation (ABA-Eval, Table 1) we would see that the body language of the participants was tense or even unusual. The interaction with the therapists was negative or even extreme. The art began with Mom being cautious and ended with Mom's refusal to participate. The interaction with the art task was extreme, in that both parents participated in only one drawing. Psychological insight appeared to be lacking, yet the content of the artwork itself was illustrative of the family dynamics. All figures were unattached and floating. Mom's feather-like tree is indicative of a psychologically barren individual who is unstable in even a light breeze (Wench, 1980). Following Mom's instructions to draw a tree, and then being scolded because she did not approve, placed Gary in a double bind. He was wrong when he drew and he was wrong when he did not draw.

Dad's drawing of the horse (particularly the phallic symbol in the anal area), coupled with Gary's drawings, which were largely phallic in nature, suggested that Gary may have experienced homosexual molestation or incest from his Dad. Additional assessment was recommended.

Follow-up

In follow-up sessions, Gary told the therapist that his Dad stabbed him every day, and that his dad felt so bad about it that it was making him sick. He also freely discussed that his two brothers had molested him since he was six years of age. Gary's delusional system centered on a belief that snakes and cobras were in his bed at night. Themes of snakes as metaphors for Gary to reveal his sexual molestation now became clear (Burns & Kaufman, 1972). Sexual abuse was reported to child protective services at this time.

Discussion

Prior to Gary's admission to the long-term facility, he had been in individual and group therapy for three years. The family had been included for consultations only, and Gary had never been assessed with his family or with an art-based assessment. The Family Art Evaluation (FAE) attempted in the facility identified several functions that Gary's manifested paranoid psychosis served in the dysfunctional family system. His psychosis fit with the familiar, although chaotic and confused, family operations. Paranoid feelings became

Table 1. ART-BASED ASSESSMENT EVALUATION (ABA-EVAL)

Name _____ **Age** _____ **Date** _____

Contract is for the procedure: the process, the product, and the perception

I. Quantitative: Procedure and Process - focus/distracted

	Relaxed Tense Present 0	Unusual Present 1	 Present 2
A. Body language			
Head (eyes, face)	_____	_____	_____
Energy, breathing	_____	_____	_____
Legs, arms, hands	_____	_____	_____
B. Level of interaction with:	Neutral 0 Positive 1+	Negative 2–	Extreme 3x + or –
Therapist	_____	_____	_____
Staff	_____	_____	_____
Family members	_____	_____	_____
Materials	_____	_____	_____
Art tasks	_____	_____	_____
C. Feeling management & insight	_____	_____	_____
D. Decision making	_____	_____	_____
E. Developmental age	_____		

   Score – 0–4 - Normal; 5–8 Caution; 8+ Test further, treat, or refer.

   F. Diagnostic Impression Axis I ____ Axis III ____ Axis IV ____ Axis V ____

II. Qualitative: Product and perception - identify & isolate art components

   A. Overall affect - positive, negative, anxious, chaotic, empty, realistic, bizarre.
   1. **Center interests and symbols** - house, trees, person, animal, environmental, repetitive, dramatic, other.
   2. **Color sensitivity** - always on continuum (i.e., associations, fit and prominence are important. They are indicators of personal associations with mood states).
   3. **Content and symbolism** - meaning - archetypal, cultural, personal, realistic.
   4. **Line quality** - soft, hard, normal, limited, energized, excessive, extreme.
   5. **Movement** - direction, forward, backward, cultural implications, in-out, right to left, stagnant, chaotic. Perception of movement that does not exist.
   6. **Overlay** - colors, patterns or symbols, sequence, first, second, third, etc.
   7. **Placement** - space, right, left, top, bottom, center, empty, integrated.
   8. **Relationships** - people, animals, absent, close, color and size fit, symbols significance.
   9. **Vista** - Perspective (bird's-eye view - broad brush and distant—work's eye view - details, and close up, direct).
   10. **Decision making and problem solving** - controlling impulses, setting goals.
   B. Defense mechanisms - denial - absent; undoing - destruction; encapsulation - enclosed; projection - symbol; isolation of affect - color continuation; regression; regressed beyond known ability.

III. Focus on perception: Teach clients to see descriptively. When the art has been completed, have the client place it on the wall or a table. Step back and observe the art as if for the first time. **What do your eyes rest on first, second?** *DO NOT TALK. Guard against projection.* **Ask the client, WHAT DO YOU SEE? Discuss what the client sees, using your knowledge and experience** (Betensky, 1983).
Use other side of this paper if needed.

clearly understandable in a family system where incest occurred and was protected. More importantly, Gary's behavior was identified as keeping the family secret and observing the family rule of denial. For example, in the middle
of the session Mom stated that Gary was not to be believed because he was
too crazy. Gary's manifested psychotic behavior permitted him to remain
loyal to his Mom, respect the family rules, and protect other family members
at his own expense. With the art-based assessment, Gary, for the first time,
was identified as a victim and the therapists were able to take a protective
stance. Unfortunately, Gary's basic trust of others and himself was so diminished that his prognosis was extremely poor.

A Review of the Goals

A review of goals in family therapy indicate that the therapist is not necessarily concerned with insight on the part of the clients, or with helping the
clients understand how they got the way they are. Rather, he or she is concerned with customizing the clients' perspectives, empowering growth, and
maximizing the potential of each member of the family. In other words, therapists want to effect change in family systems in the "here and now" so the
family members can get the most out of their present and future lives and
relationships. Family therapists do this however they can. They coach, construct, draw, observe, provide paradoxical strategies, and teach. When family therapists intervene in ways that bring about systemic change without
making the family members aware of what they are doing (Nichols & Everett,
1986), they are using paradoxical tasks. Paradoxical tasks often result in alter-
ation of behavior without a direct connection being apparent to the clients.
Family therapists do this by "establishing an atmosphere of safety and hope,
making it clear that all members of the family will be (heard verbally or visually) and dealt with fairly" (Christensen et al., 1998, p. 186). As seen in Gary's
FAE, art in therapy provided an additional language for Gary in which he
could feel safe and even talk without words. Art in therapy allowed all three
participants the opportunity to make unique visual statements and be
observed in a step-by-step process. It facilitated graphic expression by all participating family members for later assessment, goal setting, and individual or
family treatment planning.

A Review of the Client

In family therapy, the client can be either the entire family, a subsystem
of the family, or an individual family member. The work involves the developmental assemblage of related personalities and events. Family therapy,

whether the therapist is working with an individual in a family or with several family members, is concerned with current or historical family dynamics, experiences, or functions and how those affect the client(s) in relationships. In other words, the therapist can intervene in a family system with only part of the family present because the nuclear family is always present in the internalized family genogram. "Conversely some therapists can interview an entire family and still deal with the system as if it were merely a collection of individuals, never identifying or recognizing the interactional processes present in the family" (Nichols & Everett, 1986, p. 2).

The following introduction of Anne will help identify how a therapist, when working with a single family member, can focus on family losses and loyalties that often affect human SPIRIT and behavior for long periods of time. With Ann, art therapy became her vehicle for communication.

ANNE: A GIRL AND HER SECRET

Anne, a beautiful, well-dressed, unmarried professional in her late thirties, came in to therapy because, she said, her kitty had died and she was deeply upset. The therapist handed Anne a paper with two folds that met in the middle. She asked Anne to use the side with the two ends folded inward as if it were one piece of paper and to use any of the art materials available to draw how she presented herself to the world (see Appendix B–Intervention H, Outside and Inside). When she finished, she was directed to open the two folds and, on the inside, draw how she thought or felt inside. Anne used oil pastels to draw an attractive, somewhat smiling face that did not look directly at the viewer. On the inside, Anne, drew a small figure with a similar face with freckles on the nose, and softer eyes that looked to the left side. There was no smile. When asked to name the two pictures, she named the one on the outside *Smiling Depression* (Figure 19) and the one on the inside *Pensive* (Figure 20). When asked to place the picture on the wall and talk about what she saw, Anne, who appeared to be bright and articulate, had very little to say. She appeared to be frozen in time.

John Allan (1988) identifies the stages of serial drawing as used in therapy:

- The initial stage gives a view of the artist's internal world, often reflecting his or her feelings of hopelessness. The art represents a vehicle for establishing the initial contact with the helper, a way the client and the helper can join.
- The middle stage, when trust is beginning to be established, allows for the expression of raw emotion and the struggle with ambivalent feel-

Outside and inside drawings

Figure 19. *Smiling Depression* by Anne.

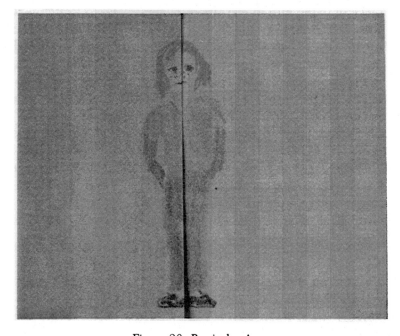

Figure 20. *Pensive* by Anne.

ings. During this stage a deeper relationship with the helper is established, allowing for the disclosure of deep issues.

- In the termination stage, the art displays healthy images of mastery, self-control, self-worth, humor, and the establishment of a central self-figure.

The family art therapist knew from looking at the images and their titles that Anne was in a beginning stage of trust. She had shared a concern. She had participated in making art that revealed both inner and outer feelings and she had identified her deeper feeling of hopelessness by titling her picture *Smiling Depression.* Her picture was a mask of what? In both pictures, her eyes looked into what? The freckles on Anne's nose related to a much younger self, perhaps in the role of a child and a daughter. Her eyes looking away were a clue to the therapist that Anne wanted help with a deep concern or secret issue that she was fearful to reveal. As often happens in therapy, little was known about the client at the beginning. As more and more memories are shared, trust is established, feelings are discovered, and hope is nourished.

For Anne, who was as yet unable to speak about her deep issues, making art helped establish an initial contact with the therapist. The therapist, honoring Anne and the art process, provided a safe and protected space for Anne to move at her own pace and slowly test the pain of further disclosure.

As shown earlier, the therapist working with a family member or a family may gather information with a genogram, take a history of relevant information, and inquire into the ways the client/family has tried to solve the problem in the past. The therapist will build a relationship with the participant(s) in the process. The therapist will take note of the issue that eventually brought the client/family into therapy, and when the client/family gave up trying to solve it themselves, they sought help from a therapist. Therefore, asking a family or an individual to use art media to express emotions or materials to answer questions about the family or determine why they came to therapy often solicits curiosity from the client(s) while providing family history and symbolic information to the therapist.

Chapter 3

THE CYCLE OF LOVE

Love fuels the cycle that gives birth to the human Soul, says Zaslow. (cited in Cline, 1991, p. 15)

FROM MID TWENTIETH CENTURY, psychotherapists observed the interactional context, within which both personality and symptomology evolved.

It is fairly obvious that, under existing social conditions, the psychological atmosphere of the home life, with the complex emotions and sentiments aroused by and dependent on the various family relationships, must exercise a very considerable effect on human character and development. Recent advances in the study of human conduct indicate that this effect is even greater than has been generally supposed. It would seem that, in adopting his or her attitude towards the members of his family circle, a child is at the same time determining to a larger extent some of the principal aspects of his or her relations to fellow humans in general; and that an individual's outlook and point of view in dealing with many of the most important questions of human existence can be expressed in terms of the position he or she has taken up with regard to the problems and difficulties arising within the relatively narrow world of the family. (Frugel, 1948, p. 4)

Satir (1972), a pioneer in family therapy, supported the theory that personality is made in families that serve as a kind of factory where socialization occurs. Within this factory, all behavior is seen as communication, and therefore, "understanding personality is impossible apart from comprehending the context in which it is formed and sustained as a system and subsystem in a hierarchy of subsystems" (Nichols & Everett, 1986, p. 93).

Family therapy, by its very identity, facilitates both the family and the therapist in thinking of families in terms of family members living and developing in nuclear and extended family systems. Exploring both cognition and

50

affect, using graphic expression and symbols, family art therapy allows the clinician not only "to think systems, but to see" them as well (Arrington, 1991). This new way of seeing provides space for co-creating new perspectives and new meaning in treatment (Christensen et al., 1998, p. 185).

FAMILY INFLUENCES IN PERSONALITY DEVELOPMENT

From the very beginning, a human child is always in relationships. Mother and Dad are the first objects of the child's affection and attention. From their acceptance or rejection, children learn behavior. Major personality theorists share appreciation for these early parental influences. "In the family," Zaslow continues:

> there is an almost magical *cycle of love* that gives "birth to our soul." Soul is used because it expresses unique, special human qualities of thoughtful caring for others and the internal belief of something beyond us and far greater than we ourselves are . . . Erikson speaks of Basic trust, Martin Buber talks of I/Thou, and Christians talk of grace. (Zaslow, 1975, cited in Cline, 1991. p. 15)

This magical cycle is what, with Foster Cline's permission, I call the *Cycle of Love*. It results in basic trust and attachment while providing safety and security. This trust is established in our most vulnerable years, and continues in a variety of forms throughout life. It begins in the womb and continues with the 4-hour feeding rhythm of the infant. In the first 6 months of an infant's life this cadence of need and relief is repeated approximately 800 times. It is deeply imprinted in the human brain as a two-step dance between the infant and the caregiver. The number is appropriate. It does not include the innumerable times during this same period that the infant is patted, changed, cuddled, or kissed. This *Cycle of Love* is the caring actions given by primary caregivers to their infants and young children. Perry (1997) says that these early life experiences literally mold and shape the core neurological organization of human beings. "Indeed it is the primary relationship of infancy and childhood that determine the core neurobiological organization of the human individual, thereby allowing this incredible social specialization. Early life experiences determine core neurobiology" (p. 126). They facilitate, except in the rarest of circumstances, social specialization of humans. It is these associative rhythms in the *Cycle of Love* that introduce humans to the interactive dance of life and relationship. *Cycle* is indicative of each individual life pattern and, at the same time, this *Cycle of Love* is the continuous connection from one generation to the next (Stevens, 1983).

Table 2. THE CYCLE OF LOVE: Trust and Attachment

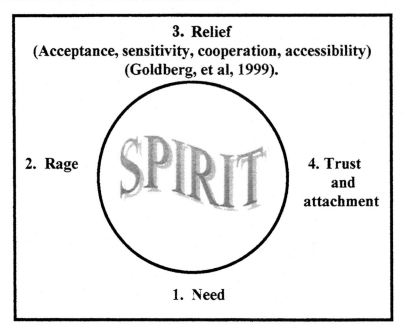

Source: Adapted from Cline, 1991, p. 16, with permission.

Families are our first school for emotional learning. They are where we do the fieldwork for attachment and bonding. Family life molds the human brain. Infants learn about the world through their families. It is within family that children, with their bundle of needs, learn to express or curtail their emotions and where this cycle of love is played out, or broken (Bronfenbrenner, 1979).

EMOTIONAL NEEDS

Human emotions provide the impulses necessary for action. These are regulated in the three interconnected parts of the brain as they "continually exchange and interpret information" (Levy & Orlans, 1998, p. 25). When we are angry, fearful, or otherwise emotionally aroused, the reticular activating system (RAS), our fight-or-flight response, takes over, releasing blood to the arms, which encourages fighting, and releasing blood to the legs, providing energy to flee (Bowlby, 1969/1982). An angry and needy baby, for its own sense of survival, shakes its arms and legs in its desire to fight or flee. The emotion of surprise provides alertness, allowing the eyes to open wider.

"When we are relaxed, not perceiving threat, the cortex is switched back on, allowing logic and reasoning to return" (Levy & Orlans, 1998, p. 25). The emotion of happiness provides energy and inhibits negative feelings, whereas the emotion of sadness reduces energy and keeps one close to home. The emotion of disgust reacts to offensiveness in taste and smell. The emotion of love, facilitating cooperation, provides calm, care, contentment, and basic human and mammal development (Sapolsky, 1998). Emotional intelligence, made a household word by Goleman (1995), is the power to understand these emotions and to develop their use effectively and efficiently.

Before one understands emotions and learns to use and control them, they exist as ways to grow and meet or express survival needs. For instance, the infant needs relief, and expresses frustration at not getting his or her needs met immediately in the only way he or she can, through the emotion of rage, which erupts in crying (Cline, 1991, p. 16). The mothering agent, usually Mom but just as easily and effectively Dad (Silverstein & Auerbach, 1999), needs to be at least one responsible, caring adult who has a consistent and positive emotional relationship with the child (p. 398), providing security, acceptance, and sensitivity (Goldberg, Grusec & Jenkins, 1999). This agent, wanting to provide relief to an enraged infant or child, reacts with her (or his) senses of sight and sound. She sees, hears, and responds. She may even note the infant's anger, using motherese, "You're really mad." Mom continues to respond to the baby's needs of touch, taste, and smell. She combines "sensitive care of the baby, individual needs and a firm sense of personal trustworthiness (Erikson, 1963, p. 249). She carefully picks up and supports the baby, trying to satisfy first with her movement, her soothing body fragrance, and then with food that is warm, satisfying, and easily digested, or with a soft and comforting dry diaper. Humans encode through their senses; first through movement, then through image, and last through language (Geller, 1978). Just picking up the baby begins to relieve the baby's sensory need for movement and relationship, thus building *trust* between the infant and the world, as the infant perceives it. Movement refers to labyrinthine stimulation. "The labyrinth is that part of the inner ear associated with motion and position" (Cline, 1991, p. 16). Checking on, picking up, cuddling, changing, feeding, kissing, tasting, and singing to an infant provide an infant's essential human contact. Caring for an infant includes the provision of a human face, eye contact, a reciprocal smile, a familiar fragrance, a light touch, and soft sounds. Caring for an infant provides multiple opportunities for emphatic human interaction, such as recognizing and identifying the baby with words, as in "There, there, it's okay! Hi sweetheart, aren't you a big girl?" all of which build ego and identity.

"Trust born of care is the touchstone of the actuality of a given religion," says Erikson, (1963, p. 250). Trust and security, predictability, and consistency are generally found in the mothering agent that is present, emphatic, and readily available. To the child, mother, as she was in ancient societies, is warmth, safety, goodness, wisdom, paradise, all-provider, all-god or goddess. Like Kohut, Lackman-Chapin (1983) believes that in the earliest months of life, failure in this empathic position "has a causal role in the development of relational conflicts later in an individual's life" (p. 3).

Childhood psychopathology is generally caused by severe breaks in this initial love cycle, according to Bowlby (1969/1982) and Mahler et al. (1975). Breaks or even fragmentation in the relationship between infant and mothering agent caused by abuse, some adoptions, neglect, and trauma often result in anxiety, distress, mistrust, and anger. The severity in the pathology depends upon the age of the infant at the break, the length of time that the cycle is broken, as well as the genetic and ego strengths of the infant. Where there is even a temporary absence or separation from mother, there is anxiety for the infant. The infant's greatest source of terror is solitude or the absence of the soothing mother.

The infant separated from his or her soothing agent anxiously yearns and searches for her. When she is not to be found, the infant is overcome with deep sadness, and increases his or her protest, following it by intense anger, and then by severe distress and depression. When mother does not return, the child, over time, develops ambivalence toward her and then detaches from her. When there is a permanent loss of the mothering agent before ten years of age, without a loving replacement, attachment and a solid sense of trust of self and others may never develop (Cline, 1991).

For the family therapist, family is tied to lifetime environmental experiences that include bonding, loyalty, and what Brazelton (1990) calls *Heart Start*. Heart Starts are those "goodly doses of life's little challenges" (Goleman, 1995, p. 192). Toddlers, with their insatiable wants, are perfect candidates for Heart Start.

> If a child is to experience an age-appropriate grandiose self-image, he or she must feel that exhibitionistic display is safe and effective. The child is assured that this is so by the mother's (and significant others') mirroring, and the gleam in the mother's eye. The child's efforts to exhibit him- or herself represent first attempts at individuation, at leaving the symbiotic ties with mother. To be successful, these feats of grandeur and omnipotence must be greeted by the mother (and significant others) with approval and admiration. (Lackman-Chapin, 1983, p. 4)

MICHELLE LEARNS THE TWO-STEP IN THE DANCE OF LIFE. Michelle, a verbal 18-month-old, and her parents were having dinner with close friends. The conversation shifted from Michelle to adult issues. After several minutes Michelle got down from her chair, stood about five feet from the table and

Figure 21. *Michelle as Belle,* illustration by Amanda.

sang in her loudest voice, " Beauty annnd the Beaaasst." Then she twirled around with arms outstretched and bowed deeply, imitating Belle in the video, *Beauty and the Beast* (Figure 21), which she watched often at her home.

The precocious toddler got just what she was counting on from a surprised and appreciative audience: applause, approval, and admiration. Michelle, in the beginning phases of rapprochement (Mahler et al., 1975), was beginning to explore satisfying and appropriate images of herself, separate and apart from her mother.

Over the next 18 months, Michelle often visited with those same close friends without her parents. One day when she was about two and a half, she was creating, playing, and singing happily in their front yard when her parents drove up. Michelle, surprising everyone, began to cry and run to the car. Seeing her mom had negated her own sense of self. From a Jungian viewpoint, Michelle's internal security, her ego self-axis, was not durable enough to function independently (Allan & Bertoia, 1992). From an object relations standpoint of neurodevelopment, Michelle's central nervous system (CNS), in a critical period, had not yet reached optimal organization or full development. When she saw her mother she realized that she had been separated and she froze in time.

About the time Michelle reached three years of age, a similar scene occurred. This time, when her parents drove by to pick her up, she continued playing. Turning to the friends, Michelle said simply, as if she remembered, "I don't need my mother all the time." Michelle's maturity did not happen just because she reached three years old. Her developing CNS, nurtured in trust, provided Michelle with basic steps necessary for growth and individuation. Children who grow up in Heart Start environments that provide positive affective experiences (love, approval, opportunity, and flexibility) learn to move and dance, first with their primary caretakers, then with significant others, and finally with life in general.

PSYCHOLOGICAL INFLUENCES ON PERSONALITY DEVELOPMENT

Whereas art and image are prescientific and have existed as long as humanity, psychology is a relatively new scientific discipline, only 150 years young. Psychology consists of a variety of theories and modalities that study, explore, and care for an integral and inseparable part of the human being referred to as the mind. The roots of psychology are grounded in disciplines of philosophy and medicine. Infused with theories and logic, philosophers have long pondered humankind's ultimate concerns as they related to mind, will, and knowledge. Medicine germinated in both biology and physiology. In past and recent cultures, individuals in these sciences continue to explore and expand knowledge of human behavior. Psychology cultivates these rich disciplines for continuous illumination and energy. The following chart (Table 3, Comparison of Theories of Personality Development) comparing theories of personality development illustrates with a broad brush how the different developmental theories interrelate and overlap through age and experience. Brief comments that focus on family influences follow the chart.

Psychosexual Theory (Freud)

Although Freud chose to focus on individual and intrapsychic material rather than family dynamics, he was aware that parents and other family members are the first objects of the child's culturally unacceptable wishes (Rychlak, 1981, p. 108). The familial environment, particularly the mother/child relationship, determines to some extent whether individual needs are satisfactorily met. In addition, successful progression through the

Table 3. COMPARISON OF THEORIES OF PERSONALITY DEVELOPMENT

Physical	Psychosexual (Freud)	Object Relations (Mahler)	Jungian (Jung)	Psychosocial (Erikson)	Cognitive (Piaget)	Artistic (Lowenfeld)
0–1 year	Oral	Autistic/Symbiosis	Childhood	Trust/Mistrust	Sensory/Motor	
2–3 years	Anal	Separation Individuation Differentiation Practicing Rapprochement Object and self constancy			Autonomy/Shame Initiative/Guilt		Random Scribble. Circular and
4–6 years	Phallic			Industry/Inferiority	Preoperational	Horizontal forms. Sun shapes.
7–11 years	Latency				Concrete-operations.	Preschematic. Schematic.
Puberty & Adolescent	Genital		Puberty	Identity/Role confusion	Formal-operations	Realism.
Young Adult			Before 40	Intimacy/Isolation		
Adulthood			Maturity	Generativity/Stagnation		
Seniors				Ego Integrity/Despair		

Freudian psychosexual stages by the developing child requires appropriate responses by parents. Discussing Freudian theory, Hampden-Turner (1981) notes that "the child is at first entirely dependent on a crucial relationship with his or her mother—who can gratify every whim or, withhold herself" (p. 42). Freud divided the brain into conscious thoughts and experiences that people knew and remembered, preconscious thoughts and experiences that reappeared because of sensory stimuli, and unconscious thoughts and events that were blocked from conscious memory. Freud believed that early experiences with primary caretakers, often lost in the unconscious, had a causal effect on later behavior. Freud's developmental structure, the "id" and the "ego" (or the "it" or "I" in Latin) and the "superego," were part of his new view of the mind.

In the first three stages of Freudian development—oral, anal, and phallic—sensations of pleasure are concentrated in the specific body areas mentioned. During this time, from birth to approximately three years of age, the mother, the breast, the provider of affect and nourishment, is barely distinguished by the infant as a separate person but is loved as a life support system. . . . with the dawning awareness of the mother's separate existence, an emotion akin to sexual love begins to replace infant narcissism. It is at this point that "boys feel rivalry, even hatred, for their fathers" who share their mothers' attentions (Hampden-Turner, 1981, p. 42).

Girls feel similar rivalry for their mothers who share their fathers' attentions. As children grow through the latency period (6 years to 12) and into the genital stage (12 years to maturity) the Oedipal and Electra conflict is usually resolved and teenagers' pleasurable interests shift from emotional dependence on parents to emotional friendships with peers. This resolution occurs because the defense mechanisms and the superego have been exercised and formed. "The resolution of the Oedipal conflict is a pattern for the development of personality" (Hampden-Turner, p. 43). Children begin Freud's genital stage at puberty or slightly before. At this time, adolescent interests turn to the opposite sex, not only for sexual stimulation, but also for satisfying and growing relationships. The ego, maintaining a balance between id and the superego, begins appropriate channeling of instincts and energy into love and work relationships.

According to Becvar and Becvar (1988, p. 45), Freud was a forerunner of the family therapy movement. With Freud's supervision of "Little Hans' father, it appears that he was the first to practice family therapy in the sense of working with more than one family member." Rubin, an art therapist, psychologist, and pioneer in the use of art with children and their families (1986), suggests that Freud was the first to practice family art therapy in that "Little Hans" drew because Freud believed that Hans was not ready for free association.

Jungian Psychology (Jung)

Like Freud, Carl Jung also identified three areas of the psyche, the conscious, the personal unconscious and Jung's unique contribution, the collective unconscious. According to Jung (1954/1974), the collective unconscious is made up of archetypes, biological or primordial images influenced by age, experience, and culture. They give meaning to life because they are both image and emotion. Connected to instincts, archetypes act as a primary ordering system, fostering self- regulation. They exist and remain similar from generation to generation and from person to person and are found in personal dreams, art, and mythology. When seen as inherited dispositions, archetypes provide a blueprint for development (Samuels, 1983). Jung (1964) contended that cultural symbolic archetypes become collective images accepted by civilized societies as universal and eternal truths expressed in their arts, politics, and religions. Consequently, the understanding of myths and symbols is essential to understanding individuals and societies. Despite the collective, transpersonal aspect of the psyche, each individual finds a relevant way of expressing his or her inner images that is totally personal and gives meaning to life. For Jung, this often meant painting, drawing, and sculpting his own thoughts and feelings (Arrington, 1986).

HUMAN LIFE CYCLE. Jung (1933/1955; 1954/1974) identified his developmental theory of the human life cycle as the individuation process.

- This process begins collectively with childhood, from birth to puberty. This is a state of unconsciousness, when the individual is under the care and guidance of parents, particularly the mothering agent. Early ego development is so much under the domination of the mother that "the chief concern is the relation, not of the ego but of the child's total self to body, to mother, and to mother as representative of the world" (Neumann, 1976, p. 137: Allan & Bertoia, 1992).
- Jung's second stage, youth, begins adult consciousness and extends from puberty to midlife. "Only with the progressive development of the ego does automorphism become evident as a tendency of the psyche to let the individual develop in his or her uniqueness." (Neumann, 1976, p. 129). Integrating the duality of feminine and masculine (anima and animus) archetypes is important in this stage.
- The period of midlife, from 40 to 50 years of age, is the period that Bridges (1980) describes as liminal, the threshold, the gap. This is the period in one's individuation process that one looks inward, exploring the development of the self archetype.
- After 50, Jung's third stage, wisdom, is seen as a period when consciousness calls for a dialogue between the ego and archetypal images

Table 4. DYNAMICS AND STRUCTURE OF PERSONALITY ACCORDING TO JUNGIAN PSYCHOLOGY

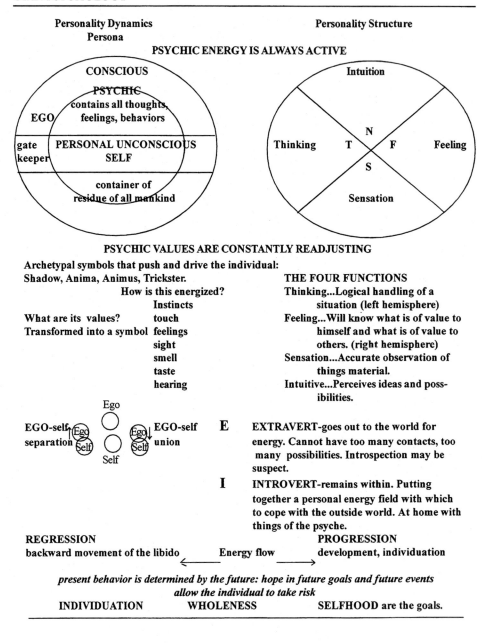

Personality Dynamics
Persona

Personality Structure

PSYCHIC ENERGY IS ALWAYS ACTIVE

CONSCIOUS

~~PSYCHIC~~

contains all thoughts, feelings, behaviors

EGO

gate keeper

PERSONAL UNCONSCIOUS
SELF

container of
residue of all mankind

Intuition

Thinking T   N F   Feeling

S

Sensation

PSYCHIC VALUES ARE CONSTANTLY READJUSTING

Archetypal symbols that push and drive the individual:
Shadow, Anima, Animus, Trickster.

How is this energized?
Instincts

What are its values?   touch
Transformed into a symbol feelings
sight
smell
taste
hearing

THE FOUR FUNCTIONS
Thinking...Logical handling of a
situation (left hemisphere)
Feeling...Will know what is of value to
himself and what is of value to
others. (right hemisphere)
Sensation...Accurate observation of
things material.
Intuitive...Perceives ideas and possibilities.

Ego

EGO-self   EGO-self
separation   union

Self

E EXTRAVERT-goes out to the world for
energy. Cannot have too many contacts, too
many possibilities. Introspection may be
suspect.

I INTROVERT-remains within. Putting
together a personal energy field with which
to cope with the outside world. At home with
things of the psyche.

REGRESSION   PROGRESSION
backward movement of the libido   Energy flow   development, individuation

⟵   ⟶

present behavior is determined by the future: hope in future goals and future events
allow the individual to take risk

INDIVIDUATION   WHOLENESS   SELFHOOD are the goals.

Table 5. LIFE CYCLE ACCORDING TO JUNGIAN THEORY

Childhood	A state of unconsciousness.
Puberty	The beginning of youth that extends to mid-life (35–50) Consciousness is concerned with ego development and master of age specific life tasks.
After 40	Bridges (1977, p. 15) refers to the period after 40 as the "gap" when paths cross and humans explore personal dreams and self-images previously unrecognized.
Maturity	Wisdom develops and conscious moves inward calling for a dialogue between the ego and the self.
Aging	Occurs at the age that consciousness recedes into unconsciousness.

reflected in activities of the self. And, now, the ego loses its importance to the self.

- Aging, Jung's final stage, occurs when consciousness and the ego recede into unconsciousness.

Jung believed that the ego, located initially in the unconscious, develops through consciousness and individuation. In this lifelong process, humans become aware that there is no individuation, no wisdom, without relationship.

Jung's archetype of the Self is essentially an innate, unconscious psychological structure that orchestrates psychological growth and development. It is both the creator and the source of psychic life (1933/1953). At birth, the Ego archetype, the center of consciousness in Jungian terms, is embedded in the archetypal unconscious matrix and is "present in a weak and undifferentiated form" (Allan & Bertoia, 1992, p. 6). During the first year of life, in early stages of ego development, the infant's physical and psychological need for nourishment and nurturance is ongoing. Rocking, holding, nurturing, and feeding the infant reduces the rage that results from his experience of unmet needs and provides momentary relief. Relief nurtures the child's ego, mediating between inner drives and outer reality, i.e., "I have a need and it will be met." When, however, infant needs are not met or the infant feels threatened, when there is no relief, or inadequate relief, the infant "must defend itself against threat or be annihilated or overwhelmed" (Allan & Bertoia, 1992, p. 9). The psychic energy of a threatened human, child or adult, will call in the defense troops and build both biological and psychological defense mechanisms. Over time, these defenses will become thick and rigid, with accompanying physical and psychological behavior expressed as anger, anxiety, body posturing, denial, paranoia, repression, and projection. Frequent volcanic explosions of anger and violence will erupt as psychic energy breaks through the defenses that try to keep it in control. In contrast, when the defenses are "seemingly nonexistent" and impulses cannot be contained, children will become "hyperkinetic, impulsive, and undersocialized" (Allan & Bertoia, 1992, p. 9).

With a healthy relationship between self and mother, there is what Neumann (1976) refers to as the alignment of the ego-self axis. This is an alignment between the ego and the self, the conscious and the unconscious (Allan & Bertoia, 1992; Edinger, 1973; Neumann, 1976). With appropriate parenting the normal child's ego can handle pain and pleasure appropriately. The child can cry when hurt, verbalize feelings when angry, seek parental help when needed, take in pleasure, and experience affection, laughter, and humor. For healthy emotional development, the ego (consciousness) learns to look at painful experiences, feel the pain, understand the significance of the experiences, and then let go and move forward. Jung likens the development of ego throughout life to a heroic struggle.

Childhood Ego Developmental Stages (Neumann)

Identified by Neumann (1976), these stages include:

- The phallic-chthonian stage, both vegetative and animal;
- The magic-phallic stage;
- The magic-warlike stage;
- The solar-warlike stage; and
- The solar-rational stage.

These stages are often seen symbolically in the art and play of children, adolescents, and even adults. The child's ego, in the first vegetative and animal stage under the direction of the mothering agent, is unconscious and passive. It is reflected in the great and giving mother, goddess, virgin, witch, and evil stepmother. The ego in the second and third stages develops activity under its own magical direction. It reaches beyond the archetypal nature of passive mother to the active archetypal nature of father. In the fourth stage, the solar-warlike phase, the ego identifies itself solidly with the father archetype. This is seen in the child's fascination with stories of princesses and knights, cowboys and Indians, space wars and Power Rangers®.

Jung (1964, p. 185) identified stages of adult development (puberty to aging) in the stages of Anima development: Pure instinctual biological sexual relations; Romantic and aesthetic love, Spiritual love; and Wisdom. He identified Animus developmental stages (p. 194) as Physical power; Planned action; The word; and Meaning.

Although Freud (1900/1958) emphasized the language of the unconscious in dreams and symbols, it was actually Jung (1954/1974, 1964) who, by valuing archetypes, recognized the importance of visual imagery and universal symbols in human personality development. For example, Jung (1960/1978) identified the masculine personification of the unconscious in females as the animus and noted that a woman absorbs her animus from growing up with her male caretaker. Likewise, he identified the feminine personification of the unconscious in males as the anima, noting that a male absorbs his anima from growing up with his female caretakers (Arrington, 1986). Becvar and Becvar (1988) wrote that in many ways, Jung's thinking was consistent with the assumptions underlying the practice of family therapy, although little is mentioned of his thought in family therapy literature.

Discussing the marriage between art and psychotherapy, Edwards (1987) says that for the client(s) in [family] art therapy, the artwork both simplifies and complicates the therapy. It is simplified because the client/therapist relationship . . .

> takes place partly through the artwork, which can variously be described as a buffer, filter, screen or container . . . and the art work mediates between patient (client) and therapist. . . . From the moment of the first expressive gesture, the subsequent stages of creating do not usually conform to will or expectation. Even a consciously planned and deliberately executed image has a way of seeming to speak back to its creator with a personality of its own. What is more, the personality of the image may not be immediately likeable. It frequently, even usually, has an alien aspect, a quality of "otherness." And yet, it has to be faced that the image, despite its alien characteristics, definitely belongs to the person who made it. The dialogue now begins between the person and the image the person has made (for the person and the behavior). At the same time, the image itself is still in a process of transformation or resolution. It calls for attention. The "otherness" of images can be disconcertingly unpredictable (and inordinately curious. It is not easy to know what the) image is asking from its maker. (p. 101)

This personification of image initiates inquiry today, next year, or in years to come because energy is contained in the image. The energy, however, may be oblique, or may make the individual feel too vulnerable, too exposed, too powerful, or too frightened, to assimilate it. The therapist assumes responsibility to connect with the energy in the art, to receive it and assist the client(s) in bringing it into culture, tradition, and understanding where the therapist can mediate between client and visual expression.

ELIZABETH RECONNECTS THROUGH ART. Elizabeth, a middle-aged professional, was recovering from the loss of her friend, and romantic companion of 10 years. With his passing, her dreams of home, family, children, and continuity also faded. Early childhood feelings of abandonment, isolation, and loss resurfaced. She felt as if she were spiraling downward, depressed and depleted. A deeply religious person, her physical, emotional, and spiritual pains gnawed at her like a hungry animal. Her eating went out of control. She never felt satisfied. Elizabeth's pain was the dominant feature of her life. She was caught between isolation and exhaustion, praying too many unanswered prayers, working too long and too hard without satisfaction, being numb, confused, and unfocused. She thought that her therapy was going nowhere. Questions of spirituality and ultimate concerns plagued her. Who could fill this calamitous canyon of feelings? What would her future be? When would this excruciating pain go away? Where was her security? Why did she lose this friend, this love, this partner in relationship?

An associate, a ceramicist, began experimenting with clay and special earth tone glazes. He encouraged Elizabeth, who had taken ceramics in college, to try her hand with the clay. Working alone and reminiscing over weekly interactions with her therapist, she spontaneously made a portrait of her feelings in the shape of a small bowl, the shape she came to call her family forms. Elizabeth, in an altered state of mind induced by her creative process, returned to an earlier time in her life. In this meditative state she worked in the soft, cool, mud intuitively, without thinking. She relaxed. She could manipulate the material without pressure or expectations. Her first small bowl was half the size of her fist. A tiny figure grew out of the bottom of "the cave" with several other figures swirling around and above her, always out of touch or reach. A cave, according to Cooper (1978, p. 31) represents the womb and mother earth, a place of burial and rebirth. Elizabeth glazed the pot and fired it with her friend's special glaze. She showed her therapist. She then made another, and then another, repeating the small bowl-cave shape with first one tiny figure and then others swirling out of the depths but never touching, all covered in the same earth tone glaze.

Elizabeth's archetypal earth tone forms reflected feelings that she had felt in her early family life, and now, in her grief, here they were again, reflecting her feelings of abandonment and isolation.

The next bowl Elizabeth made was slightly larger with the small figure at the bottom and the rim lined with people touching hands. She painted this one in colors. With each newly fired group, Elizabeth shared the family forms and their meaning with her therapist, who encouraged her to risk and explore her feelings in the non-verbal media. She began a series of family forms that included lighthouses, and turtles. Turtles, according to Cirlot (1962) represent "the synthesis of heaven and earth" (p. 95), perhaps the reemergence of Elizabeth's inner divinity. "Light is traditionally equated with spirit. . . . becoming illuminated is to become aware of a source of light, and, in consequence, of spiritual strength " (pp. 187–188).

Observing the pots and her process, Elizabeth was encouraged to follow the lead of her forms and images, and reach out to other people. Her spontaneous art had become a symbol of her prayer life, her inner power and a vehi-

Figure 22. *First Cave* by Elizabeth.

cle for communication with her therapist. Her art process had become a sacred process of recovery. As Elizabeth reconnected with her soft, tender center, she was able to reach out and touch the tender centers of others.

Today, she continues to construct clay forms that include many images (Figure 24). Elizabeth has extended her family and her art has become her spiritual companion in her ongoing individuation process.

ATTACHMENT AND OBJECT RELATIONS

For good or ill, children are malleable, capable of being shaped and formed, easily controlled or influenced, and adaptable, but all within limits, and often only in critical periods. During the first two to three years of life, patterns of attachment are the property of the relationship. The mothering agent is in charge. If parenting changes, patterns will change accordingly, but patterns of attachment, once established, tend to be self-perpetuating. Attachment patterns, formed in the context of the family network, stay with us the rest of our lives, and dictate many of our actions as they relate to language and relationships.

Figure 23. *Family Forms* by Elizabeth.

Figure 24. *Family Forms with Lighthouse* by Elizabeth.

"Attachment is an affective bond characterized by a tendency to seek and maintain proximity to a specific figure, particularly while under stress," notes Bowlby (1969/1982, p. 12).

Infants, have a built-in need for object attachment and relationship. "(This) attachment develops apart from feeding experiences but also where releasing stimuli of many types activate the process"(Anthony, 1994, p.184).

Fairbairn (1954), a forerunner in object relation influences on personality development, believed that child-parent attachment was primary to healthy child development, noting that early childhood experiences, positive or negative, psychologically imprint the child.

Building on the premises of both Fairbairn and Bowlby, Mahler et al. (1975) researched object relations and the mother-child relationship. Their data identified stages of object constancy development and led them to believe that these retained experiences, or introjects, affected responses and reactions to others in later life (e.g., spouse or friends) in the same manner that a child "perceived, reacted, and responded to parents in earlier years" (Wilcoxon, 1987, p. 3).

Kohut (1971), in his parent-child attachment studies, identified the first stirring of selfhood as the self-object, the archaic grandiose self. Perhaps Kohut would say that our young performer of *Beauty and the Beast,* Michelle, had developed cohesion of the self. Her grandiose self had been mirrored, she had learned to self-soothe, and because of these things she was becoming more independent of her parents. Jungian developmental theorists (Allan & Bertoia, 1992; Edinger, 1973; Neumann, 1976) would say that Michelle's ego-self axis (a good relationship and connection between the unconscious [Self] and the conscious [Ego] mind) was in alignment. Throughout her life, Michelle's early longings, like those of all of us, will continue to need "self-objects," those people or things valued for making us feel good, special, and important.

Caring parents also provide developing children with information for living in relationships. This includes the discipline of limit setting: roles, rules, restraint, and containment. "Parental disapproval creates negative feelings in the securely attached child, extinguishing unacceptable behavior and leading to the development of a conscience. Pride emerges when the child receives parental approval and then feels good about him or herself" (Levy & Orlans, 1998, p. 42).

TUCKER TESTS AUTHORITY. Tucker was overextended in play. As bedtime approached, the almost three-year-old became more and more impatient with his toys, his sister, and his parents, whining, crying, kicking the toys, and throwing his arms around. Tucker's mother put the objects of frustration in the toy box and firmly but lovingly picked Tucker up and held him tightly as she carried him to bed. He relaxed in her arms and for a few minutes after she

Figure 25. *Testing Tucker,* illustration by Amanda.

left everything was quiet. Then Tucker, testing, ran back in the room screaming. In a rage, little Tucker positioned himself, feet apart, hands on his hips,
and then he stuck his tongue out at his Mom (Figure 25).

A surprised Mom contained her smile. Dad, watching the confrontation
from the couch, spoke with authority. "Tucker that is naughty, goodnight."
With that Tucker ran back to his room crying. Quiet quickly settled over the
house. Five minutes passed and out of the bedroom came Tucker, skipping,
laughing, and singing the taunt, Da da da da da Da - Da da da da da Da.
Repeating his earlier performance, but this time in a playful and teasing way,
Tucker stood with feet apart, hands on his hips, smiling, tongue sticking out.

Mom and Dad purposely ignored the performance and pretended to read
while Tucker skipped around and repeated his song and stance one more
time. With the help of his parents, the toddler was now in control of his rage
and once again felt good about himself, appearing like a much older child
who had been embarrassed by parental disapproval. Tucker tried, in his own

way, to communicate that he really was not naughty. He had only been kidding. Letting Tucker complete his performance, his parents looked up and said firmly, "Tucker, goodnight" and Tucker ran to his room and went to bed.

Children are born more nice than naughty. But all children at some time want their way, even as they need the love of their parents. When they are out of control, children need to know that someone is there to hear their need and help them tame their rage. Discipline, from a caregiver of a young child, is a necessary component in the *cycle of love*. Children develop beliefs and expectations about themselves and others based on attachment patterns with primary caretakers. External and loving discipline provides relief for a young child's rage before he or she learns to internalize self-discipline through the development of a conscience. Caregivers who do not provide stable environments that contain infantile rage foster uncontrollable behavior that explodes in latency or adolescence, requiring social involvement of community agencies, mental health services, and/or medical personnel and police.

BEHAVIORAL SCIENCE DEVELOPMENT

In recent years, a paradigm of developmental behavioral science has evolved "encompassing the concerns that neighboring disciplines (anthropology, cognition, economics and sociology) have with the social environment of human action" (Jessor, 1993, p. 117). The key points that contribute to this paradigm need only be noted here, as they are discussed at length in Jessor (1993). Any understanding of personality development must include understanding of the society, not just the family, in which the person is raised.

Psychosocial Theory (Erikson)

Erikson's psychosocial theory of development supports the importance of social behavior learned in families and committed relationships throughout the life cycle (Erikson, 1963). Family support begins and is significant as a foundation in early developmental years. Erikson believes that the "cornerstone of a vital personality" is formed in infancy as the child interacts with parents or other caregivers (Rice, 1997, p. 216). Erikson's social development evolves through the a series of eight psychosocial stages (Table 3). It suggests that internal individual needs and the external demands of society put pressure first on the family, and then on the individual as he or she makes directional changes moving from stage to stage. Although stages overlap and are not completed at specific times, inadequate resolution of crisis at any stage hinders the development of succeeding stages. Erikson (1963, p. 68) goes so far as to say that "when crisis is not resolved, or a developmental need not met, a deep rage is aroused comparable to that of an animal driven into a corner." With children, it is the parent's job to provide opportunities for relief to them, be it acceptance, containment, or sublimation, for their internalized rage.

Cognitive Theory (Piaget)

Whereas Piaget's (1971) periods of development are cognitive rather than psychosexual, psychodynamic, or social, they also assist families and professionals in understanding age-appropriate behaviors, expectations, and thinking (Table 3). Piaget's cognitive developmental stages are integrated into understanding the whole person.

- *Sensory-Motor (age birth–2):* Piaget's first stage, involves learning to respond through motor activity to the various stimuli that are presented to the senses. At this stage, action is knowledge (e.g., crawling, walking, talking).
- *Preoperational (age 2–7):* Piaget's second stage, includes the ability to think, to connect words to objects and events, and to communicate using those words. The action is language, verbal or nonverbal, and thought that equate to personality.

Gardner (1973) says Piaget is interested primarily in those mental processes that result in scientific thought and can be expressed in logical terms. An example of Piaget's preoperational (second) stage, in which the child develops the ability to think, to connect words to objects and events, and to communicate using those words, can be seen in the following story of Carl as he tries to make sense of and a connection to the words he hears.

CARL TRIES TO MAKE SENSE OF WORDS AND BEHAVIOR. Carl had just turned three when his PaPa Lou died. Standing quietly in his new vested suit in the cemetery in front of the skirted casket that was carefully centered over a recently dug hole, Carl was taking in the experience. He had witnessed all of his relatives come together in a church in the middle of the afternoon. Many of them cried. Strangers brought food to Grandma Judy's, kissed his mother and father, and patted Carl on the head.

At the cemetery, his mother held him close and pointed to a metal marker at the edge of the casket skirt. She softly explained that Grandma Dorothy was right there next to PaPa. That aroused Carl's curiosity. Carl looked closely. He didn't see anyone. Carl was at the stage where he was developing language and memory skills, this episodic event was about to take root, and Carl was trying to understand what his mother meant. First, he looked under the skirt to see if anyone was there. Still he did not see anyone. Carl spent the entire burial service folding his tiny body over to see if anyone was in the hole he saw beneath the skirt. When he did not see anything but darkness, he tried lying on his stomach on the metal marker, slowly and quietly inching toward the raw earth. He tried very hard not to disturb the adults talking around the coffin and the skirt. When the talking stopped and people moved away, he waited a few minutes and then he lifted the casket skirt and peered into the darkness. Unsatisfied, he walked to all four sides, repeating his actions. Finding no person, no Grandma or PaPa, Carl left the coffin and the skirt and went from one metal grave marker to the next in the park. Few adults noticed this small child as he ritualistically jumped on each marker. He bowed his head and stood quietly. Then he raised his arms and his head. Looking at the sky, he released a long and low "Ahhhhhhhhh." With drama, movement, and voice, he physically honored something; he wasn't quite sure what it was, but he knew it was important to his family.

In Piaget's preoperational stage, Carl understood that his mother's words were representative of something important, but he did not have enough experiences to make the connections. Gardner (1973, p. 30) suggests that the only way to understand human development is to psychologically analyze both the art a human creates and the artist who creates it. If we could understand Carl's artistic drama, it would be necessary to have observed Carl and the events leading up to his presentation. Children who learn open and direct communication do so from caretakers who are sensitive to their needs to live and experience family events and emotions.

VISUAL CONSTRUCT DEVELOPMENT

As early as the nineteenth century, it was known that "all children possess a universal language of visual symbols" (Troeger, 1992, p. 30). This nonverbal language, like other developmental processes such as attachment, cognition, individuation, object constancy, sexuality, and social ability, develops generally in a predictable sequence (Table 5) (Anderson, 1992; Harris, 1963; Kellogg, 1969–1970; Lowenfeld, 1957).

Pioneer art therapist and educator Thomas Pasto (1968) identified the impact the family, in the crucial years, has on the child's expressive development. At year one, the child expresses himself through "swing scribbles, the sound of joy, and the feel of muscle" (p. 66). A child around two years of age "will attempt in his circular swings to fence in his mother and himself to create a cosmos which revolves about him and which he controls. The mother image and the circle become associated together, and so will remain for the rest of his life" (p. 65). At age three, the child faces opposition and the prob-

Figure 26. *Examples of Basic Visual Construct Development.*

lem of integrating the masculine and feminine. In the fourth year, "the child draws a rectangle, the sign of the ego" (p. 66) (Figure 27).

By the mid-twentieth century, research on child art development by such notable art educators as Goodenough (1926), Schaefer-Simmern (1950), Koppitz (1968), DiLeo (1970, 1983), Jolles (1964/1992), Machover (1958), Drachnik (1975, 1995), Gardner (1985), and Ulhin (1981) had a major influence on the interpretations and expectations of children's artistic expression.

Table 6. VISUAL CONSTRUCT CONTINUUM

Human Drive Toward Making Patterns and Meaning

All individuals consciously and unconsciously communicate their fundamental thoughts and inner feelings through selecting and spontaneously expressing visual constructs (Arrington, 1986). Certain basic visual constructs appear consistently in a person's artwork. The appearance of the constructs is developmentally predictable (Kellogg, 1967; Lowenfeld, 1964) and implies parallel stages of psycho-social-emotional stages of maturation. They move from the presymbol making stage (chaos) through stages of increasing ability, awareness and maturation to a point of high or symbolic art. They move from unstructured to structured. The creative process hooks into the right hemisphere and allows patterns to form and emerge through the left hemisphere.

DEVELOPMENTAL CONTINUUM	BASIC VISUAL CONSTRUCTS (BVC)	VISUAL CONSTRUCT CONTINUUM THEMES
1. Random Scribble		1. Chaos - Stage of rhythmic and kinesthetic exploration - the beginning of pattern.
2. Circular, vertical, and horizontal forms		2. Cluster - Attempts at integration. The mind tries to hook into patterns already there.
3. Sun and sun shapes		3. Centering - Ability to center and define self and others.
4. Preschematic		4. Body image - Growing awareness of self. Refinement of personal boundaries and composition of variety of body image projections. These may include animal forms as a way of distancing from self.
5. Schematic		5. Takes on a consistent pattern of body image.
6. Line detail and pictures		6. Grounding and environments - awareness of self and others in space (land, water, sky).
7. Color		7. Color and energy - Awareness of color in natural relationship (emotions) and with unnatural color used expressively.
8. Depth perception		8. Directionality -Awareness that things change over time and have natural process either defined or implied. Values established.
9. Symbolic art		9. Realism

It is important to note that high psycho - social - emotional development indicates that the person is free to use any and all basic visual constructs to create symbols that best express thoughts or feelings wishing to be conveyed.

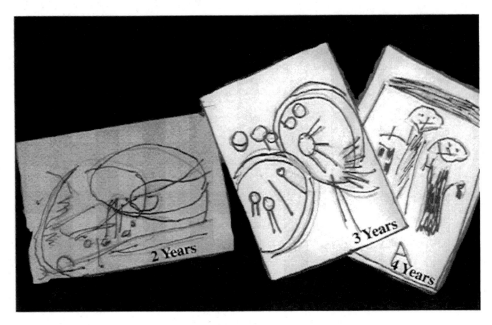

Figure 27. *Examples of Visual Ego Development.*

Feldman (1980) extended Piaget's unilineal developmental scheme to include five domains that affect artistic development. These include universal development, which is achieved by all humanity; cultural concepts, which are achieved by all members of a culture; and skill and craft development, which are discipline-based (this is achieved by a small segment of a culture), and lastly, idiosyncratic development. Although each individual is unique, only a small number of a culture achieve idiosyncratic development.

Empirical research conducted on children's art developmental level by Levick (1983) revealed that children in preverbal, sensorimotor development, unconsciously connect basic visual constructs with their primary care-givers (mother, fathers, and siblings) and their environments. These universal and predictable constructs (Kellogg & O'Dell, 1967; Kellogg, 1969-1970) "serve as an index of ego function in spontaneous drawings of children and adults" (p. 18). They develop in a "hierarchy of perceptual experiences" (Wilson, 1987, p. 46) along with personality development and serve both "adaptation and communication" (p. 57). Gerber and Lyons (1980) found that levels of development portrayed in adult drawings can also be assessed for points of childhood fixation and/or degrees of regression. In 1991, Troeger (1992, p. 32) concluded that Piaget's (1971) "concepts of normal cognitive development provide a structure for identifying images which are atypical at particular levels of growth."

Chapter 4

THE CYCLE OF VIOLENCE

A HUMAN BRAIN, that has been nourished and nurtured, can, with its intricate interaction of neurons invent ways to survive and repair unfair treatment or abuse. One that has not cannot without help. Alice Miller writes:

> For although I had undergone two complete analyses as part of my training, the analysts had been unable to shake my version of the happy childhood I was supposed to have had. It was only my spontaneous painting, which I took up in 1973, that gave the first unadulterated access to my early reality. In my paintings I came face to face with the terrorism exerted by my mother, at the mercy of which I had lived for so many years. For no one in my environment, not even my kind father, could ever notice or question the child abuse committed under the cloak of child rearing. (1990, pp. 6–7)

VIOLENCE

Somewhere between World War II and the turn of the century, the United States, as viewed on television and in the newspapers, became a frighteningly violent country in an equally frightening and violent world. Countries act and react to other countries with extreme, intense, sudden, and unjust force or destructive action. In epidemic proportion, families and individuals in families often follow suit, living on a behavioral continuum from excellence to evil, nurturance to neglect, social to isolate. Batterers batter and kill their spouses and children because, as they often report, they "love them so much they can't live without them." "The number of youth held in juvenile facilities has increased 41% in the past ten years. . . . The number of children seriously injured by maltreatment quadrupled from 1986 (140,000) to 1993 (600,00)" (Levy & Orlans, 1998, p. 4). Homicide, the eleventh cause of death for all

Americans, is the third leading cause of death for children between five and fourteen (Children's Defense Fund, 1994, p. x). Information from *The State of America's Children Yearbook* (Children's Defense Fund, 1994, p. xii) continues:

- Every 5 seconds of the school day a student drops out of public school.
- Every 26 seconds a baby is born to an unmarried mother.
- Every 30 seconds a child is born into poverty.
- Every 4 minutes a child is arrested for an alcohol-related crime.
- Every 7 minutes a child is arrested for a violent crime.
- Every 2 hours a child is murdered.
- Every 7 minutes a child is arrested for a drug crime.
- Every 4 hours a child commits suicide.
- Every 9 hours a child or young adult under 25 dies from HIV.

Teen pregnancy, abuse and neglect at home, inadequate child care, poor schools, and lack of health care are among the biggest dangers threatening America's children (Torassa, 1999, p. A-14). But, when these news headlines affect our neighbors, our friends, or our family members, we rant in disbelief. Like Psyche, in the myth of Psyche and Cupid, when in crisis we seek out Pan for answers (Neumann, 1956). How can this be? What is the cause? What can we do?

In ancient societies, humans formed skills and strengths in response to their environments and experiences, and the range of meaning those experiences held for them. Neurobiologists tell us that this continues to be true. Preverbal experiences of infants provide the organizing structure for underdeveloped infant brains (Perry, 1997). These early experiences are recorded in our senses (taste, touch, sight, smell, sound, and movement), not in our words. This neural human armature composed of three brains in one (the brain stem, the limbic system and the cerebral cortex) holds the neurons that actually determine who we are. These areas, molded by sensory experiences at critical periods, determine core neurobiology (Damasio, 1994; Goleman, 1995; Lambert, Bramwell, & Lawther, 1982; LeDoux, 1996; Perry, 1997). This brilliant, intricate, non-verbal brain system allows humans to breathe, move, feel, fight, flee, assess, plan, think, and visualize. It is a testimony to the healthy human brain's great plasticity that, when the individual is nurtured, intelligence and creativity are fostered, and yet, when the individual is exposed to neglect, stress, and trauma, he or she becomes emotionally vulnerable and intellectually unstable. Neurochemical responses to malnutrition, disease, and violence during the first three years dramatically mold the young brain structure, resulting in the anxiety, depression, and aggression that thwart learning and development.

In the aftermath of the Columbine High School massacre, we are told that children's brains are shaped by the multiple images to which they are exposed. Their cognitive muscles, weaned on *Sesame Street* and nurtured on *MTV* and computer games, reflect what the environment has inputted and downloaded, developing young brains at rates different than the rates at which their elders' brain developed (Jennings, 1998). Although older humans have similar brains, changing environments shape brains differently, causing individuals to think and react accordingly.

Humanity, with its expanding scientific and technology resources, has not been freed from its dependence on interpersonal relationships reflected in image and symbols. Indeed, it could be argued that science and technology have increased humanity's need for both. Contemporary societies are constantly searching for more elaborate and refined expression of symbolic outlets, as seen in our advertising, cyber-communications, entertainment, religions, and space explorations. A recent commercial made by Reebok contained eight images in a single second in an effort to attract the attention of a generation whose brains have been bombarded, pierced, and shaped by visual information. The format of the commercial is an athlete rapidly jumping rope. Supposedly there are 480 single-image landscapes and actions that enhance this image. But they appear so quickly that they are difficult even to identify (Shank, 1998).

Through neurological imaging procedures, scientists identify areas of the brain responsible for retaining and reacting to multiple experiences. These sensory experiences both dwell in and construct convergent zones (small ensembles of neurons) in our brain. Beginning in the brain stem, these dispositional representations, or neural patterns, react and respond, ordering other neural patterns about. When they fire back to early sensory cortices, located throughout the higher-order associated cortices (in the occipital, temporal, parietal, and frontal regions), and in basal ganglia and limbic structures, they result in *images* of either response or relaxation. Human brains cannot respond and relax at the same time (Erickson, Rossi, & Rossi, 1976; Damasio, 1994).

Our brains, influenced by environmental experiences and feelings such as love and joy, hunger and fear, react in *images* that affect the interactions of the convergent zones, inhibiting or enhancing our human behavior, cognition, and emotions. The results, good or evil (Crick, 1994), weave our social tapestry. What is extraordinary is that we know this, but as yet, we have not taken the steps necessary to reduce, if not eliminate, early human suffering.

Violence, with its severe and damaging consequences to human functioning, has always been a part of human behavior, but in recent history we have been led to believe that one could recognize "good guys and gals," by their symbolic white hats. Today, with instant and global communication, diverse and confusing belief systems and erratic behavior models, much of the "white hat" symbology has turned to gray. When Americans hold homes, schools, or communities as sacred, we are left to wonder how violence can happen there. Home, after all, is one's dwelling place. It is the abode of one's family, and supposedly a place of domestic affection, not domestic violence. In our symbols and mythology, home is where "good guys and girls" live, people who love, nurture, and protect, not ones who scream, terrorize, and abandon. Now, however, through seductive symbols and images, violent, self-serving behavior, with its instant and direct exposure into homes through television and the Internet, is often seen as the norm. This "pyramid effect" (Levy & Orlans, 1998, p. 5) of abuse, neglect, and abandonment is transmitted intergenerationally to children, who are made to feel worthless as they grow up and replicate their childhood experience.

Like the *Cycle of Love* in the previous chapter, the *Cycle of Violence* begins with need, human need. When, as pointed out by Erikson (1963), need be it for love, sustenance, or limit setting is not met, it turns to deep rage. As humans age and are more able to delay gratification, the rage becomes more internalized and less obvious, unless it explodes in some violent way. Whenever rage is met with inconsistent relief, no relief, or even abuse, insecurity and broken trust follow. When abuse or unfair treatment, without human care, continues over even a short time, human withdrawal and isolation are the result. When abuse or unfair treatment, without human care, is continued over an extended time, humanity creates a formula for developing violent and dangerous human beings that require expensive and extensive social interventions.

VIOLENCE ASSOCIATED WITH MALNOURISHMENT AND MALNURTUREMENT

Today, when an estimated 13.5 million children in the U.S. live in governmentally defined poverty ($16,400 a year for a family of four, according to Torrass, 1999, p. A14), one must consider malnutrition as a major form of violence committed upon the young. Malnutrition is not only damaging to infants and toddlers, but to latency age children as well (Brown & Pollitt, 1996). Malnutrition creates life-threatening need, disrupting cell functioning that often results in irreversible damage to the nervous system and emotional stability. Affected even by how recently one has eaten, energy necessary for exploration and learning is sapped, reducing an individual's "interaction with other people and with their surroundings" (Brown & Pollitt, 1996, p. 40). This intellectual and physiological damage negatively affects personality development, mental functioning, and all manner of behaviors. Federal and state school breakfast and lunch programs are provided as a result of these findings.

Table 7. THE CYCLE OF VIOLENCE: Broken Trust

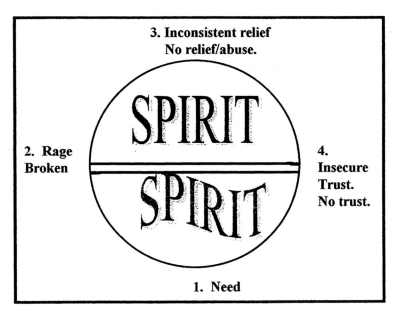

Source: Adapted from Cline, 1991 with permission.

Malnutrition also alters the immune system. The immune system, physiologically and emotionally entwined within the human body (Goleman, 1995), travels in the bloodstream like a blue dye, tainting every cell for good or ill. Those cells that the immune system recognizes leaves them alone; those it does not it attacks, defending the body against diseases like cancer, or creating its own problems such as allergies and autoimmune diseases.

As significant as the information on malnutrition is, it is equally relevant that research can now identify the effects of malnurturance or violence on humans (Sapolsky, 1998), particularly children. For children, abandonment or separation from their significant love objects can be considered as malnurturance and violent trauma. When there are early separations, when human ties break or get lost, as in abuse, abandonment, death, neglect, and traumatic or serial divorce, the negative memories, experiences, and relationships cling to us like lichen keeping us the bottom feeders in our environments. Perry (1997) calls this "emotional retardation" (p. 5) and points out the far-reaching destructive influences that emotional retardation has on personality development and interpersonal relationships.

Nerve terminals in the autonomic systems communicate directly with immune cells. Under stress, these cells are influenced or even suppressed by elevated hormones known as adrenaline and noradrenaline, cortisol, prolactin, and natural opiates. When hormones, such as cortisol, wash over a youngster's tender brain, they react like acid. They literally eat away new and soft regions in the cortex and in the limbic system that are responsible for essential human thinking and emotions such as attachment, concern, and empathy. In abused children, these areas are "20 to 30 percent smaller than they are in non-abused children. In abused children, activity in the brain structure involved in survival (vigilance and arousal) is left more exposed, thereby increasing problems in attention, regulation and self-control" (Gunnar, cited in Begler, 1997, p. 32).

People who experienced chronic anxiety, long periods of sadness and pessimism, unremitting tension or incessant hostility, relentless cynicism or suspiciousness, are found to have double the risk of disease—including asthma, arthritis, headaches, heartaches and ulcers. This order of magnitude make ongoing and negative emotions as toxic a risk factor as high cholesterol or smoking—in other words, a major threat to health (Goleman, 1995, p. 169). When we consider all of this, we are truly led to wonder, what kind of interventions and government programs are, or should be, available for children who are malnurtured?

CHAD AND BETHANNE, HOMELESS BUT NOT HELPLESS

Chad and Bethanne were poor children, born into a poor family, but it is doubtful that they started out as children-at-risk. It is doubtful that, as infants, they were malnourished or mal-nurtured. Actually, they were six and twelve when the storms of violence began raining on them. Their story, of two at-risk but resilient youth (noted as one of the most distressing cases seen in the agency where they were treated) follows.

Chad and his family were recommended to the nonprofit agency by local school administrators worried about this new nine-year-old who rarely smiled, played, or did his school work. Often he just sat, staring into space. After some difficulty locating the family by phone, the therapist sent a note home with Chad asking his parents to call for an appointment. Surprisingly, Dad called and on the appointed day Dad came in, leading the family. Warm, overweight, full-bearded, looking a little like Santa Claus, Dad introduced his significant other, his fifteen-year-old daughter, Bethanne, and his nine-year-old son, Chad. Dad said simply that the children had recently come to live with him and he wanted to be as helpful as he could. Dad did most of the talking, with little interaction from either of the emotionless youngsters. Completing the intake materials, Dad made a single appointment for the following day. When he returned, he came in sighing, lit a cigarette, put it out, and

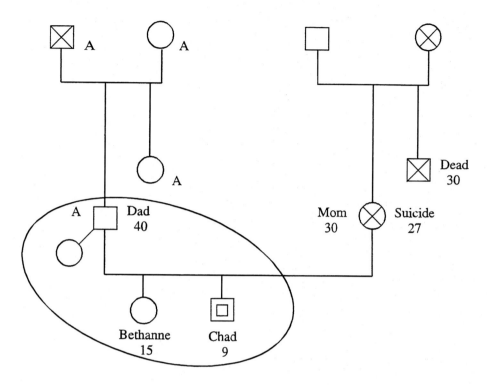

Genogram 3. Chad and Bethanne's Family.

then, in bits and pieces, began telling his story, often responding to the therapist's questions by saying he couldn't remember, he wasn't there, "maybe," "yeah," or shaking his head.

Dad noted that while he was using drugs and alcohol he had made some poor choices and ended up in the state penitentiary for armed robbery. Prior to going to jail, Dad said the family had lived the good life. He worked as a plumber and Mom worked as a waitress so that she could be with the kids. They lived in a trailer in the woods where, with friends, they partied a lot, a whole lot. One evening while Dad was in prison, Mother went out to buy bread and never returned. She took a drug overdose and died in her car. Child Protective Services picked up the children, from their life-long home, and sent them with one suitcase apiece to live in a new community with their closest relative, Mother's brother, who had a long history of drug dealing. About the time Dad got out of jail, Mother's brother torched his house in the middle of a drug raid, and the kids, now, with only the clothes they had on, were held in protective custody until the father, out of prison, was located.

Dad and his current significant other met after he got out of jail. Although Dad didn't feel that he really knew the kids (he had been away four years), he

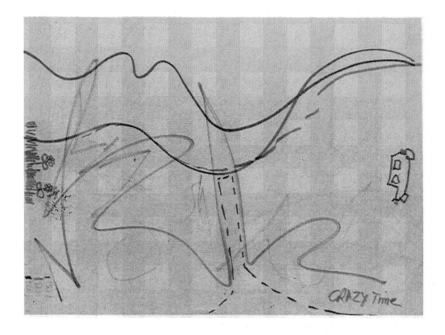

Figure 28. *Crazy Time* by Chad and Bethanne's family.

appeared to want to help them. But with Dad's history of alcoholism, the chances of his staying clean and sober with his new family pressures and responsibilities were slim. Bethanne and Chad had become children-at-severe-risk.

The initial family art-based assessment with the family included Landgarten's (1987) Nonverbal Family Art Task (Appendix A-2). The family titled it *Crazy Time* (Figure 28).

The first assessment, drawn with markers, was made with no interaction, no talking, no touching, and no overlapping of colors. Dad and Joy sat on one side. Bethanne and Chad sat across from them, male opposite male, female opposite female. Each person worked in his or her own space in front of where he or she was sitting. The family worked, nonverbally, on a single piece of paper, each with a separate color marker. When they were finished they stopped and Dad decided on the title.

The second assessment, made with colored plasticene, was created in a similar fashion. Although they were told they could talk, Dad was the only one who actually spoke in sentences. The others just grunted or made brief comments. Throughout the process, the family, except for Dad, was solemn and still. Dad and his significant other were the only ones who were some-

Figure 29. *Space Dog* by Chad and Bethanne's family (plasticene).

what involved. When they finished, after a brief discussion, they named the creation *Our Space Dog* (Figure 29).

Following the family evaluation, the therapist, concerned about the children, particularly Chad, felt it was important for them to work through their grief (Figley, 2000). Assessing Chad for a cognitive and affective baseline, the therapist had him draw a house, a tree, and a person (Buck, 1948).

The visual syntax of the art-based assessment (Figure 30) further indicated Chad's emotional fragility. Light line pressure, slanted placement, and the bottomless, unstable, ungrounded house depicted Chad's living condition and his internal lack of stability. The crown of the tree indicated severe confusion and the tiny, fraying stick figure indicated loss and a sense of disconnection.

The family briefly attended a group the agency held for families. When they stopped, the therapist went to the schools to see the two children and drove by their house to see if Dad was home. Although cars were in the driveway, the shades were pulled shut, and no one responded to the bell. Slowly, consistency, and participation in art projects helped build a relationship with Bethanne. Board games, and shared walks and treats built one with Chad, one that reduced his resistance and lack of trust. By December, Chad began sharing his concerns, verbally and in art.

Chad 's disclosure to the therapist that he and his sister often slept in the closet with pillows over their heads while Dad and his significant other drank

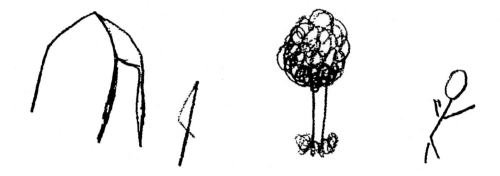

Figure 30. *House-Tree-Person* by Chad, age 10.

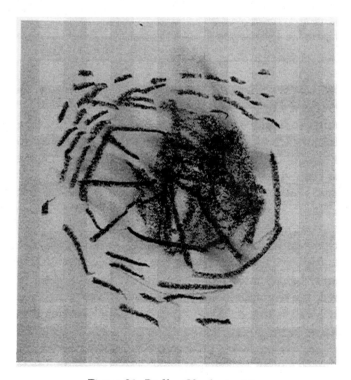

Figure 31. *Dad* by Chad, age 11.

and fought was the reason for the therapist's initial call to Child Protective Services. At the next meeting, Chad, anxious and agitated, reported that Dad, in a rage had broken "lots of things" in the house, thrown all of his girlfriend's belongings into the yard (in the rain) and told her to leave. Quickly the problem escalated. Bethanne moved out. After some time, the therapist located Bethanne, who had moved in with a friend's family. Providing Chad additional support, the therapist began seeing him twice a week.

Panicked and anxious, Chad left a message insisting on seeing the therapist as soon as possible. When he saw the therapist he gasped, "My dad and I got evicted after someone came by and shot in the house. We are living in the car and there is no food." Then he asked the most basic of questions, one that few therapists ever hear: "Who is going to feed me?" The therapist intensified her efforts to get social services involved. But, when she finally connected with them, the therapist was told that Chad was lucky. Social Services would provide food stamps, but Chad had a Dad and they had a car. However unstable their circumstances the boy and his dad had a place to live. Within a week, Chad was no longer in school. He and his dad, living in the car, were moving from one state park to the next with two-week permits. Occasionally Chad would show up at school and call the agency to see his therapist. He always asked the question, "Why won't someone adopt me?" Knowing the nonprofit agency's limitation to facilitate physical change without doing harm to members of the family, the therapist felt impotent.

Finally, one cold blistery day, Chad and his dad disappeared. No one, Bethanne, school, agency, or friends, knew where they had gone.

The following September the therapist received a message from the school that Chad had reenrolled and wanted to see her. Chad, in a more positive emotional state, verbal and open, reported that when Dad had been sent back to prison he left Chad in Southern California with his aunt, who also drank a lot. He continued, "One day Bethanne came down to see me. She brought me home and I never went back. No one has ever come looking for me. Now, Bethanne and I live with her boyfriend in a garage apartment at a really big house."

Bethanne's boyfriend, 19, also homeless, had made friends with the homeowners. The boyfriend lived in the garage apartment for free, while working as the gardener. It appeared that Chad's ultimate concerns, food, shelter and being with nurturing family members had been met. Chad, now began to use therapy to help him understand what had happened to his life and family. One week, a large cardboard box appeared in the playroom. Chad used the box again and again to replay the last time he saw his mother (Figure 32). He persuaded the therapist to get in the box and close her eyes, and often he requested she fold her hands together while holding a flower. He placed her as if she were lying in a coffin and then asked her to lie still. Next

Figure 32. *Memories of Mom* by Chad (Polaroid Collage).

Chad would use the agency's Polaroid® to take pictures of the therapist "laid out" in the box. This occurred again and again, until the large box, battered and worn , was finally discarded and Chad had some kind of understanding of what it meant to bury someone.

Chad had been young and confused but Bethanne had had to grow up fast. She learned the meaning of "parentification" early. Not quite 17, Bethanne was going to school, working as a waitress, and with the help of her boyfriend, supporting herself, and now her brother. She seemed better pre-pared than anyone else to care for both herself and her brother. There appeared to be no alcohol or drug use in her life. She met the requirements for emancipation, and with the help of the agency, these two at-risk children became a family. In the emancipation process, the therapist asked Bethanne how she avoided getting in trouble. Poignantly she replied, "I knew that if I ever got in trouble no one would get me out."

RANDY R. SEARCHES FOR HOME

Both financially and emotionally, Randy was at the opposite end of the continuum from Chad and Bethanne. He lived the first five years of his life in a privileged but chaotic and malnurturing environment. He lived with changing authority figures, and inconsistent love and attention. Randy had no shots fired in or at his house. His parents were not addicts or alcoholics. His father did not go to prison. His parents did not use or sell drugs or drink themselves into oblivion. But Randy was exposed to emotional neglect and physical violence in both behavior and abandonment. Research evidence indicates that emotional neglect, and psychologically unavailable caregivers, are more harmful to children than physical neglect or other forms of maltreatment (Hetherington et al., 1998).

Through Randy's early years, constant factors in his life included his brother and his grandmother's luxuriously appointed environment. Sending Randy alone to his Dad's, away from his brother and the environment in which he had grown up, was the beginning of a violent loss and the continuation of a cycle of negative events.

On the other hand, Randy's Dad and Stepmother lived in a typical middle-class suburb, and as much as they might have loved and wanted to help Randy, they, like most other young couples, had only their own childhoods as examples of how to raise children. They were at a loss as to how to help a confused and labile five-year-old.

Dad, an upward-moving executive, traveled a great deal of the time, leaving much of Randy's care to Stepmother. Stepmother, from a hard working and thrifty family, had chosen a career over children. It had never occurred to her that her new husband's children, or child, might come to live with them. With limited perception or interest in what had been Randy's prior sense of place, it wasn't long before, through the use of timeouts and restrictions, Stepmother had Randy under control, cleaning his room and doing his own laundry.

Stepmother would set rules for Randy and enforce them through timeouts and chores. She volunteered that she did not use physical punishment, as she had seen her dad use when punishing her brothers; instead, she had Dad spank Randy if Randy had not followed the family rules while Dad was away. Each week when Randy relayed to grandmother, by phone, his sad situation Grandmother would resolve it as she always had, by sending expensive and inappropriate presents such as tape decks, camcorders, and cameras, com-

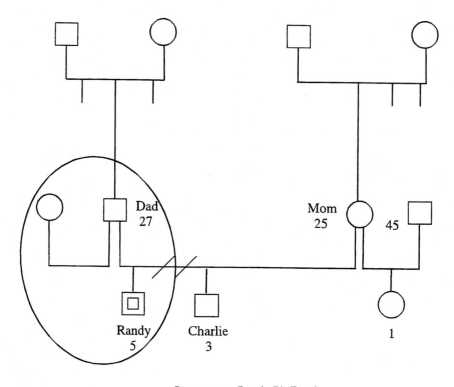

Genogram 4. Randy R's Family.

pounding the new family's problems with the bonding process and further confusing Randy.

A tenacious individual, Stepmother knew that she could provide a home for Randy. But it wasn't going as she had envisioned it, nor was her marriage, for no matter how hard she or Dad tried doing what they knew how to do, this sad and serious youngster continued to be in pain, leaking his distress onto everyone around him. The parents, out of despair, moved in the right direction, and sought therapy.

Like family therapy, one of family art therapy's modalities is brief therapy (8–10 sessions), focusing on problem solving and helping individuals in a family, or the family as a whole, use their resources and move on to their next developmental levels intact. The process includes gathering information, listening, asking questions nonjudgmentally, and encouraging the repair of previous hurts while building positive relationships. If therapy needs to be extended beyond the brief model, that is often an option. One never knows when therapy begins how long it will take. In this case, the R. family continued in treatment off and on for over six years.

Figure 33. The R. Family Lifetime.

Initial formalities with this family included (a) a verbal and written family and medical intake, (b) a family interview using a genogram (Genogram 4), a visual interview using a Family Lifetime Chronology (Figure 33), and a Family Art-Based Evaluation (Appendix A-1). The R. Family Genogram at the beginning of therapy revealed known family structure and facts.

The Family Lifetime chronology integrated visual and verbal memories and events, what and where, as in a family blueprint (Figure 33). In the family lifetime, the therapist encouraged all members of the family to present general information about the present family and their perception of how they came to this time, even if each person's story was different (Satir, 1967). Then the therapist encouraged the family to expand the lifetime to include how they met, their thoughts and feelings about that, and what their lives were like before these particular problems arose. Beginning at the present and moving back to a more positive time decreases fear and increases hope (pp. 112–134).

With positive affect, the couple revealed that they had known each other for six months before they married. They had married six months before Randy came to live with them and he had been with them four months.

The couple, unprepared for Randy's profound lack of trust, was at a loss to know what to do for him (Erikson, 1963, Visher & Visher, 1988). Open and raw, he grieved his core attachments: home, mom, grandmother, and brother. "One of Bowlby's postulates is that the loss of a mother figure between six months and 3–4 years has a high degree of negative potential for subsequent personality development due to the occurrence of mourning processes" (Malmquist, 1994, p. 187). Randy's persistent anger was an essential part of his unconscious efforts to recover his losses. With the early loss of both of his parents, Randy's young developing brain had allowed him to mourn vicariously by attaching to his grandmother and becoming his younger brother's guardian. But now, both were gone. Although his Dad was available, Randy had not attached to his Dad. Everything was different and Randy was angry. He projected his anger randomly and intermittently both at home and school. Denial "on a conscious level" of the permanence of the situation, and Randy's inability to "engage in normal mourning processes, [eventually] necessitated a split in his ego" (p. 188). Or perhaps, as Goleman (1995) notes, he established "two memory systems, one for ordinary facts and one for emotionally charged ones" (p. 21). Randy had been denied the power to recover his losses. His emotionally charged memories overwhelmed him, marking his behavior with (a) temper tantrums and provocative language, which had been learned and accepted in his other life, (b) pleasing and coercing both his Dad and Stepmother, and (c) finally giving up in despair. Randy's confidence in parent protection or power was diminishing.

FAMILY ART EVALUATION (FAE)–THE R. FAMILY–A FAMILY ART-BASED ASSESSMENT

Prior to establishing goals with this family, the therapist asked them to participate in a Family Art Evaluation (FAE) (Kwiatkowska, 1978; Appendix A-1). She began by asking the family to use the materials freely and draw whatever came to mind.

First art task: Draw whatever comes to mind

Dad used oil pastels to draw something he could see in the room (Figure 34). Stepmother drew what may have been a memory of her past (Figure 35) and Randy drew a house (Figure 36). Randy's house was large, grounded and well-structured. Smoke was coming from a reinforced chimney and a flower and sun were on the left side. A symbol Randy identified as a doorknocker was on the door with a doorbell on the right of the door. Perhaps the door-

Figure 34. *The Office Plant* by Dad.

Figure 35. *The Horse* by Stepmother.

Figure 36. *A House* by Randy.

knocker was symbolic of Randy's openness for help. Drachnik (1995, p.53) sees emphasis on the chimney as a possible sex abuse symbol.

The second directive, "Draw the family doing something together" followed

When asked to "draw the family doing something together" all three family members drew the family in a line with limited interaction or touching. Dad drew the family, as they often were at home, in sweats (Figure 37). Mom drew the family as she described, on their way to dinner (Figure 38), and Randy drew the family and Rob the large turtle that lived in the garden (Figure 39). In Randy's picture (Figure 39) Randy is almost invisible. Dad and stepmother have on strange hats. Drachnik (1995, p. 42, citing Oster & Gould,

Figure 37. *The Family in Sweats* by Dad.

Figure 38. *The Family Going Out* by Stepmother.

Figure 39. *Family members and Rob the Turtle* by Randy.

1987) sees hats as indicative of exerting energy to control angry feelings. Randy's anger is understandable when you look at the world from Randy's perspective. It is certainly probable that Randy could believe he was taken rather than sent from his mother's home. It is also common for humans to project their anger on the family member who they have rather than on the family member who they have lost.

When the family was asked to draw the third directive, abstract family portraits, Dad drew three books: an appointment book for himself, a checkbook for his wife, and a school book for Randy. Stepmother drew a cup of Starbucks® coffee for herself, a golf club for Dad, and a heart for Randy. Randy drew a baseball bat for Dad, a Big Mac® and fries for Stepmother, and a figure of himself. (Figures not included.)

The fourth directive (Figure 40). The therapist asked the family members to create a joint scribble, allowing each family member to enhance a shape or symbol they identified in the scribble. Together the family was asked to create a story about the shapes.

Fourth art directive: "Find three objects in a joint scribble and create a story about the shapes"

The picture developed from Stepmother's heart, Randy's balloon, and Dad's curvy road. The heart and the balloon on a curvy road to somewhere

Figure 40. *The Heart and the Balloon on a Curvy Road to Somewhere* by the R. Family.

pretty well described the family at this time and in this space. The final direc-tive was once again, *"Draw whatever comes to mind."*

Dad drew a roller coaster seen from above as a bird's-eye view (Figure 41). Stepmother drew a perspective view, a walkway into a garden with a flowerpot at the end of a path (Figure 42). This time Randy drew a house from a worm's-eye view, large, less structured, and somewhat overwhelming (Figure 43). The house has a bright red door and many different size win-dows. A bell is in the triangular attic. A thin-lined rainbow, a symbol of pro-tection, was in the sky on the left (Ulhin, 1974) and a small red flower was on the bottom right.

By providing the family with an opportunity to use the non-verbal lan-guage of art, all of the family members–Dad, Stepmother and Randy–could communicate at the same time, be heard and therefore, treated fairly. In addi-tion, the family would be seen together sometimes, and at other times, indi-vidually or in coalitions (Dad and Stepmother, Dad and Randy, Randy and Stepmother). There would be no secrets between the therapist and any of the family members. What was revealed in one session might come up, with the help of the therapist, in another. The immediate purpose of therapy was to assist these family members with parenting, congruent communication (Satir, 1964/1967), and in an appropriate way, match feelings with effect.

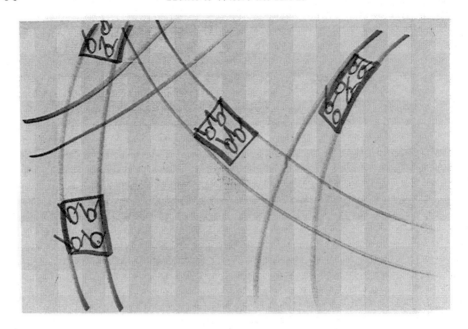

Figure 41. *The Roller Coaster Ride* by Dad.

Figure 42. *The Pot at the End of the Walkway* by Stepmother.

Figure 43. *A House* by Randy.

Randy was part of a family, a network of family structures, hierarchical organizations, and subsystems. By focusing on the family context rather than the individual context, Randy's symptoms could best be understood. Both Randy's mother and Dad used patterns of isolation and avoidance. Randy, a bright and forthright child with many unmet needs, provided additional stress to both his Mother's and Dad's new relationships. In both instances, the universal pattern of hierarchical organization (parents have more power than children) was left to and assumed by the stepparent, resulting in weak and ineffective parental subsystems. Whereas rigid boundaries existed between child and stepparent, diffused boundaries existed between child and parent.

Dysfunctional alignments of triangulation (child, parent, and stepparent) were the results.

As seen in the Introduction, the therapist's goal was to join with Randy, his Dad, and his Stepmother, observing how the family achieved balance and homeostasis and to help the family members look at their perceived realities. By doing that, family members, particularly Randy and Stepmother could reduce their feelings of isolation, triangulation between Dad, Stepmother, and Randy could be avoided; and the family could stay more focused on positive affect and relationships.

As with most plans, however, there were flaws that were not immediately evident. The major flaw was that not all of the players, i.e., Randy's Mom and Grandmother, would never be in therapy, but would always be in the picture. Randy was caught in a double bind by both Mother and Father. Mother and Grandmother used money to give Randy messages of love and at the same time they enforced transactional patterns of rejection and isolation by sending him away. Father and stepmother used words and actions to give Randy messages of love but at the same time they punished and disciplined him. Something that had been lacking in his early childhood.

The next house that Randy drew (The House and a Fuzzy Sun, Figure 44) was large with a red door and a doorknocker. It was on the left side of the picture. On the right he drew a rainbow encapsulating a cross. In the middle above them he placed a smiling, fuzzy sun. Drachnik (1995, p. 63) sees the sun in the middle or on the right-hand side of the paper as representative of the father. She sees the sun on the left as representative of the mother (personal communication, Drachnik, 1995). The house and the rainbow were placed on a solid area representing ground. The picture, more positive, suggested that Randy felt better about his surroundings.

But for Randy, a gifted child who was in Erikson's (1963) industry versus inferiority stage, the focus was always on family. It was not surprising that whenever Randy, either with his parents or alone in the playroom, was asked to "draw or paint whatever you like," he generally started with a picture he called "Home."

Figure 45, *The House and a Rainbow* is no exception. This time Randy's house is smaller, well structured, centered with lots of smoke coming from the chimney. This one, like the others seen, is age-appropriate; drawn with a grid, as if he is trying to organize the environment in which he lives. This house, like earlier ones, has a small, pointed roof and his door has a knocker. This picture includes a picture of a tree, larger than the house. The tree has five apples. Four of the apples are grouped together, as if representing his home with his original home, mother, father, Charlie and himself, and then one apple is alone. The tree has turned-up roots and the trunk is unusual, with multicolored layers. Drachnik (1994) refers to turned up roots as a rejection

Figure 44. *The House and a Fuzzy Sun* by Randy.

of mother (p. 33). The house and tree are placed on two layers of earth. Did the multicolored tree trunk and earth represent the many homes in which Randy had lived? A red quarter sun appears on the right side of the picture.

Figure 46, *Families Need a Home* begins to reflect Randy's diminishing coping ability. Although the house is drawn with a grid, similar to the last one, entrance into it is more difficult, the door is turned sideways. It appears that a garage and an extra side have been added to the house indicating perhaps that Randy does not feel part of the family. Dark smoke is coming from the house. Randy wrote "Families need homes" in the left top of the picture.

Drawn several months later, Figure 47, *The House and the Hill* is different yet similar. There is a large hill covered on the top with round shapes. There is a small fruit tree encapsulated by the hill with upturned roots and a large knot hole. A small flag is next to the tree. A small house on the right of the hill is recognizable as Randy's. It has a grid and small door with Randy's door-knocker. The picture is disturbing in several ways. No longer are there windows in the house. A balloon of smoke emits from the chimney. Red quarter

Figure 45. *The House and a Rainbow Tree* by Randy.

suns appear in both the right and left corners of the picture, and a large flower is haphazardly drawn in the sky. Peterson and Hardin (1997) list seven serious indicators for screening children's drawings. These indicators include encapsulation and added fruit trees (p. 25). Drachnik (1994, p. 48) sees kites or balloons as a desire to get out of or above the family environment.

Randy's art reflected life, not necessarily as it was, but equally disconcerting, as he was experiencing it. Not only did Randy have a family life with his father and stepmother, he also had daily or biweekly phone calls from his mother and grandmother. Figure 48 has no grounding for the small red house, the tree, or the three snow-tipped mountains. A large red quarter of a sun appears in the left corner. The house has no windows, grid or knocker.

Figure 46. *Families Need Homes* by Randy.

The tree, larger than the house and the mountains, is between mountain two and mountain three. The knothole on the tree is larger than those previously seen but the roots of the tree still turned upward.

In Figure 49, *The House, the Trees, and the Flowers* has no base or foundation. The little red house is smaller than Randy's other houses and unstably leans to the right. The house is on a plain with two flowers, a tree, three flowers, a tree, a flower, a tree, two flowers, a tree, and three flowers. The therapist questioned if these were combination of families with whom Randy had lived? All of the trees, strange, even bizarre have long, wavy limbs and no leaves. The red quarter sun is on the right side.

Figure 47. *The House and the Hill* by Randy.

In Figure 50, *The Smoking House,* the red house with a door stands on the ground in a bleak environment. Wavy lines indicating smokes reach from the left bottom of the house to the sky. The red quarter sun is now on the right.

During the following year, Randy and his family continued therapy. Art and verbal interventions included free drawings, scribble chases, instant collages (magazine pictures) of future dreams; word tapping, talking about or drawing the event named, and making Me and We Boxes together (Appendix B–G).

Randy responded to suggestions to draw something or someone that could protect you, (Appendix B–J) with a figure he identified as the Lone Ranger (Figure 51). The Lone Ranger, a figure on a horse and a teepee began appearing in his pictures.

In Figure 51, *The Lone Ranger,* on his horse is facing the small red house. Smoke from the house aims at the large half-sun seen on the right. Two large clouds appear in the sky. Burns (1987) sees clouds as "anxiety, something hanging over one's head" (p.149).

(Whereas standardization of symbols in the United States is fairly accurate and continues to be researched, it is, in its infancy universally. In my family, art therapy work and research with poor, homeless children, and families in both the Ukraine and Guatemala (2000) clouds appear consistently in their pictures, even when they are drawing "their favorite kind of day." No research

Figure 48. *The House and the Snow-Topped Mountains* by Randy.

Figure 49. *The House, the Trees, and the Flowers* by Randy.

Figure 50. *The Smoking House* by Randy.

has identified, however, whether this is true of all individuals in those countries or just those who are anxious.)

Although Randy and his family had some successes during his first year with Dad, involvement in Cub Scouts, a few friends, with his soccer team (with Dad as coach) advancing to the playoffs, Randy's cycle of malnurturance continued to evolve. The following summer, Randy's Mom invited him to visit for a couple of weeks and see his brother Charlie and a new baby sister. Visiting his Mom and his brother and stepsister reopened Randy's painful wounds. When Randy returned to Dad's house a month later, his unresolved infant narcissism increasingly put him at a disadvantage with his peers. Randy set himself up to get bullied and teased. This allowed Randy to nurse his hurt feelings, rejection and depression.

Randy's art continued to reflect his state of mind. Figure 52, *Three Hills in the Rain* reflects Randy's growing depression. The house, hardly recognizable as Randy's, sits on the center of three hills. A smudge of dirty green (possibly trees) is on each side of the house. The house is wide, with a door, a red roof and chimney. There is a red quarter sun on the left. Three clouds and spatters

Figure 51. *The Lone Ranger* by Randy.

of rain cover the picture. Drachnik (1994, p. 48) sees this as indicative of depression and low self-esteem.

The following winter, Mom's family dynamics changed, but her personality patterns did not. She divorced Stepfather #1 and moved in with a new boyfriend. Under the new boyfriend's influence, Randy was placed in greater peril. Returning for a visit the following summer, Randy was invited by Mom, with no prior discussion with Dad and Stepmother, to stay. When Randy, now eight years old, with limited coping skills and an expansive fantasy of what it would be like to again live with Mother was pressured to stay at Dad's, his suicidal tendencies surfaced. Randy hung ropes in trees and then put a noose around his neck. He stood on deck railings acting like he was going to jump. He tested the waters and hinted at killing himself.

On a large sheet of paper, Randy drew himself in his bed. A small, sad face looking at the viewer. The background is colored in gray (Figure 53). The therapist, after consultation, met with Dad recommending that Randy go to his Mom's. The decision was made knowing that (1) Randy certainly could be depressed enough to follow through on his ideation, (2) if he did stay with

Figure 52. *Three Hills in the Rain* by Randy.

Dad, his anger would increase and he would surely project it onto Stepmother, and (3) perhaps Randy and his Mom could reunite.

Randy, depressed and with suicidal thoughts, moved into his eighth home and with a mother who had no idea how to live with a now completely confused and despondent child. Living arrangements had not been thought through and the maid's room, separate from the family wing of the house, was made into Randy's bedroom. Randy, angry and disappointed, had wanted time with Mom; instead, he shared whatever time Mom would give him with her new boyfriend, his brother, or his little sister, and then Mom got pregnant again. Randy's misery infected everyone. Even Charlie, his little brother, asked him why he had come back because he was so bad. Mom and her boyfriend battered and yelled. The boyfriend set rules even stricter than those of his stepmother. From Randy's point of view, the boyfriend had no right to do that; he wasn't Randy's Dad. Split between two families, Randy felt like an outsider and was treated like one. Five months into this unhealthy arrangement, with Randy's ego-self-axis out of alignment (Allan & Bertoia, 1992), Randy's thick defenses snapped. He painted expletives on the walls with markers, dumped glue on the rug, and tore the doors

Figure 53. *The Bedroom* by Randy.

off the cupboards in his bedroom. Mom's boyfriend took raging Randy to the acute psychiatric setting for children, where he was diagnosed as severely depressed and treated as an inpatient for a month with medications and follow-up upon his release. Randy learned a lot there. The next time boyfriend came after him with a belt, Randy showed the bruises to his teacher, and boyfriend, charged with child abuse, left the house and left Mom. Randy, however, more hostile and belligerent, faced more losses and stress. Having rebelled against Mother's toxic environment, Randy was rapidly returned to his Dad and Stepmother and his new baby sister, at Dad's home (Forward & Buch, 1989).

By the time Randy returned to his Dad's, Randy had been so physically and verbally abused that he was brittle and defensive. Not able to hold his Mom or Dad in contempt, because he would surely lose their love, he held their partners in contempt, stonewalling any attempts at nurturance or repair.

Randy was in a crisis. Even with more care, the mold had been cast. Randy, now in late latency, was taking an internal position of "no trust." Fig-

Figure 54. *The Black House* by Randy.

ure 54, *The Black House* shows a lonely house. This one is black, but still with a door and a doorknocker. The house sits on one of three hills. There is a swirling sun on the left, and many anxious-looking clouds moving toward the right.

Randy's family did not go to therapy that year. Therapy came to the family. Randy's Dad and Stepmother, recognizing their limits, placed Randy in therapeutic day treatment where the family received home visits and guidance in behavior modification, and Randy received medication. Medication was ruled out as ineffective, but behavior modification was not. Through all of this, Randy communicated his needs and confusion nonverbally, through art, and his Dad, acting as assistant scoutmaster, worked to keep him appropriately involved with other children.

About Christmas time of that year, Randy painted a moose on top of three strange-looking mountains underneath four clouds connected by a swirling sun (*The Moose on the Mountains*, Figure 55). The entire picture was covered with rain, or self-deprecation marks. The moose, a large relative of the stag, is associated with Hercules as a symbol of an individual freeing him-

Figure 55. *The Moose on the Mountains* by Randy.

self in the quest for immortality from his sins and errors, monsters and struggles (Cirlot, 1962, p. 145). Randy had been shifted and moved so much that his emotional bank account of human attachment and stability were depleted. But his unconscious searched for images to sustain him.

Randy no longer felt safe in his environment. He had internalized two cultures, his mother's and his father's (Hong, Morris, Chiu, and Benet-Martinez , 2000). Both cultures lived inside of him. Never integrating, but often motivated by cultural images, they took turns guiding his thoughts and feelings. For example in his mother's home, he would get a $20 bill to buy candy at a movie. In his father's home he was expected to do chores and got money, ($5 bill) only for extra work in the house or the yard. Gradually, Randy's compulsivity helped him defend against his depressive "frame switching" and loneliness (Malmquist, 1994). Randy's family tried to help as he tried to hold his world together whatever way he could. In many pictures Randy drew during this period, he literally had a stake and a spike nailed into the earth

Figure 56. *Holding the World Together* by Randy.

holding it down. In this picture the stake is holding down half of a hill that is on the left. On the right is a tree leaning to the left. The tree has a knothole but no roots. A flower is drawn on each side of the tree. A teepee, often drawn for the Lone Ranger is under the tree. All of this sits on a grassy base. A round, stitched bush sits in the middle. The sky is filled with clouds from one side to the other. Lightning is coming down on both the right and left sides. The sun is split in the middle.

With a heavy dose of tough love and tough peers, Randy sealed over his emotions and learned to live with his perceived reality of his family and his home life. He internalized both the good and the bad. He drew two houses that connect like a duplex. They sit on one of the two hills. His tree has deprecating marks in it. The house and the tree slant with the landscape. The round object (sun or moon) in the left sky is colored white. The colors are gray and gloomy.

Within family constellations, family development and dynamics are ever-changing. The year following therapeutic day treatment, crises continued to evolve. Randy's misery was now in pubescent bloom. This time the crisis

Figure 57. *Split House* by Randy.

came via Stepmother. Triangulating his father, Randy pushed buttons that made others feel as miserable as he did. Stepmother, in her efforts to control Randy, was pushed beyond her limits. She emotionally and physically abused Randy. Unhappy with her home life, she and the baby moved into a separate apartment. Dad and Randy continued part-time therapy.

Randy's stress level was greatly reduced when he had Dad to himself. In junior high school, at home, and in scouts, his behavior stabilized. In therapy, Randy chose to work in clay (Figure 58, a self-portrait in clay). He made a ceramic self-portrait. Painted white, the eyes suggest a woman's breasts, indicative of the nurturance that he had never received. The slashes in the face reflect his self-deprecation.

Grandmother became more involved as Randy moved into high school. She offered to send Randy to the military school that his uncles had attended. On the surface, Dad and Randy found this to be a good option. However, after Randy left and Dad reunited with Stepmother, Randy felt disillusioned and betrayed.

Figure 58. A self-portrait by Randy (clay).

GOTTMAN'S MODEL FOR POSITIVE AFFECT BETWEEN COUPLES

Gottman (1998) organizes and describes his theoretical concepts and therapeutic process for couples therapy as a "Sound Marital House" model with seven floors. The foundation is comprised of what he refers to as "Love Maps" (couples learning and continuing to know one another through discussion and questions). The second floor he refers to as the "Fondness and Admiration System" that recognizes the importance of and encourages psychological soothing. The "Emotional Bank Account," teaching couples to turn toward rather than away from each other, is on the third floor. The fourth floor contains what Gottman describes as "Positive Sentiment Override." His research found that if couples were to have satisfying relationships, relaxation and reduction of both physical and emotional stress were necessary. The fifth floor deals with "Effective Problem Solving" and learning to dialogue with, and about, personal differences and perpetual problems found in every relationship. The sixth floor helps couples avoid "Marital Gridlock" by helping each other make dreams and aspirations come true. The top floor or the "Attic" is the place of dreams, narratives, myths and metaphors. Gottman sees the "Four Horsemen of the Apocalypse" (criticism, defensiveness, contempt, and stonewalling) as the most destructive elements to the Sound Marital

House and personal relationships. Whereas Gottman's research (1993, 1994, 1996, 1998) is focused on couples, and I have not found any research by Gottman on families or children, applicable to families. I believe, that in the future, that his Sound Marital House Theory, and his positive affect approach to and focused treatment will be equally applicable to families.

NANCY EXPERIENCES THE HORROR OF HORRORS

Throughout the world and in America today, things happen that are just too horrific to imagine. The following story is the beginning of one of those nightmarish events experienced by Nancy and her family.

After school, one afternoon in April, Grandmother Nancy, an "art-doer" with exceptional talent and a special education teacher for severely learning disabled fifth-graders, received a call from her youngest daughter, Kerry, who hysterically sobbed in the phone, "Nathan has been killed." No one, not the police, the firemen, or the mortician, would let Kerry see the body of her eleven-year-old, who had been shot point-blank in the face by a neighbor boy with a history of fascination with guns.

Calls to Nancy's other children, relatives and friends flooded the lines. Nancy and her husband left to be with her daughter and her daughter's family. There, until the middle of August, Nancy stayed, except for brief visits back to her own home. Nancy's large and close family had been fractured by the event. Nancy, mother *par excellence,* knew that somehow, someway, she would protect Kerry. Being with Kerry and her little family could ease their pain and reduce her frightful sense of disruption, disorder, failure, and shame. Yes, shame. Kerry's shame was, "I am the mother who let her child be killed." Kerry's husband Tom's shame was, "I am the father who did not keep Nathan safe," and Nathan's sister Rachel's shame was, "Why didn't I go with Nathan to protect him?" But Nancy found that she could not ease anyone's pain, not even her own. She felt betrayed by her basic trust system.

Recurring Images and Art Solutions

From zigzag images discovered on bones in Europe 50,000 years ago to web sites created in cyberspace today, symbolic images are synonymous with humanity. They reveal the inner lives and outer experiences of their creators. Over the years, therapists from many persuasions have continued to find that graphic images express inner feeling and ideas and blocked or distorted thoughts. Scholars who have studied archetypes and images can identify symbolic themes and images (Arrington, 1986; Goleman, 1995; Howowitz, 1970;

Keyes, 1983; Miller, 1990; Peterson & Hardin, 1997; Ratcliffe, 1977; Rhyne, 1979; Ulhin, 1972; Wadeson, 1980; Wilson, 1987).

Nancy reported having constant internal images of herself, her daughter Kerry, Kerry's husband, Tom, and their daughter, Rachael, bobbing up and down in silent, ice-cold, dark blue water. There were no sounds other than Nancy's mournful internal screams that seemed to go on forever. Although many friends and neighbors tried, there was no one who could help or in any way relieve Nancy's despair.

In August, Nancy had a second image. This time the image included a life preserver floating in the water. It wasn't close, and none of the family survivors tried to reach it.

Then Nancy had a third reoccurring image. A distant cruise ship, laden with bright lights, and filled with noisy, partying people, floated by in the darkness. No one on the ship could see the four people bobbing in the frigid, inky surf. Still, Nancy was unable to express her image.

Nancy's school staff and her friends did not believe that Nancy could return in September to her fifth grade class, a class of eight children all the age of Nathan. But in August as she began preparing to return to her school and students, she began thinking of the school's curriculum theme. For the first time in her 15 years of teaching, Nancy selected Alaska, the frozen northland. Intuitively, Nancy had found a way to survive with her cold and life-threatening images. She froze the water. She led her class as they studied the flora and fauna of Alaska; Alaskan Eskimos; housing; food sources; transportation; entertainment; and the Iditarod race, where competitors travel along hundreds of miles in the frozen darkness to their destination. The students made Eskimos and Alaskan animals out of newspaper and fur.

During the fall, Nancy lived painfully with her grief. As Christmas neared, she began making gifts for her large and extended family. She made snowmen in all sizes and shapes and painted snowmen on t-shirts, sweat shirts, and book bags.

Sealing over her feelings but filled with questions, Nancy was encouraged by her therapist to go back to the horror of horrors and to picture what had happened to Nathan the day that he was shot point-blank in the face. She bought a snowman that she rocked while she watched TV or sorted through all of the possibilities and impossibilities of that devastating event. By February, Nancy was making long-eared snowmen for Easter. She called them her "Long-eared friends" (Figure 59).

The following spring, as winter thawed, Nancy was also able to reach deep into her soul and recover the images that she had been unable to draw before. One image Nancy pictured was of Kerry's home during the past summer. It was a small house encircled by a briar patch. She felt the inhabitants could cook, clean, do the laundry, or garden, but because of the briars and

Figure 59. *Homemade Friends* by Nancy.

thorns, they could not leave the house, nor could anyone enter. Pain and shame encircled it.

Then Nancy visualized a bust of a figure in the dark, cold water holding a baby. The stark head had a skullcap but no hair, and the upper body looked androgynous. There was a crimson blush on the heart area. Nancy referred to the image as a priest. In the background was a warm and rosy portrait of Nathan as he had looked before his death.

At this point, Nancy was free to paint all of the images in one picture.

We leave Nancy here for a time, as images flooded her mind again and again. Art became the way she organized psychic material and transcended her horrific experience shared. The images, pregnant with healing messages, allowed Nancy to function, honor Nathan, and bring meaning to human tragedy.

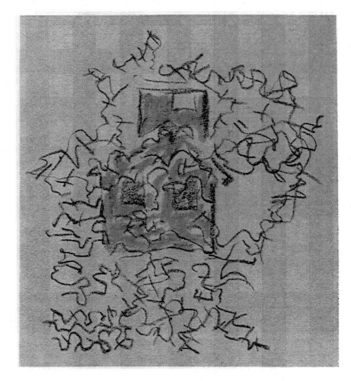

Figure 60. *Kerry's House in the Briar Patch* by Nancy.

Figure 61. *The Priest, the Baby, and the Boy* by Nancy.

Chapter 5

AND THE CYCLE GOES ON AND ON

They tried to force it,
"It didn't fit—So it broke
Now it may be beyond repair"
Jym Marks (1992, p. 28)

THE MOST COMPREHENSIVE COMPILATION of youth-offender data in the 1990s reported by the U.S. Justice Department noted that in the past ten years, juvenile arrests for major violent crimes had grown by one third and the number of juvenile homicide offenders had doubled. "At-risk behaviors in which adolescents engage are related to but distinguishable from the manifold conditions to which youth are exposed. Adolescents are dependent on the living conditions of their parents and families and hence are vulnerable to the impact of conditions well beyond their control" (Jessor, 1993, p. 129). "Juvenile violence is tied to family socioeconomic conditions as seen in poverty, homeless families, runaway and throwaway kids, and drug use. One-fourth of the adolescents aged 10 to 18 in the United States live well below the federal poverty level" (Snyder, 1996). In addition, families most likely to be poor are families headed by single mothers, America's most popular family constellation. The Census Bureau in the early 1990s found that poverty was a reality for three in ten Americans, with children being poor no matter what the measure (Children's Defense Fund, 1994).

Today, however, it is not just poor youth or adolescents who commit crimes. Youths from all social classes are committing horrible, senseless acts. Society would like to know if this is due to bad parenting as indicated by abuse, neglect, lack of discipline, or too much exposure to computer and television games. Perry (1997, p. 5) found that in cases of severe emotional neglect, affective blindness made their young victims into sociopaths unable to connect to other human beings with what we know as empathy. Stone Philips (1999), investigating the Columbine tragedy, found something surprisingly more lethal, lethal because it would appear to be a normal American youth pastime that is imprinting our youth. He found that many American youths repetitively play violent games on videos and computers, the same games that are used for training sharpshooters in the Secret Service and the Federal Bureau of Investigation.

Today, the disturbed youth who commit the crimes we read about appear to have no thought or care for their victims. It appears that not only are these perpetrators emotionally retarded, they appear even to have lost their souls, laughing as they draw blood. Daily, the media report events relating to this national plague. Six-year-old kills six-year-old. Outcast youngsters with guns and automatic rifles kill peers and teachers. Adolescent boys drug and rape young females. Teenage girls rob their victims of shoes and clothing and then kill them for no reason. Children set community fires and torture family pets. Adolescents abandon neonates in dumpsters, strangers' trucks, dance hall restrooms, or at the airport. Kids kill other kids, or adults, or even infants in drive-by shootings, and on, and on, and on. All of these young people, perpetrators and their victims, have families with mothers, fathers, sisters, brothers, grandparents, aunts, uncles, cousins, friends, and teachers whose lives are forever changed because of these tragic events.

At a conference, Gilligan (1995) described a PBS special on the juvenile criminal system:

> I don't remember the evening but I do remember the story that left me with many images. One segment of the show was of multicultural girls, who were killers for really no reason. For things like, I want your jacket. They gave them the jacket and then *Bam Bam,* they were dead. The extraordinary thing about this story was that there was a program in the prison whose major purpose was to try to get the kids to be aware that they had killed a human being, that they had done violence to a human being. Not only was that human life taken away, but it affected so many other people, the victims, yes, but also their family members. The incredible thing was that these kids had no idea that they had murdered a human being. They did not have a sense that it was a person that they were relating with. Only with long-term and creative treatment were the souls of the youngsters in this television feature being restored.

TV exemplifies the problem of trauma experienced by children. Ed Bradley (1989), in a 15-minute segment of *60 Minutes* called "Growing Up in LA," interviewed school personnel and young children and relatives in the Watts area who had seen loved ones murdered: mothers run over, brothers shot, uncles knifed. Relatives seeking help for these youngsters found it unavailable until one school principal, Dr. Melba Coleman, organized a pilot-counseling group. The group, led by a counselor and a psychologist, was established for those in most need, so they could talk about the fears, hurts, and pain that were the results of their traumatic experiences. Because there is so much the young victims cannot talk about, drawing has become an important part of the program, both in creating images and then reflecting on them. Coleman admonishes that society cannot afford to write these children off. She continues, noting that if the children are to become productive citizens rather than mental health patients or incarcerated adults repeating the crimes that they have witnessed, help in the way of professional nurturing must be available now.

CATHY AND SAM AND PAINFUL PARENTAL FAILURE

The following story of Cathy and Sam looks at why and how parents sometimes fail. Cathy and Sam came to conjoint therapy because they were in crisis; their family stress level was out of control. Cathy wasn't sleeping, and to use their term, their communication was becoming mean. With Cathy's initial call, the process of therapy had begun. It continued when they arrived, on time, at the office. Cathy, a slender, attractive woman wearing a lot of makeup, dressed in short shorts, a tank top, and sneakers. Sam, also attractive, was dressed in a collared shirt and khakies. The intake included the necessary agency forms and a rather lengthy family questionnaire. The therapist's first interaction was to ask them what brought them to therapy at this time.

Cathy began. Sam, a business executive, had lost his job through downsizing six months earlier. He had gotten a nice settlement package but it was running out; the bills were piling up, and soon the family would not have health insurance. Cathy had been a stay-at-home-mom, but had recently taken a job as a waitress to earn needed extra money. Her two teenage sons from an earlier marriage were not doing well. The youngest was in a group home for drug rehabilitation, and now the oldest was apparently also using drugs and skipping school. Cathy continued, complaining about her out-of-state alcoholic parents. Becoming more agitated, she said her mom called each week to see how she was, but before the call was over her mom was criticizing her about her wild children and her jobless husband. Finally, Cathy said she wanted Sam to get a job, stop drinking beer in the garage with the neighbors (while she worked two shifts), and be less critical and more understanding of her two older boys. Then she sat back and waited.

Sam sat quietly watching until Cathy finished. Then, almost too calmly, he defended himself, saying that he had several interviews lined up and he knew one of them would work out. It was obvious that Sam couldn't rush the job search because he was not going to take a job that paid less than he had been making. Sam said that for the nine years that he and Cathy had been married, he had tried to work with the two older boys, using both punishment and rewards, but the three of them just did not understand each other. He did not understand where they were coming from and he was sure they did not know where he was coming from. He was hurt; he had helped them more than their own deadbeat dad had done, and they seemed to dislike him all the more for it.

Using Satir's growth model (1964/1967), the therapist asked the couple to tell her about themselves and how with all of the people in the world the two of them had gotten together. What drew them to each other? The therapist searched for a warm clue to assess the love connection between the couple and to see if their individual and shared dreams had futures.

Cathy began with her own family of origin, noting sadly that she had grown up in a chaotic and often violent environment. Both of her parents drank, as did her uncles, who were often at the house. To keep from getting beaten, like her brothers, she tried to stay out of her parents' way. In junior and senior high school she played school sports and worked as a waitress. She married at eighteen to get out of the house but the couple moved in with her husband's parents. After two children, and a move to California, Cathy divorced her first husband because, she said, he drank too much. She relayed a long medley of family worries and crises. She brightened when she talked about how Sam had pursued her when she went to work at the same company. He was handsome and bright, with a good future. He had a nice family. She thought that he was unlike her dad, and she felt safe with him. Cathy had finished high school and taken a couple of college courses, but she said she just couldn't concentrate. She was proud of Sam because he had a master's degree, but she continued to feel less and less comfortable around Sam's family. As they accomplished more professionally, she felt more inferior. After they married, Cathy quit work to have their son. Several times Cathy commented that she really could not see how she could work for long because she was "the chief cook and bottle washer" in the family. It was quite clear that Cathy's unspoken dream was that Sam would love and take care of her and her children. Through the roles and rules in her earlier experiences, Cathy had learned that women need to be in charge of their home, their kids, and all of the household expenses. Cathy's world view was that any alcohol could put you on the road to destruction and destroy your dreams. Rightly or wrongly, she was paranoid about Sam's drinking.

Sam listened intently to Cathy as she talked about her family. He rolled his eyes as she talked about her boys, or his drinking, and then smiled with her as she talked about their courtship. Following Cathy's lead, Sam also

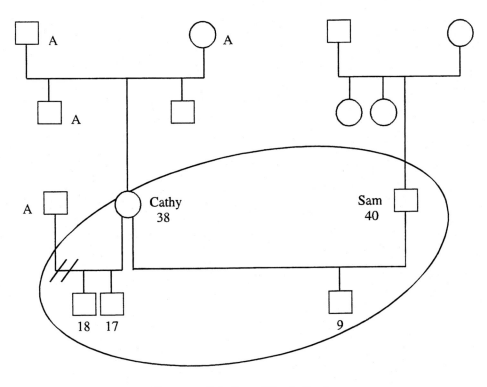

Genogram 5. Cathy and Sam's Family

began with his family of origin. He was a local from the next town. The youngest of three children, he felt close to his family. He, Cathy, and the kids often spent holidays with his family. He felt that Cathy resented them. She interrupted, commenting that his family barely tolerated her sons. Sam responded that Cathy exaggerated everything.

Sam's experience growing up was quite different from Cathy's. Life had been fun and safe. His family was supportive and had helped him succeed. He happily returned their affection. He was the one who often planned family events with his siblings because he liked being with them. He had no understanding and little empathy for Cathy's older boys, who did not share his world view of a supportive family that encouraged hard work and hard play. He had given the boys a home with lots of material goodies. He had paid their expenses and coached them in soccer, but felt their resentment for what he had done for them.

Cathy was happier being in control of the money, so Sam let her run the family finances. Sam's dream was of living in a happy family, as he had experienced in his family of origin. He had learned that as a male he could provide the money for the home but he did not have to be responsible for the way it was run. For now, this family hierarchy was out of balance. Sam was living off of his severance package and Cathy's tips. The former roles and rules no longer applied. Family rituals, like dinner and quiet family evenings, had changed or become nonexistent. This family needed to address workable alternatives. When the therapist asked Sam what had drawn him to Cathy, he smiled and looked at her, and in a broader version validated Cathy, saying she was beautiful, and smart. Dreams were still alive. Both Cathy and Sam exhibited warmth in relationship, and love underneath the hurt. Satir (1964/1967) refers to this area of the interview as a Family Life Chronology, a good starting point in which to look for love energy and trust learned in their family of origin.

Next, the therapist began asking questions about areas that appeared to be unclear. The therapist inquired as to how they had handled finances in the past. What did they do for recreation now and in the past? And, what they had meant by the statement, "The communication often became mean"? Bypassing all other questions, the therapist allowed Cathy's hurt to surface. Cathy jumped right in, saying Sam was verbally abusive. Sam retorted bluntly, saying that if they were arguing and she didn't like what he said she threw things. She would pick up the closest thing to her and throw it, usually at him: her brush, her jewel box, or a perfume bottle. Cathy quickly defended herself, saying that that was the only way that she could get him to pay attention to her. He rolled his eyes again, and responded with, "Oh sure, how could one not pay attention to you?" A spontaneous enactment had occurred (Minuchin, 1974). Obviously, the domestic violence scene was a perpetual problem, one that the couple had played out again and again. It could be scripted, as in a play, diagramming what happened first, what happened second, what happened third, etc., with both knowing how the scene would end (Bowen, 1978). The therapist's task was to help family members change early behavior in the script so that the scene could end differently.

As mentioned earlier, negative behaviors are corrosive to a relationship. Gottman's research (1998) indicates that negative behaviors are often gender specific. Women generally are more critical and men stonewall. In the first interview, the therapist had witnessed Cathy and Sam interact in a both non-threatening and concrete manner as well as in a critical and defensive manner. The therapist had watched, searching for a point of entry, "the lens with which to see the family" (Riley, 1993, p. 253). The therapist stayed in the present, guided by the interaction of the couple. To reduce the tension and physiological flooding and to level the communication field, she introduced the couple to art as communication. This concrete form of expression gave the couple something to hold, look at, and explore at that time and in future sessions.

SELF PORTRAITS TO BE EXCHANGED WITH THE PARTNER– CATHY AND SAM–A FAMILY ART-BASED ASSESSMENT

The therapist had the couple complete an art-based assessment protocol (see Appendix A-4) using:

1. a free picture, Draw whatever comes to mind" (to help them feel at ease);
2. a Kinetic Family Drawing (KFD, a picture of the family doing something together to focus on family issues [Burns & Kaufman, 1972; Petersen & Harpin, 1997]); and,
3. a self-portrait, to be exchanged with the partner's (Wadeson, 1980) and help the couple focus on their relationship.

Cathy, who was a quilter, drew a well-defined quilting pattern in her free picture (Figure 62). Sam drew a sailboat (Figure 63). In Cathy's KFD she drew the family standing in a row (Figure 64). Sam, on the other hand, drew a snow scene with the family lost among the other people in the picture (Figure 65). When Cathy drew a self-portrait, Sam made it into a beach scene with an umbrella and a hat in her hand (Figure 66). He enhanced her figure. When Sam drew a self-portrait, he drew his head (Figure 67). Cathy enhanced his hair and glasses and placed a light bulb with a picture of a sailboat in it. Both were more complimentary than critical.

Art interventions provide an evolving and "expanded focus of observation" or what Minuchin would refer to as spontaneous enactments (1974, p. 451). A spontaneous enactment often helps identify dysfunctional learned family scripts that both influence and are influenced by the family system. In this family, Cathy's defensive scripts included both avoidance and blaming to evoke guilt. She was hypervigilant, anxious, and alert to many nonverbal cues. She had grown up observing, but staying out of the way of the violence in her family of origin. Besides the fights that occurred between her parents, her younger brother, at fourteen years of age, had been hospitalized from a beating by her dad. Her younger brother had run away from home and only reconnected with Cathy after her move to California.

Sam's learned family scripts included avoidance and super-reasonableness that evoked resentment from Cathy. Art bypassed the couple's avoidance script and leveled their blaming/super-reasonable communication field. It revealed sensitive issues, and identified family strengths.

Growing up in a violent and abusive home, Cathy was traumatized by her family of origin. Her stress and anxiety had been reactivated when Sam lost his job and again Cathy felt totally out of control. Although in the beginning of therapy Cathy would have been the last to admit it, her language and blam-

First Art Task: Draw whatever comes to mind.

Figure 62. *A Quilting Pattern* by Cathy.

Figure 63. *Sailing* by Sam.

Second Art Task: KFD, Draw your family doing something together.

Figure 64. *The Family* by Cathy.

Figure 65. *Skiing* by Sam.

Third Art Task: Draw a self-portrait and then exchange it with your partner for their additions.

Figure 66. *Self-Portrait* by Cathy with additions by Sam.

Figure 67. *Self-Portrait* by Sam with additions by Cathy.

ing script indicated that she was more likely than Sam to be the harsh disciplinarian, particularly of her older sons.

EMOTIONAL HIJACKING. Research now tells us that our early, preverbal, sensory experiences create highways that, in emotional circumstances of anger and fear, allow our impulses to outdistance and override our rational mind almost instantaneously. Goleman (1995), reporting on emotional hijacking, says, that neurologically, first, a visual signal goes from the retina to the thalamus, where it is translated into the language of the brain. Most of the message then goes to the visual cortex, where it is analyzed and assessed for meaning and appropriate response. If that response is emotional, a signal goes to the amygdala to activate the emotional centers. But a smaller portion of the original (visual) signal goes straight from the thalamus to the amygdala in a quicker transmission, allowing a faster (though less precise) response. Thus, the amygdala can trigger an emotional response before the cortical centers have fully understood what is happening (Goleman, 1995, p. 21). Most moments of emotional arousal, stored in the amygdala, are imprinted in memory with a tremendous impact, providing the brain with "two memory systems, one for ordinary facts and one for emotionally charged ones" (p. 21). The emotionally charged memory system matches data associatively rather than precisely and often acts with outdated information even before all of the current information is available. Goleman notes that our neural memory alarm system is sloppy, sloppy because many significant memories occur in the preverbal years, in the relationship between an infant and its caregivers. This is especially true for traumatic events of neglect and abuse. "These earliest emotional memories" perceived through our senses of taste, touch, feel, sight, and smell, "often date from a time early in our lives when things and events were bewildering and we did not yet have words for comprehending them" (p. 22). At this early stage of life, parts of the brain have not fully developed. Thus, storage of information is diffused and therefore less controllable later in life. Known as emotional hijacking, this phenomenon "presumably involves two dynamics: triggering of the amygdala and failure to activate the neocortical processes that usually keep emotional response in balance (i.e., recruitment of the neocortical zones to the emotional urgency)" (p. 26). "Over time, and under the right conditions, the prefrontal cortex circuitry effectively intakes, comprehends, and governs our emotional reactions regulating our responses" (p. 25). On the other hand, and important to note, "the amygdala can react in a delirium of rage or fear before the cortex knows what is going on because such raw emotion is triggered independent of, and prior to, thought" (p. 24).

Johnnie, Cathy's middle son, was about eight when he went to visit a friend after school. After the visit, as prearranged, he was to meet his mother at the corner of a busy intersection. But, as he walked to the corner, it started to rain. The rains became fierce. Johnnie, dripping wet, went to a house near the corner and asked if he could call his mom, who by now had already left for the corner. When Cathy did not answer the phone, Johnnie called a neighbor lady, who was happy to come pick him up. Cathy, in the meantime, had arrived at the corner, where she parked and waited. Sitting in the pouring rain, she began to worry. As time wore on she became more worried. Like any anxious mother, she wondered what had happened to her precious boy. She waited, becoming more agitated. Returning home, she waited by the phone. But no one called, so frantically she returned in the rain to the corner. Johnnie in the meantime had been picked up, dried off, put in warm adult clothes, and served milk and peanut butter cookies. Mom returned home with catastrophic fantasies of her child being lost, kidnapped, or even worse, dead. The kind neighbor finally connected with Cathy to say Johnnie was at her house. When Johnnie came home, warm and loved, Mom was relieved that he was all right but distraught and out of control from fear. She beat him with a belt for not minding her. She beat him for leaving the corner, even though it was storming. She beat him because she had been so afraid something awful had happened to him. She beat him because she loved him so much. No one called child protective services for Johnnie. But Cathy, grievously saddened by her horrific, out-of-control behavior, lived with this guilt and shame a long time before she brought it up in therapy during a session when she was alone. There she recognized that her explosive anger was not in response to Johnnie but in response to her own inner fear and loss of control (Figure 68). Cathy, with limited parenting knowledge passed down in her family of origin, had been genuinely fearful of losing Johnnie, but in her fear her emotions had been hijacked.

The significance of this story is the intergenerational transmission of violence and negativity by Cathy. Cathy and Sam were two nice and normal people, but her two older children were highly at-risk. Cathy learned something the day she beat Johnnie (Figure 69), but, punished and hurt for taking care of himself, what did Johnnie learn? What form of trust, or mistrust, was engraved on his memory?

Talking about her first marriage, Cathy said she and her first husband were mere teenagers with limited role models and resources. She never remembered being happy when she got married. She just wanted to get out of her parents' house. The couple had no money and no plans, and what she knew about parenting she had learned at home. The boys were already having behavior problems before the divorce, but when she became a single mom they drove her crazy. She often found herself overwhelmed. Both of the boys, who had needs that she could not meet, would throw "real temper tantrums." She thought they would get better when she married Sam, this nice stable man who could act as their father, and she could become a stay-at-home mom. When this actually occurred, certainly her stress level was

Figure 68. *The Way It Was* by Cathy (Instant collage).

Figure 69. *The Way I Wish It Had Been* by Cathy (Instant collage).

reduced, but it is doubtful that her empathy level increased considerably with the children. Being a stay-at-home mom with significant money met Cathy's needs and gave her more peace and control. She was relaxed, and the new baby was calm because Cathy was able to meet his needs more completely. Sam and the boys were good mother's helpers but the two older boys were still a handful, both at home and school. They got their share and more of criticism, spankings, time-outs, and grounding. Cathy was actually relieved when her middle son was diagnosed as having Attention Deficit Hyperactive Disorder (American Psychiatric Association, *Diagnostic and Statistical Manual of Mental Disorders,* 1994, p. 78–83), placed in special classes, and given medication. Her guilt was relieved. The problems had not been her fault. She believed that she would finally get help. In elementary school, she did get help from special education personnel. But by the time the boys went to junior high school, negative interactions had taken their toll. Distancing from family and school and feelings of isolation from mainstream society had been established, leaving the boys to work their problems out alone or with other isolates. Each older boy lived his life parallel to all other family members. Cathy's middle son, socializing with children in similar pain and circumstances, was quickly involved in drugs and vandalism. The family with one world view could never tell what and when the youngster with another world view was going to do. He fought authority at home and at school. For him there was no relief. There was no trust. The world was not safe. There was only rage. The family burned out (Figley, 1997); fearing for his safety and the safety of others, his parents gave up and placed him in a group home.

The couple referred to the oldest as a sweet kid, totally unmotivated to do *the right thing* (which was to be like Stepfather). Instead, the boy used pot, skipped school, and ran with youngsters with similar backgrounds. As he got older, once again, the couple gave up and let him "do his own thing," reducing his chances for a life-style with fewer problems. According to Newcomb and Loeb (1999), "in adolescence family support and bonding reduces later adult general deviance for men and psychological distress for women" (p. 178).

The boys, who had been raised in poor circumstances, had even fewer resources when Cathy divorced. Research indicates that "poverty itself corrodes family life, delivering emotional blows to children with reduced affection, abundant parental depression, and a greater reliance on harsh punishment" (Goleman, 1995, p. 256). Rich or poor, a happy childhood makes life easier but not necessarily a cakewalk. Abuse, even abuse thought to be discipline, may over time disrupt the normal tasks of child development such as the formation of attachments, the development of interpersonal abilities, and growth of trust, resulting in anger and low-self esteem (Emery & Laumann-Billings, 1998). In light of Gottman's (1998) research with couples, hypothetically, is it any wonder how rapidly children, exposed in their families to abuse and domestic violence, will separate themselves from the family in whatever way they can? Will children who separate from their families later in childhood do so because of the early general absence of love, empathy, and positive support? Cathy's middle son had experienced the most family conflict. Early, he found a way to separate himself from his family. The older son just slowly slipped away.

Psychologists and educators know that from ages 0–3, high cortisol levels "increase activity in the brain structure involved in vigilance and arousal" (Perry, 1997, p. 32). They are reactivated on a high-trigger alert whenever the child thinks about prior abuse or is reminded of it by the mere presence of the abusive person. The slightest stress releases hormonal activity that creates hyperactivity, anxiety, and impulsive behavior, imprinting and forming a receptive brain. Chronic neurodevelopmentally traumatized children have behavioral impulsively, cognitive distortions (Pynoos, 1985; Pynoos, 1993), and a persistent fear response. Males with this response will easily misinterpret a behavior as threatening. Responding in a fight or flight response, they will more likely be violent, whereas females who respond are more likely to dissociate. "Similarly, a young man may find the only escape from the distress and pain caused by the emotional emptiness resulting from neglect, or the anxiety of a persisting fear response is with drugs or alcohol" (Perry, 1997, p. 9). Perhaps both of Cathy's older sons fit into this category. The boys were in a conflictive home that provided either negative or limited monitoring. That in itself was a "potent pathway to the development of delinquency, alcoholism, and substance abuse" (Hetherington et al., 1998).

To maintain a healthy, lifelong sense of self, all humans must, on a continuing basis, feel that they are loved, admired, and belong in some way to another human being. When this admiration and approval is missing or deficient, humanness and selfhood are diminished. The individual who has a hard time loving and being loved is a serious threat to self and to others. For humans, the earlier the neglect and the rejection, the more significant the damage, both in the brain and to selfhood. The more damage to selfhood, the more damaged are inner thoughts and feelings, and the less one can reach his or her full potential or be a contributing member of society. One child's thoughts of confidence, optimism, and trust, and his or her ability to have fun and be free, versus another child's thoughts of restriction, failure, hopelessness and unrequited rage are shaped in the first few years of life. They are reinforced or repaired as the child grows older.

Children learn ways to gather information, communicate, and to behave in their families. If they don't get their needs met, they learn violent ways to compensate or treat others. The following story is about three youngsters and a mom who lived in the battered women's shelter for six months.

HOW AM I SUPPOSED TO PAY ATTENTION IN SCHOOL?

Mother and three sons, Andre (8), Barry (6), and Clay (3), all presented to the therapist as guarded, mistrusting, anxious, and emotionally and physically agitated. The boys had limited attention spans; they were unable to concentrate or attend to a task for more than fifteen minutes. All of the family's speech was rapid and anxiety-laden. Collectively, the three young brothers told stories of horror, terror, abuse, police arrests of the father, driving for the father when he was drunk, what it looked like to stab someone (including a demonstration of how the body will physically react) and what it means to shoot up. They spoke of witnessing physical and verbal abuse of the mother by the father and of being physically beaten by both their parents.

When six-year-old Barry talked about his art, he verbalized his fear. "I'm afraid that my Dad is gonna get me. He could drive over here right now and just take us. Mother wouldn't do anything. He has custody. It's lucky he doesn't know where we are or he'd come get us. Dad goes to work early, like 2 a.m. in the morning. Sometimes before he leaves he beats my mom. The last time he hit her in the back of the head, she cried and her head bled. He comes in to eat then he beats, eat then beat, eat then beat. All this at 2 to 4 in the morning and I had to go to school and I didn't get any sleep. Every night this happened. How am I supposed to pay attention in school?" The therapist encouraged the child to draw how he felt (Figure 70).

At the beginning of their participation in the Family Art Therapy Program, the majority of the art works and play scenarios by the boys contained reenactment themes of fear and violence. The boys spoke of, played about, and created images of anger, rage, terror, mutilation, drowning, falling from roofs, killing, death, and destruction. They created images of and acted out scenarios dealing with their fears, concerns, anger, sadness, depression, and explosive rage. They employed terrifying movie characters and monsters, and frightening, powerful animals as metaphors for how they had been traumatized. Mother's art was dark and confused. Her verbal themes were also of fear and violence.

Although Clay, the three-year-old, continued to play the "drowning and rescue game" until he left the shelter, his images changed radically during his stay there. They changed from violence to rescue. The two older boys created much-needed strong, protective defenders (see Appendix B), the beginning of stronger and more protective egos. The themes and images in their art became less aggressive, indicating a shift in their psyches, with less need to constantly defend themselves against threats of danger and even possible annihilation. The images and stories in six-year-old Barry's art-based assessments (H-T-P) indicated that even though he felt that he had survived, he was

Figure 70. *Beat and Eat, Eat and Beat* by Barry.

still just a baby and needed to grow. When the therapist asked him what he thought it would take before he could stop lying and stealing as a way of acting out his anger, Barry, the sage, stated matter-of-factly, "Probably a lot of education."

By the time mother and the children were ready to leave the shelter, the children had greatly reduced their verbal and physical aggression toward one another. They seldom reported that one of their siblings had hit or bitten them and they were calmer. Their conduct in the shelter became appropriate. They were mindful of community books and toys in the art and playroom. The boys became more and more cooperative, communicative, and relaxed. They were no longer vigilant or hyperactive, and their motor skills had improved, as did their cognitive skills. Without late-night fighting sprees and constant fear, the boys could focus and attend to tasks for an hour or longer. With mom no longer fearing for her life, she no longer modeled helplessness and despair.

ANNE: TRUST BUILT ON CREATIVE EXPRESSION

Now we return to Anne, our mysterious and lonely young professional who came into therapy because her kitty had died. We might wonder what family or social event had shaped her life path. What malnurturance had caused her pain and brought her smiling depression to therapy? The therapist wondered if perhaps the kitty's death, however painful, might have been a catalyst for reminding her of some deeper human loss. She asked Anne to draw a picture of her family doing something together.

A Kinetic Family Drawing (KFD)–Anne–Family Art-Based Assessment (Appendix A-7)

Using pencil and paper, Anne drew a picture of her dad and younger sister in a car facing right or forward in the left top quadrant of the paper (Figure 71). Filling the right bottom quadrant, she drew her mother sitting at the kitchen table facing the left side, or the past, and her older sister on the left, facing right or the future. Both women were encapsulated in a square representing the kitchen. Revealing her isolation, Anne placed herself outside the square, and under the car, sitting on the "basement" stairs. There were no figures in either the top right quadrant or the lower left quadrant of the paper. Anne commented, "This is where I sat every afternoon after coming home from my Catholic girl's high school. I would come in and then sit on the stairs listening to my mom and my older sister gossip about the day's events." She added, "This is before my mom had her heart attack."

Anne, in John Allan's (1988) initial serial drawing stage, had drawn a picture of her internal world of a time long ago when she, a middle child, was a teenager. She placed herself outside of either Mom or Dad's inner circle. There were no pets in the picture.

Kwiatkowska (1975) indicates that the first drawing is an introduction of the self and may represent the family issues. Looking back at Anne's first drawing, her inside/outside drawing (Figures 19, Smiling Depression and 20, Pensive) was her introduction of the self. Following Anne's lead (naming her picture Smiling Depression), the therapist assessed Anne for a cognitive and affective baseline. She asked Anne to draw a Kinetic Family Drawing (K-F-D, Figure 71) and a House, a Tree and a Person (H-T-P, Figures 73, 74, and 75).

Anne's K-F-D (Figure 71), provided a rationale for all of her later actions. It visually depicted Anne's isolation, but the picture allowed her the freedom to share what she chose about her family. Anne reiterated that everyone in her family lived in a little town a thousand miles away except her. When questioned by the therapist as to why she lived here and they lived there, Anne had no answer. There was no question that Anne loved and felt love in her family of origin, but somehow, somewhere, a rigid boundary had been established. What had limited Anne's basic trust? What need had not been met? What had driven Anne away from that little town and her close family?

Figure 71. *My family* by Anne (drawn from a 16-year-old's perspective).

Figure 72. *A House* by Anne.

Figure 73. *A Tree* by Anne.

Figure 74. *A Person, Female and Male Figures* by Anne.

Using the Art-Based Assessment Evaluation (Table 1), Anne's body language was both tense and full of energy. She appeared cooperative but it was clear, she did not want to lose control. Her interaction with the therapist and the art task (HTP) was positive. Her interaction with the materials (pencils) was neutral. The drawings were conventional, consistent and on a superior intelligent level. Qualitatively Anne's affect and the affect of the drawing was positive. Anne's line quality was brisk covering all quadrants of the picture. All figures were direct views. Defense mechanisms were not evident. Anne's House had two sections, indicating Anne's separation from her maternal home. Bushes buttress the house indicating a lack of security in the home. The double front doors are drawn with door knobs and a double supportive line. Drachnik (1995) sees double doors as often a symbolic of a sexual entrance and doorknobs as indicators of isolation (p. 23). The walkway is long but structured indicating aloofness and self- control (p. 25). The two different trees, open to the earth, have no root systems. Anne's tree (Figure 73) also has no root system. The trunk is long and slashed. Drachnik (1995) sees the length as representing Anne's high goals and the slashes as representing her real or psychic wounds (p. 32). The crown of the tree is filled with scattered, open branches that do not connect to the trunk. According to Drachnik (1995, p. 30, 32) these indicate some confusion, and lack of impulse control.

Anne drew a woman first and then a man. Both figures are drawn on the left side of the paper. Buck (1966/1978) sees this as an over-concern with the past (p. 105). The woman uses her right hand to lean on the left wall again indicating the significance of the past. Emphasis is placed on the face implying a conscious effort to maintain an acceptable social front (p. 95).

The male figure is drawn in a suit and tie with a brief case. Large buttons appear on the coat. Drachnik (1995) sees the tie as a phallic symbol and the buttons as dependency symbols (p. 42).

Searching for inroads and answers from this smiling lady, the therapist asked Anne if she would like to make a Me Box (Figure 75) at home, placing how she thought others saw her on the outside but how she honestly felt on the inside (Appendix B–G). Although somewhat resistant either to the art or to the revelation required, she agreed to try.

The following week, Anne returned carrying a large box covered with cut-out pictures and words. Anne was beginning to communicate with her inner world and it was obvious that she was intrigued. Together the therapist and Anne reviewed her work. The top looked much like Anne presented. Pictures and profiles of beautiful women held large cut-out words: "music," "always rich," "on my mind," "natural high," "intense solutions," "mending," "now," "verbal-self-defense," "tough stuff," "intense solutions," "today," and "solid." Small words catching the therapist's eye included: "lying smiles," problems? What problems?" "Without a shadow of a doubt," "questions

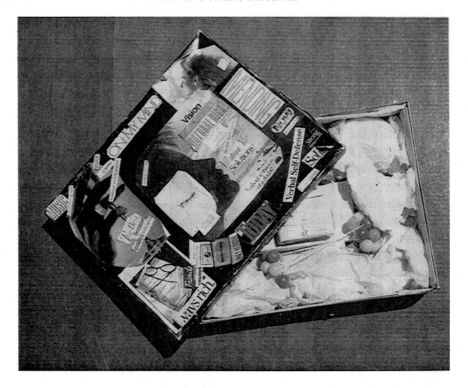

Figure 75. *Me Box—the Outside and the Inside* by Anne.

remain," "boyfriend," "absolute control," "membership has its privileges," and "only human." All four sides of the box continued with word themes from the top: "no more trouble," "in a safe place," "a different kind of love," "woman involved with a married man," "beware," "living dangerously," "right or wrong," "the wild pair," "making choices," "marry or stay single?" "have children or not," "women at work," "warning," "don't think," "valuable," "when a woman loves a man" and a picture of a kitty sitting on the words, "establishing roots."

The inside of the box was filled with soft pastel tissue, two small replicas of a cluster of balloons, and two small boxes tightly wrapped in yellow with cut-out phrases, "The vision of the future," "Where happy endings begin," "Classified."

When asked to talk about the Me Box, Anne responded, talking benignly about obvious words, such as "music," "always rich," and "natural high." The therapist, looking for circular family patterns, asked Anne about the more evocative words like "lying smiles," "problems," "woman involved with a married man," "beware," and "living dangerously" that she had included. Anne talked about a man that she had been seeing for over ten years. After a few minutes, obviously feeling safe, she became more descriptive, adding that he was a successful politician, married, with children, who lived on the other side of the continent. Relieved at having said it out loud to someone she was beginning to trust, she sighed. Although Anne was evasive about the inside of her box, from her selected images, Anne's mystery for seeking therapy continued to emerge.

The therapist asked Anne to write her autobiography using word tapping from the Life Cycle Log (Appendix B-1). Within a week or two, Anne, ready to explore her thoughts and feelings, lifted her mask and disclosed deep emotional scars: family expectations and the social/psychological violence that she had experienced as a late teenager that forever changed her life. In Chapter 6, we will have a chance to learn more about Anne and how art and writing helped her identify her sacred concerns, honor the energy and power of being rather than just the experience of living and free her SPIRIT.

Chapter 6

THE CYCLE OF HEALING

INDIVIDUALS AND FAMILIES who show up on the doorsteps of our agencies or offices are in physical and psychic pain. It is a scary time for them. They don't know how to verbalize their inner feelings because they are unable to make any sense out of them. Their families may be, or may have been, profoundly problematic, living in disadvantaged circumstances. Steven Gilligan defines our job as psychotherapists as "sponsoring the awakening of someone's soul, their deep tender center so that over time we can recognize, accept and reflect their inner language, expression, courage, patience and trust in whatever way it works" (Gilligan, 1995). Many people, be they children, adolescents, adults, or seniors, create this inner language in art or in images because it works better than using words. Art lets you see what you are thinking and feeling (Arrington, Eslinger & Virshup, 1975). Seeing your thoughts and feelings is another way of accepting them (Koplewicz & Goodman, 1999). Art, according to Arnheim (1997) is "a helper in times of trouble." It is a means of:

> understanding the conditions of human existence and of facing the frightening aspects of those conditions. It creates meaningful order—welcome aids that are grasped by people in distress and used by healers who come to their assistance. But, the blessings experienced in [using art in] therapy can reach further: they can remind artists everywhere what the function of art has been and will always be. (Arnheim, 1997)

In my family I was the worrier. Thinking back over many small and unimportant events in my life, I often whined about what could happen. My dad, now my hero (but certainly unrecognized as such at the time) often greeted my painful lack of control of my environment with a favorite Bible verse, insisting that I learn it: "Take, therefore, no thought for the morrow; for the morrow shall take thought for the things of itself. Sufficient unto the day is the evil thereof" (Matthew 6:34). Up until my adult life, I saw this as a foreign lan-

140

guage, a koan maybe, but certainly not a rule of life. Today, because of a myriad of events, I worry considerably less; however, on more occasions that I would like, my unconscious takes over and my body worries for me. For example, on nights before my husband and I leave the country for a long trip, I have been known to end up in the hospital for tests for botulism, or heart failure, or fingers that need stitching. In recent years a reggae tune popularized my father's same admonition: "Don't worry! Be happy!" Simplistic? Maybe not. For it is true, "Which of you by taking thought can add one cubit unto his stature?" (Matthew 6: 27). Sapolsky (1998), professor of biological sciences and neuroscience at Stanford University, tells us that "the diseases that (currently) plague Western societies . . . can be either caused or made far worse by stress," anxiety, worry, psychological and social stressors, and our ability (or lack of ability) to cope (pp. 2, 5). His work with both animals and humans and his subsequent findings "identify [universal] simple answers to coping with stress that are far from simple to implement in everyday life" (p. 325). These universal answers include (a) find a personal and compatible outlet for life's frustrations and (b) practice it regularly; (c) in the face of horrific and non-changeable news, cope by denying; (d) in the face of lesser problems, "hope, but protectively and rationally" (p. 336); (e) seek control of what you can change and let go of what you cannot; (f) seek predictable and accurate information but not too soon, too late, or even too much; and finally, (g) seek relationships versus mere acquaintanceships.

Those of us who do not fill all our leisure time with sports events or nature fill it with some form of the arts: music, movement, or modern-day drama, and television with its universal myths and symbols.

Goleman (1995), echoing Naumburg (1917), says:

> The emotional brain is highly attuned to symbolic messages and to the mode Freud called the "primary process": the messages of metaphor, story, myth, the arts. This avenue (art therapy) is often used in treating traumatized children. Sometimes art can open the way for children to talk about a moment of horror that they would not dare speak of otherwise. (p. 209)

Professional healers both now and in the past believe that art and image open the way for all ages and all cultures to remember and reflect not only on inner beauty and peace, but also on inner memories of horror, pain, and confusion. In Charles Allen's (1949) classic book, *Healing Words,* he notes that when a word is allowed to dwell in the mind for any time, it forms a picture and that picture "sinks deeply into the subconscious influencing within for either good or evil" (foreword). When one is too young, too old, too fragile, too frightened, or too confused to verbalize inner thoughts, images, and disenfranchised feelings, art that bridges inner and outer perceived realities is both a coping mechanism and the expression of choice for the therapist working with such a population. In a safe and protected environment, creating and selecting images provides concrete exercises for reducing stress, rebuilding abused, burned-out, or damaged emotions, and reframing experience. Gilligan (1995) admonishes therapists, that if someone is not there to bless the pain, the behavior, and the symptom, "to connect with it, to bring it into culture, and tradition, the experience will have no human value whatsoever." Using images is less stressful than using words and helps individuals look into their own hearts and rekindle their lost and forgotten dreams.

RESILIENCE

> Long-term studies of hundreds of children brought up in poverty, in abusive families or by parents with severe mental illness show that those who are resilient even in the face of the most grinding hardships tend to share key emotional skills. These include a winning sociability that draws people to them, self-confidence, an optimistic persistence in the face of failure and frustration, the ability to recover quickly from upsets, and an easygoing nature. (Goleman, 1995, p. 256)

Goleman continues, noting that optimal prevention programs include a list of key skills necessary for resilience. These include self-awareness, identifying alternative actions and their consequences before acting, reading social and emotional cues, listening, being able to resist negative influences, taking others' perspectives, and understanding what behavior is acceptable in a situation (p. 259).

Protective factors can offset risk factors (Jessor, 1993). Protective factors include cohesive families, mothers, fathers (Silverman & Auerburg, 1999), quality schools, neighborhood resources, involvement in church or community clubs, and interested adults who value a child's achievement and health and are intolerant of deviance from ethical standards. Risk factors include some aspects of biology and genetics (identified as alcoholism or substance abuse), social environment (identified as poverty), and perceived environment (identified by the presence of models for deviant behavior). More risk factors may be identified by examination of personality (identified by low self-esteem and low perceived life chances) and behavior (identified by smoking, driving recklessly, sexual irresponsibility, substance abuse, and truancy).

Children are malleable, not resilient argues Perry (1997). Children don't recover and return to an original shape. Rather, they adjust to changing circumstances. When protective factors are not available, treatment helps children adjust. This treatment, however, calls for simpler, not more complicated, methods. Treatment methods need to be regressive, pegged to the developmental levels where abuse and mistrust were first experienced, including communication with and about all that is known and experienced within the family.

Under the direction of a therapist trained in art or symbols, there is a cycle of healing that integrates the creative process with the stress, trauma, and isolation imprinted in the amygdala at this early period. In a safe environment, valued by the therapist, the client is encouraged to communicate in new and varied ways by using art and image. As in the case of prayer, when one is actively involved in this creative process, cortical focus narrows, kinetic movement increases, and fresh oxygen infuses the brain, creating an altered state of consciousness. Negative feedback loops are stopped, reducing stress, if only for a moment. One cannot be positive and negative at the same time. When the experience is in a positive state of flow, Csikszentmihalyi (1999) refers to it as an "autotelic experience" (p. 824). People around the world interviewed by Csikszentmihalyi refer to this experience as "ecstatic," in other words, as being somehow separate from the routines of everyday life, sometimes "like you almost don't exist." Creating provides immediate and personalized internal feedback. The creator observes the product "to be right or in need of revision" (p. 825). In a moment-by-moment process, memory, communication, and a concrete product, an image or symbol, of the feeling or thought emerge. In this emotionally healing experience, the person abandons censorship, allowing himself or herself to "feel good, natural, and spontaneous, as his (or her) abilities match his (or her) opportunities for action." This focused, self-soothing, but spontaneous approach serves to relax the individual and reduces stress. Remembering and retelling in art and image allows past physical or mental insults to lose their importance so they may be forgiven or forgotten, and the person can move forward. In the creation of the product, trust builds through confidence, first with self and then with others. As trust is built, hope is reestablished, facilitating the dreaming of dreams and the empowerment needed to acquire the mastery necessary to live them out. When facilitated by a family art therapist, the cycle of healing is integrative. It begins with images that reflect historical family material, positive and negative, as they reflect on current concerns.

A CASCADE OF STORIES FROM AN ART THERAPY APPROACH TO FAMILY THERAPY

The following stories about Sharri, Mary, Humberto, Jenny, Sallie, and Ron and the conclusion of the stories of Anne, Nancy and Randy are examples of this creative cycle of healing.

Table 8. CYCLE OF HEALING: Being Valued–Treating Trauma, Stress and Isolation

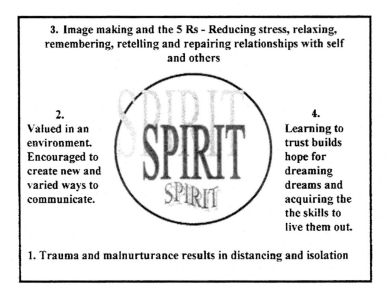

3. Image making and the 5 Rs - Reducing stress, relaxing, remembering, retelling and repairing relationships with self and others

2. Valued in an environment. Encouraged to create new and varied ways to communicate.

SPIRIT SPIRIT

4. Learning to trust builds hope for dreaming dreams and acquiring the the skills to live them out.

1. Trauma and malnurturance results in distancing and isolation

Sharri's Healing through Art

Sharri, an only child, was age seven when her mother, an avid gardener, teacher and artist, died after a brief illness. Sharri had grown up following her mom from one "hands-on" project to the next, digging in dirt, planting bulbs, mixing paints, and designing jewelry, believing that her father did not value art because he was a "businessman." At the funeral, Sharri's grandmother provided her with a coloring book and crayons and Sharri colored the Easter bunny black. Following the funeral, her relatives went home, her father went back to work, and Sharri, cared for by a maid, soon returned to school. But Sharri was not ready. Intuitively, Sharri knew she needed a safe environment in which to express her inner feelings. Pretending to leave with father each morning, she would wave goodbye as he left for work, and then she would return home. Back in the house she would set up a card table in the living room and proceed to create "op art" (her term) from a process using paper and starch that she had learned at Brownies. To Sharri, the art was something she had to do. It was hers alone. It was not to be seen by anyone–particularly her father. It connected her with her mother. She could not relax until she had completed the ritual that she called "sacred." When her "op art" was finished for the day, or needed to dry, Sharri would hide it in her closet, take the table down, pack her books, get a note from the maid, and go to school. Often it was noon before this process concluded.

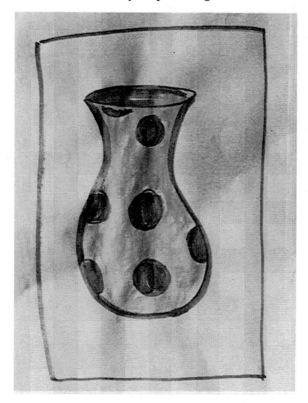

Figure 76. *Vase* by Sharri.

The first thing that she made was a large papier-mache vase (Figure 76) . She painted it yellow with green circles. This image stayed with her for years, appearing and reappearing in her doodles.

The vase, according to Cirlot (1962, p. 359), is a feminine sign representing repose, immanence, and acceptance. It is cosmic waters, the Great Mother, and the heart, and it is frequently associated with the Tree of Life symbolism. An empty vase "depicts the soul absent from the body" (Cooper, 1978, p. 184).

Between the ages of seven and eight, Sharri was often late to school, staying home to make many pieces of sacred art that she hid under clothes and shoes in the bottom of her closet. Sharri's most sacred experience was connected to an animal ritual. Sharri and her cousin, Eric, went hiking. They found themselves climbing a mountain (it may have been a hill) far from home, where they should not have been. It was there that the two children found the "dead eagle" (it may have been a buzzard). It took both of the children to drag the large, fly-infested bird back to Sharri's house, where together they dug a hole in the gravel on the side of the garage where visitors

Figure 77. *Cross* by Sharri.

sometimes parked. Next, the two children proceeded to prepare "the eagle for burial." Eric, soon bored with all the preparations of ointments and potions needed to sanctify the decaying corpse, began digging another project. Sharri was driven by her mission to honor this great and worthy creature. She proceeded alone.

When the bird's body was properly anointed, Sharri buried "the eagle." Her final task was to construct, from loose fence slats, a large wooden cross to mark the grave. When the cross was in place Sharri realized that it was not as ornate as she wanted it to be. She looked, and walked, and thought. Next, she went into the garage and searched until she found the boxes of Christmas decorations. She carefully selected and then transported her treasures to the gravesite, where she used them to enhance the cross. When the cross was royally decorated with the gold tinsel garlands and Christmas balls, Sharri felt good (Figure 77). She stood back and looked and knew it was done. Needing to make sense of what had happened in her life, Sharri, like Chad, had reenacted the trauma of her mother's death and burial. Once her tension and anxiety were reduced, Sharri no longer needed to stay home from school.

Although Sharri's cross was never acknowledged by anyone in her family, eventually it disappeared from the gravesite. Not quite understanding it,

Figure 78. *Floating on the Lake, My first memory* by Mary.

Sharri never forgot the archetypal experience of art and ritual. As an adult she often doodled the vase that she had made as a child. As an adult, years later, in an art therapy workshop Sharri was instructed to make a container. Only then did she identify the container she made as her sacred vase, the one she began making after her mother's death. The art therapist instructed Sharri to draw another picture in which she turned the vase over and poured out its contents. As Shari did, the metaphorical experience helped Sharri release the tears of grief that she had carried in the vase for her mother.

Mary's First Memory

Using oil pastels, Mary *drew her first memory* (Figure 78). It was a beautiful, golden picture of her, at age three, and her brother, age one, on a float in the middle of the lake. When the therapist asked her where the parents were, she couldn't remember. The picture was the beginning of many memories and drawings of Mary's early abandonment and neglect.

Humberto Remembers and Retells

For the first time in a supervision group for therapists, the group used the services of a family art therapist for training and consultation. The art task the therapist presented to staff was simply, "Draw whatever comes to mind." In

Figure 79. *My Homeland* by Humberto.

the following twenty or so minutes, Humberto, a young bilingual therapist and a refugee from Central America, used crayons to draw a landscape of what he described as his homeland (Figure 79). He drew five purple mountains under a blue sky with three clouds and a sky full of birds. The horizon was lined with a green hedgerow of pointed trees and a heavy brown fence. In the foreground was a lake surrounded by seven red flowers growing out of the water's edge.

When the therapist asked, "Who wants to share their art process?" Humberto, who had been feeling quite anxious over the last few weeks, quickly volunteered. The experience provided Humberto with a way to communicate his deep anguish with others whom he trusted. For the first time since he had been hired six months earlier, Humberto shared his grief, his loss, and his fear of deportation. He had become deeply afraid, with or without cause, of being returned to his country and the dangerous environment where, in a different life, in a very few minutes his trust had been fractured and his life had changed forever.

One evening, government soldiers with automatic rifles came into his village. In front of everyone, they killed five members of his immediate family, along with others. He and the townspeople quickly scattered and hid. He was able to get on a truck that was leaving town. Although he has been in contact with his family, he had never gone back to his home or seen his family or his country again. His training and skills allowed him to immigrate into this country.

Humberto began by talking about how green his country was in comparison with where he was now. He remembered his family members—his mother, his father, his brothers—and the gentleness of his country before the war. He remembered his mother's cooking and the church. He remembered the girl he had been dating. He did not know what the picture meant, but he said that it represented his present state of mind and he found it very powerful. He did identify the purple mountains as his honorable family members, brother, uncles, and grandfather, who had been killed by spraying bullets. Members of the staff pointed out that there were five mountains and five family members and that he had fenced his present off from his past. Although he did not mention it, the staff questioned his depression and anxiety represented in the three white clouds covered by many worry birds. The therapist questioned whether the lake represented his unconscious surrounded by memories of family or passionate new growth of friends, support, and trust. Humberto's art and his verbal reflections with people he trusted provided a focus for identifying personal trauma and therapeutic need.

Jenny Talks without Words

Jenny was a casualty of childhood (Kaufman & Wohl, 1991). Physically abused by her mother, sexually abused by her father, Jenny was thirteen before a neighbor finally reported this battered and neglected child to Social Services. After several days of investigation, Jenny was removed from her toxic home and placed in foster care with people who were ill-prepared to care for a child who had been treated so badly (Forward & Buch, 1989). Abused for perhaps most of her life, Jenny, like other children who have been violated, needed a way to survive (Terr, 1990). Early on, this small child survived by disassociating from her tormentors. She could close her eyes, find a white spot, and then all of her pain and everything else would be gone.

Jenny ran away from the foster home many times, but was always found. Within a year she was labeled compulsive and incorrigible. A year later she was placed in a mental institution and, because she heard inner voices, was relabeled schizophrenic. Over the next 20 years, Jenny was in and out of bars, hospitals, and jails before she found a doctor who, like a surgeon and the archetypal good mother, helped Jenny reintegrate her ego. Through Jenny's art, her therapist came to understand the hellish life Jenny and the alternate personalities, whom she called "her little people," had led.

Jenny used a variety of materials and found that "the making of art became her ritual for expression, because it allowed all of her people a say" (p. 34). She writes:

Jung says that the body wills to heal itself, and I found that art was the means by which my body, even without my awareness, started to heal itself. Even though I had no language to express myself, and there was no trustworthy ear to listen to me anyway, I could express myself artistically. As a child I enjoyed art, and in school I was thought to be good at it. I had a great imagination and I could imagine a spot in my mind and somehow go there. My process of drawing from the inside out, which I now understand to be related to my active imagination and my ability to self-hypnotize, was entirely spontaneous. I didn't know what I was doing, but I knew that the process was soothing and made me feel less threatened and less fearful. I could find brief moments of peace while I was in the trans-like state that characterized my times of artistic expression. Russell, one of my male "alters," would come and draw in a very precise, mathematical way, thereby creating an inner sense of balance, in contrast to my outer self, which always felt like it was on "tilt," a pinball machine gone awry. Art in therapy became a way for me to talk without words. (J. Miller, 1997, p. 38)

Today, Jenny, a working professional, appropriately guarded but open, speaks about her former mental illness. She says that she and her inner people have integrated. Scott, one of her most dominant "alters," was retired in good standing with the family, with a gold watch, for services rendered. Whereas in the past the "little people" had to do art, Jenny now wills to do it. "Because of art's healing properties," Jenny says with a smile on her face, she will continue (with inner personality nudges from one of her former inner personalities) to do art until she no longer breathes.

The following Figures 80, *The Uclid City* and 81, *Russell's Protection, the Coat of Armor* represent art work created by Russell, one of Jenny's alters. Figure 82, *Alchemy Village* is a painting Jenny completed during treatment as her alters integrated. Figure 83, *The Great Mother Goddess* is dedicated to Jenny's revered therapist.

Sallie's Numinous Experience

Sallie, a participant in a weekend art therapy workshop, listened as the gestalt art therapist slowly and purposefully began. "You are in your own lifetime. You have the privilege and the responsibility for claiming and being and doing in your own life space" (Rhyne, 1973). Asking the group to use the variety of art materials as they wished, she continued, "Spend the rest of the morning creating your lifetime" (see Appendix B-B).

Focusing on early memories, Sallie needed little guidance as she allowed distant scenes of her childhood to flash before her closed eyes. She remembered early feelings of innocence, support, and love. Picking up the newsprint, she cut a long and protruding shape representing her perception of her early family experiences (Figure 84).

Figure 80. *The Uclid City* by Jenny (Russell).

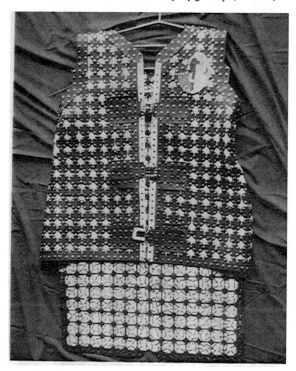

Figure 81. *Russell's Protection: The Coat of Armor* by Jenny (Cardboard and brads).

Figure 82. *Alchemy Village* by Jenny.

Figure 83. *The Great Mother Goddess* by Jenny.

Like a ribbon flying in the wind, a memory of fear waved before her. She had had the feeling many times before, but this time, in this safe and creative space, she immersed herself in the uncomfortable feelings—the pounding heart, the tightness across the chest, the butterflies in the stomach, the dry mouth. Memories of a continuing nightmare returned. She had had one just last night and her scream had awakened the roommate she had warned of her dreams. When, after a time, she could not connect the nightmare to an event, a place, or an occasion, she shook it out of her memory and picked up pastel colors of yellow and peach to brighten her picture. She sat back to find something in her early life that she could identify through memory.

Sallie thought of latency. Latency was family time: girl friends, and fun; playing things she knew, church, school, and doctor; listening to her sister's friends gossip about boys; and swimming at the community pool.

She remembered playing jacks on the cool porch cement; playing paper dolls, cut from Sears catalogues in the summer in the dark, cool living room; jumping rope; playing dress-up; and kind Sunday school teachers. She also remembered stories of children who got polio and lived in iron lungs. Then she remembered her own hospitalization and a deep fear returned to her chest. She shook the negative thought out of her memory and glued soft pink construction paper down on the artwork.

When she thought of early adolescence she remembered angrily the volcanic upheaval in her family. Her father had taken a job out of state. He had gone to find a home so the family could move. Sallie, eleven years of age, was one week into the sixth grade, a class filled with friends from kindergarten, when she came home to a strangely dark and quiet house. She looked for her mother, only to find her ill in the stillness, and her aunt in charge.

As with Humberto, although much more gently, a nodal event, an event that changed everything, had intruded in Sallie's family's life. After that day, nothing was ever the same. All Sallie had previously known changed that warm fall afternoon. Sallie felt fear, yet she was too young to understand the depth of the event or the fear.

Sallie remembers taking the train to her grandparents' house. Her sister (her roommate and protector) dropped her off on her way to enter college. Although Sallie's grandparents were kind over the year that followed, this abrupt and complete change from the known, the valued, the safe, reopened old wounds of fear and anger. Detachment settled in.

With mother well, the family reassembled the following summer in a new home in a new location, but all had been emotionally imprinted. Sallie remembered that hormones raged and opposition flourished. Family life was heavy. Although bright enough to be successful at school, the youngsters were a handful at home.

Figure 84. *My lifetime–Childhood and Adolescence* by Sallie.

Returning to the art therapy process, the "Lifetime," Sallie quickly decided to use a red paper, which she tightly corrugated, adding black patches and lines to depict this confusing period. She interspersed the red with torn patches of the natural newsprint. Then she sat back to focus on the next period of her life.

The family had changed. Her sister had married a stranger and moved away. Her older brother joined the army. The house was quiet. But the shrinking family could not attach to their new community and within three years they returned to the area that Sallie considered home. There she finished high school and prepared for college. Avoiding another separation, Sallie chose to go to a state college in the next town. Thinking that she could be in control of her own destiny, she married a local young man and, during the next five years they had a child. Her young adult years included ideal moments of love and intimacy. She remembered how she thought, "Now my life is settled." She made this area pink with blue scraps of tissue paper.

INTERACTIVE PROCESS. Art therapy involves the two-pronged therapeutic process of creating and reflecting. As Sallie worked on her Lifetime, reflection and primary process flooded her with the deep emotions of fear, pain, and confusion that she had buried. Using art materials, she was able to reflect, remember, and self-soothe. She thought, waited, and chose. She looked at the materials, and then selected where and how to use her selections. Then she began again. New feelings emerged. Looking at her art piece in the making, Sallie thought of her past and her next developmental stage. Each developmental stage reflected relationships and individuality. It included family, mutuality, intimacy, isolation, differences, similarities, joy, pain, patterns, and forms. However, each time Sallie looked at her media choices and selected from among them or kinesthetically cut, tore, crushed or painted, she was exercising deep preverbal areas of her brain. Each time she meshed them into her evolving artwork, each time she sat back to reflect before beginning again, she was awakening blood vessels, brain matter, and cognitive skills that had not been used for a long time. Acting and reacting with the art, thinking and reflecting, she was engaged in the therapeutic process of creating meaningful images. "Making art alongside" fellow participants created an "energy that enabled (Sallie) to take risks and push further" (Allen, 1995, p. 166).

Focusing on her mid-twenties, Sallie was aware that her perception of reality, affected by her current family life, no longer met her dreams, fantasies, or expectations. Her ideals of intimacy were flawed. Her sense of mastery was embryonic. She felt that she had lost control over her life and everything else. In the art, she depicted her depressed and suicidal state of mind in thin, torn, fragile strips of black construction paper. Detaching from the altered state of consciousness that she had been in, she sat back to converse with her image (Figure 85).

Just as at an earlier time she had been drawn spiritually to a higher being, this time she was drawn emotionally, with excitement and pleasure, to the physical art experience, and cognitively to its meaning. The image interwove family and self, past and present. For the first time, Sallie recognized the value not only of the positive, but also of the times she had considered negative. In this numinous experience, Sallie was spontaneously and unconsciously constructing a metaphoric container for all of the events, emotions, and relationships in her life. In this highly concentrated state, Sallie had been pulled into and autotelic state (Csiksyentmihalyn, 1999). The power of the experience was transformative. She backed up and looked at the now four-foot tall paper collage. Flooded with emotions, she recognized the symbol for the first time. It was a tree–Sallie's internalized image (Figure 86).

Figure 85. *Young Adulthood* by Sallie.

Five years earlier, Sallie and her family had moved from their home state and small community, where Sallie's forebears had settled and lived for five generations (except in Sallie's family's case, when they lived out of state for three years). Sallie's roots sank deep into her native culture. Although Sallie, her husband, and her son had only moved from one state to another and everyone spoke the same language, Sallie was in a state of acculturation stress. The culture, the food, the music, the relationships, and the values were different. She no longer felt validated and reaffirmed in a community construct of reality (Heller & Woods, 1998, p. 275). She had lost her sense of mutuality. Sallie's metaphor of the tree had begun to evolve (Lankton & Lankton, 1989). She often said that she felt as if her taproot had been cut. The move had exacerbated her feelings of anxiety and fear. Any peace and contentment that she found was in making art: drawing, sketching and painting trees, and parts of trees, that she had seen in family travels. Sometimes she drew the trunks, sometimes the root systems.

Figure 86. *It's a Tree. Aha, I Am the Tree* by Sallie.

Sometimes she drew the branches or the leaves. Sallie often included the shadows behind the branches, leaves, and trunks (Figure 87). Whether she worked in paint, pencil, pen and ink, needle and thread, or acid, her art was directed toward images of trees and tree parts (Figure 88).

In response to the isomorphic quality of trees, surges of deep emotion in Sallie were released. Thoughts came quickly. Meanings proliferated. Her hands could not keep up with her mind. She pushed to complete the multimedia collage. Sallie was aware that other members of the group were now sitting back and watching the intensity of her creative process. Jung (1938/1983) says, "When a dynamic experience seizes and controls the human subject, who is always rather its victim than its creator" (p. 239), then the experience is numinous. Sallie's experience was indeed numinous. Torn black construction paper depicted branches. Multiple media and shades of green created the

Figure 87. *Leaves and Shadows—tree sketches* by Sallie.

crown of the tree. No longer acting willfully, Sallie was seized by the moment. Her life, her past experiences with their pains and joys, fell into place with her future dreams. The unconscious and the consciousness were unified by the image. Through the symbol she had understanding.

Sallie could now see the reason for the "dark times" in her life. She went back to the beginning of the dark times. She started with the trunk of the tree and excitedly, interspersed black on one side, honoring her fears, ambiguity, and shadow, welcoming the dark times, while accepting the responsibility for, and the power of, her life.

REPRESSED MEMORIES. Over the past several years, Sallie had worked with several therapists, all whom had inquired into possible child abuse or molestation that she may have experienced as a child. The therapists often pointed out that Sallie exhibited symptoms relating to Post-Traumatic Stress

Figure 88. *Transformation—etched leaves* by Sallie.

Disorder (PTSD): avoidance of stimuli associated with trauma, inability to recall aspects of early trauma, hypervigilance, exaggerated startle response, nightmares (DSM IV, 1994, p. 428).

Sallie had no memory of abuse or mistreatment. Each time she heard this she had relooked at her childhood, but now, using the art and skills she had learned in therapy, skills of inquiry, questioning and acceptance, Sallie looked again at her ribbons of fear and where they might have attached. Her thoughts focused on her early illness. Before penicillin, antibiotics, or amnesia sedatives, before art and play therapists on children's wards, treatment of serious illnesses in children was often long, lonely, and invasive. Love and laughter were interfaced with fear, pain, and restraint. Believing that children did not encode threats to their physical integrity, or believing that they would "get over it," both family members and medical personnel paid little attention to childhood medical terror. In the art, Sallie connected with her year two and one half to three and one half when she had experienced extensive medical treatment for mastoid. The art validated what no one had validated before, her humiliation, pain, and fear from long-term medical treatment. Sallie begin to feel free, releasing the ribbons of fear, releasing the internalized memories of being held down and medically treated again and again by the doctor, nurses, and her own parents trying to save her life.

EXISTENTIAL PERSPECTIVE. In this free and creative state, Sallie reached a state of flow or a peak performance (Csikszentmihalyi, 1990, 1999). Athletes know this space as "the zone where excellence becomes effortless" (Goleman, 1995, p. 90). Sallie was dismantling meaning and remaking it. She identified with the living tree. Sallie was culturally and ethnically grounded in the image, which was more than the sum of its parts. When she drew root systems, she was drawing her family roots, her community, her culture, and her belief systems. When she drew the texture on the trunk, she was drawing how she had learned to protect her inner feelings. When she drew the branches, she was drawing her interaction, her security, her identity, and her dreams, with her family of origin, her extended family, and her young nuclear family. When she drew the leaves, she was drawing how she took in the environment and lived out her life's purpose. When she drew the shadow, she was drawing and accepting all those events, behaviors, and significant relationships that she had denied. The image illuminated her lifelong interdependence on significant relationships.

The structure of the tree, according to Cirlot (1962), with its roots, trunk and branches, stands for the relationship between the three worlds (the underworld, the earth, and heaven) or the world axis, and the central point in the cosmos. Trees grow in a cycle of seasons. Unlike the material model of planned obsolescence, trees grow richer and more beautiful from season to season and year to year. Each tree lives in the present while building on the past as it prepares for the future. New life begins before old life has fallen. Each new life grows and flowers in the soil of past experiences. Just as the protective covering of the seed must fall away before the small tree root can attach to the environment, so experiences in life begin with the death of prior experiences. The Tree of Life contains the knowledge of good and evil. Evil spelled backwards is live. On a variety of levels, Sallie saw the image and accepted its challenge "to live."

Until Sallie experienced "dark times" or Jung's archetypal "shadow," there had been limited insight, but no awakening, no change, and no inner growth. As she accepted the shadow in her symbol of the tree, she could accept each "dark time" as a necessary part of the whole, integrating self, relationships, and environment. This experience with this therapist was Sallie's treatment (Figure 86). Sallie's life was her teacher. What she needed to know met her at each crossroad. While the technique and this single experience should not be seen as "the cure," Sallie, like so many others before her, found that the creative experience, the culmination of a long quest, was curative. It validated her ability to find and integrate the answers within the image. The art experience had, as Kramer expounded, engaged all of her faculties (physical, intellectual, imaginal, and emotional) "in a supreme effort of integration" (Kramer, 1974, p. 15). Coming at the time it did it awakened Sallie's power over the events in her life. It was both a support and a catalyst for Sallie's healing journey toward individuation.

Like life, the art product reflects both age and experience (Arrington, 1998; Troeger, 1992). Linked to the artist, it bridges family, community, and culture, and expands mind, body, personality, and soul. Naumburg named this "symbolic speech" (1987, p. 4). Wadeson (1980) refers to this as "spatial matrix" and indicates that art duplicates real-life experiences "by showing closeness and distance . . . similarities and differences . . . the context of family life ad infinitum" (p. 11).

Ron Follows the Yellow Brick Road

Under the direction of a professional trained in the use of art as healing, the art process (expressing, or selecting) and product (two- or three-dimensional) foster both conscious and unconscious communication of the creator's dreams, experiences, feelings, thoughts, and sensations. In this kind of a setting, the process and the product have a proclivity to change mood, cognitive beliefs, and methods of communication.

Ron, a Fortune 500 executive, was feeling the pressure of success. For 25 years he had been a rising star in his company, attending to himself, his family, and his customers. His life had meaning. But a merger in the works had changed the rules of his work life. The company was moving into the new millennium with a mission changed from service to profit. Customers whom Ron had served for 20 years were no longer appreciated, nor was Ron or his staff. Management was playing lean and mean. Questionable deals, resulting in big and fast money, were being made daily. Employees could not work hard enough or long enough to meet the feeding frenzy of corporate dissolution. Ron and his staff could not market one project before another one was put on their desks. Eating poorly, taking no exercise, Ron was losing weight, unable to sleep, irritable, and preoccupied. He was going to work at 5 A.M. and working 16 hours a day, but even at that he could never catch up. As a premier member of his frequent flyer club, he accumulated approximately 100,000 miles a year. His wife reported that she never saw him except when he was asleep on the couch with the TV blasting. After Ron called her from work one morning at 6:30 A.M., shaking and confused, his wife brought him to therapy. According to the DSM IV, there is as much of a physical component in a mental illness as there is mental component in a physical illness. Ron was walking a thin line between mental and physical breakdown.

The therapist observed the couple, listened to their story, and then referred Ron to a physician for a complete examination. The next time the therapist met with Ron and his wife, they constructed a genogram. Ron's parents had grown up during the Depression. In his family environment, Ron had developed a strong work ethic that started from the time he sold magazines at age seven. By the age of 18, he was paying his own living and college expenses. His dad had been a company man starting at age 20 and retiring at age 65. His mother had worked for the same company for 15 years after Ron and his younger sister left the home. Ron and his wife had been married 24 years and had three teenage daughters.

It was apparent that Ron, confused about his changing identity, needed a safe and protected space where someone, outside of his family, would listen to him, value his experience, and help him make some hard decisions. Ron, a thinker and verbally well-defended man, needed a way to create a new perspective of his future. Although the therapist believed that eventually he needed to do that with his wife, Ron's emotional and cognitive state first needed to be evaluated. The therapist thought a directed art task, with color, form and symbols, would give the three of them something concrete to hold on to, look at, and ponder. She asked Ron to draw a picture of where he was in his life and where he was going. Ron used markers to sketch a picture he called The Yellow Brick Road (Figure 89).

Can participation in a creative activity really help a person's depression and anxiety? Definitely yes! If a person or a family can become engaged in a creative process for even one minute, he, or they, can stop ruminating about issues they cannot change (Haley, 1998).

Ron's picture, although composed horizontally, is a diagonal landscape. It communicates isomorphically, its creator's world view. Looking at the overall effect carefully, the height of his Promethean Mountain is significant. It covers the paper. The picture goes from left to right, from the unconscious to the conscious, the past to the present. The viewer is unable to see where the road begins or ends, but the road is a passage. It is movement through space. It represents a journey, an urgent desire for discovery and change. As interpreted in the Art-Based Assessment Evaluation Protocol (ABA Eval, Table 1), the line quality is agitated and anxious, depicting Ron's physical anxiety and struggle.

The "Yellow Brick Road" metaphor relates to direction, energy, and dreams. The color yellow relates to intuition and intellect. The lack of people in the picture suggests isolation. The numbers of objects in the picture, in this case trees, flowers and stones, often relate to significant people and events.

Figure 89. *The Yellow Brick Road* by Ron.

The number of flowers was consistent with the number of children in Ron's family. Central interests of the picture included the road and the fragile tree, or the journey and the self. Although anxiety is expressed, the picture is straightforward, with clear colors that are appropriate to the objects included. There are no color overlays, indicating confusion or historical material, or darkness, suggesting shadow content.

Ron's picture (Figure 89) prompted questions like, "Where is the road going?" Uphill, but what is at the top of the hill? Ron admitted that he had to decide whether the hard climb to the top of the yellow brick road would take him where he wanted to be. Although the picture with the sketchy lines was disturbing, as was the lack of people and sparse grass (communicating anxiety, isolation, bleakness and lack of nurturance), there was much strength expressed by Ron. The stones and the tree represented grounding, permanence, solidity, and integrity, while the three red flowers represented fragility, passion, and energy. There were strengths in the mountain itself that represented inner loftiness of spirit. The picture was a blueprint of Ron's personality, emotional climate, and current coping skills. Ron, a skilled and positive man, in a career crisis that was in conflict with his core values, was not coping well.

Before asking Ron to look at the picture and tell his wife and me what he saw, the therapist asked his wife to draw a picture that in some way related to Ron's. The therapist wanted art to speak to art.

Ron's wife drew a green mountainscape with houses, cows, and children playing. She said that it was a village outside of Zermatt near the Matterhorn, an area the family had visited years earlier. She said it was lush and peaceful. When she had been there she was amazed at how well and how simply other people in the world lived what appeared to be very satisfying lives. She had always wanted to return. Drawing to drawing, the pictures talked to each other. His wife asked him how he had chosen to follow this yellow brick road. Ron's answer was that he was not sure that he knew any other. He said he had gotten on it and it just went on and on. The therapist asked if he knew where the yellow brick road was going. He thought for a while and then said that it was going to the Land of Oz. The therapist pointed out that a misleading magician held court in Oz. Ron's wife noted that he had the brains and she had the heart; maybe together they could find the courage necessary to look at where and how they wanted to spend their future. In the individuation process, one must support not only personal dreams but the dreams of significant others.

Ron's external conflicts related to work, changing jobs, and caring for his family. His internal conflicts related to his personal integrity, and the meaning of life, work, and relationships, concepts he had learned and first experienced as a child. Ron's work issues and his family issues were woven together into his history, his relationship, and the culture in which he lived. Conflicts between his core values and life changes had triggered his anxiety and depression. The family was one of Ron's core values. The therapist felt that it was important that the couple be involved in the resolution of these conflicts. Where did they want their yellow brick road to go? Did they even want to be on the yellow brick road? As said earlier, there is no individuation without relationship. Four months later, Ron resigned from his company. Within a year, he and his wife had passed through their crisis, together and intact. They had chosen their own creative path with a color yet to be decided.

A Family Tragedy

In contemporary society, the social leper, the wearer of the scarlet letter, is often seen by society as a person, a family member, or even a family inflicted with AIDS or its precursor, HIV. Recent studies demonstrate "that children within HIV-infected families are at high risk for psychological

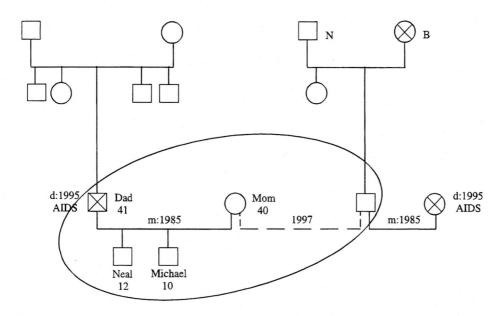

Genogram 6. Neal and Michael's Family

adjustment difficulties" (Dorsey, Chance, Forehand, Morse & Morse, 1999, p. 103). Neal, age twelve, and Michael, age ten, had two members of their family affected; Dad had died of AIDS in the Northwest before Mother, also HIV positive, and the boys returned to Mother's childhood home and entered therapy. The art in their family therapy helped the shrinking family come to terms with their life and death issues, live in the present, express the sadness of their past, and face the fears about their future.

The boys, Neal and Michael, were a behavioral expression of their fragile lives. Bright, friendly, caring to each other and toward their Mom, they were also anxious, hyperactive, obsessive, and undisciplined. For all members of the family, the art materials were like food to a starving child. They quickly tried them all, using symbol stamps, scented markers, pencil, crayons, pastels, and oil pastels on the paper provided.

The Family Art-Based Assessment (FABA) included a free picture and two family landscapes (see Appendix A-6). The FABA begins with a free picture to let clients play with the materials and relax as they realize they can be in control. The family landscape sequence begins with clients thinking of how they felt at a time between ages three to twelve and drawing this psychological space as a landscape, identifying the objects in the landscape as family members present. The FABA continues with the clients being asked to draw another landscape, this time from the perspective of the people identified in the landscape. They are asked to begin with the person who is most distant from the artist in the picture.

Although Mom presented with depression and lack of energy, her first art task, a free picture was an expression of optimism: a lightly colored floating rainbow with a pot of gold on the right-hand side. She named this picture *Rainbows*. Her second art task, a family landscape, Mother used pastels to sketch a couple, mother and her new friend, walking through a forest of five trees, she called this picture *Autumn dream* (Figure 90).

The third art task, mother's second family landscape was a picture with no people, only an empty blue car on the right side of a bridge that appeared to be heading into a rainbow in front of two mountains. The bridge, spanning rough seas, was not attached to either side. Mother called this *San Francisco Rainbows* (Figure 91). She said that she was the car and her deceased husband was the rainbow. The boys were the mountains behind the rainbow. The fourth art task, her last picture was again a lightly colored view of a distant family of four walking on the beach with their dogs. It was a picture of the family and Mother's new friend. She called this *Walk on the Beach*.

Neal's first art task, a free picture. On a very large sheet of paper, Neal compulsively filled the top part of the paper with blue and red star symbol markers (Figure 92). He included a dozen small symbols of flying birds. Under the sky, in the middle of the page, he drew an orange-striped cat with a strange set of double footprints behind it. In the lower right he drew an igloo. Directly in the middle he wrote "LOST." Neal's second art task, a landscape, he called *Sucsess* (Figure 93). On the left side in blue pastel he drew a house and a garage half off the page. A large gray tree with a large trunk and limbs is in the middle of the page. Again, Neal compulsively added limbs and branches. In black marker, he added five small figures. Neal identified Mom in the left upper corner; "me," a small person next to the left side of the tree in the middle of the page, "Cary" (Mother's new friend) in the middle; "Dad" was on the right-hand side and "Michael" was compartmentalized on the bottom right. His third art task was a second landscape he called *Graveyard* (Figure 94). Drawn in black marker and blue and gray oil pastel, the picture has a railroad-like fence, filling the left and top of the page. At the top of the page, under the fence, Neal drew three rows of grave markers. Under the grave markers he drew his perception of his Dad's funeral. Blue awnings cover the crowd of people and part of the casket. The fourth art task was a free picture (Figure 95). As a final picture he drew a starry picture and fragmented symbols. On the picture he wrote *Star Wars Triogy*.

Michael's first art task, a free picture (Figure 96), *Crazy Wolf*, was fragmented. Star, foot, and paw symbols covered the paper. A wolf, drawn in pencil was at the top right, two faces with large mouths that looked needy, and the script writing of "Crazy Wolf" on the bottom right. The second art

Figure 90. *Autumn Dream* by Mom.

Figure 91. *San Francisco Rainbows* by Mom.

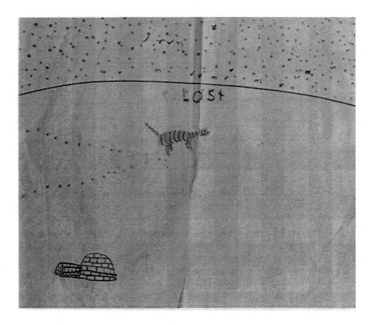

Figure 92. *Lost* by Neal.

task (Figure 97) was a landscape of two carefully drawn houses and driveways above a horizontal road. Under the house on each side of the driveway Michael wrote "Mom" and "Dad." Heads named "Neal" and "Me" are drawn in front of a birthday cake with six candles and "Happy Birthday Michael" is drawn above the house on the left. "Hay!" is written as if it is coming from Michael's mouth. A large orange sun is drawn over the blue house. *Sunny Day,* written in script, is at the bottom. The third art task, a second landscape (Figure 98, *Wonderful view*) is drawn in pencil and crayola. A large tower with a brown roof is in the middle of two large trees under an orange sun; similar to the one he had drawn earlier. The words "wonderful view" wind through the middle of the picture. The fourth art task (Figure 99) is a free picture drawn in black marker. It is a volcano with a screaming face in front of a very large orange sun. "MT. Saint Hellims" is written very large under the volcano.

This family art-based assessment acted not only as assessment but also as treatment. Having these three family members work in the same room creating symbolic landscapes of earlier times in their lives gave them a chance to talk about their immediate and traumatic past: Dad, before he was sick, his illness, and their family life now. The second landscape, a landscape drawn from the point of view of the person who is furthest from the artist, helped members of the family focus on their losses, feelings, and pain about husband, dad, home, and life-style. With unobtrusive symbols concretized on

Figure 93. *Sucsess* by Neal.

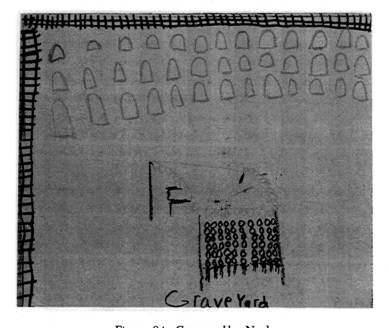

Figure 94. *Graveyard* by Neal.

Figure 95. *Star Wars Triogy* by Neal.

Figure 96. *Crazy Wolf* by Michael.

Figure 97. *Sunny Day* by Michael.

Figure 98. *Wonderful View* by Michael.

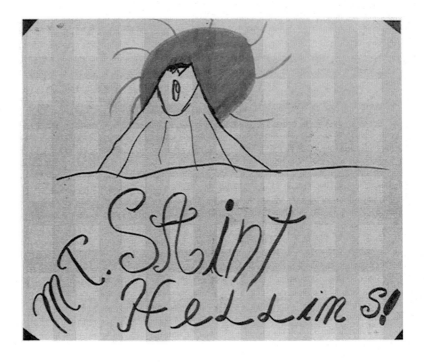

Figure 99. *MT. St Hellins!* by Michael.

paper, in a safe and protected environment, the family members felt safe to verbalize nagging fears about their future. Is mom healthy? What if mom gets as ill as dad? What if mom dies? Who will watch out for the boys? What happens to dead people? Do they live with Jesus? Who can we talk to about our fears and sadness? Following this session, the family willingly committed to attending a grief group where mom and the boys could find they were not alone, there were people who understood and had suffered from similar experiences. There they could get help and gain strength.

A RETURN TO NANCY WHEN ART RELEASES HER PAIN

Following Nathan's death, Nancy's pain was ever present. She and her husband traveled to Italy, where Nancy took pictures of doors. Were they opening or closing? Encouraged by her therapist to expand her symbols, she painted a door. It appeared to open. Behind the door was an image of a beautiful angel holding a red velvet curtain. Nancy felt it was one of the angels that had been looking after Nathan and her family. She felt the angel had been

Figure 100. *Nathan in the Arms of the Angel.*

sent to help release the family's pain. Again, expanding her images, Nancy painted the angel and the red velvet curtain. It was large and majestic. Nancy began to feel at ease.

But each time Nancy thought of Nathan's death she was again filled with horror, horror at the family loss, horror at the tragic event, horror that a young child's head had been deliberately blown off by an eleven-year-old with a gun. She could not shake that picture. At the suggestion of her therapist she asked herself, what do I believe actually happened? In a safe and protected space with a new and varied form of communication, she began to draw (Foa, Friedman, and Keane, 2000). Nancy, a craftsperson, had never had any formal art training, yet guided by her inner feelings and beliefs, she began to draw an angel holding Nathan, whole, embraced, and loved. When she finished, Nancy's heart took wings. For the first time since the accident, she experienced inner peace. She had been able to see the angel take Nathan into his arms whole and loved at the moment of his death (Figure 100).

Today, Nancy still grieves the loss of Nathan and the trauma experienced by the entire family, but the terror and depression are gone. As Nancy read the paper and watched the news on television, she saw tragedy after tragedy of children all over America killed and killing. Nancy had a photograph of her painting of Nathan in the arms of the angel reproduced and printed on postcards. She mails them, with a copy of her family story, to each family that she reads or hears about who have suffered from similar painful experiences.

Nancy believes that it was the inner images that she drew that helped her heal. She has come to see that families like hers who grieve the loss of a child due to senseless violence need to know that when one faces the truth and places value and honor on the experience, finally there is peace. This peace occurs in various ways, but Nancy wants other families to know they are not alone in their grief. Other families have gone before them and understand the depth of their loss, support them in their excruciating pain, and in their need to make sense of their experience.

A RETURN TO ANNE, WHO REVEALS, REUNITES, AND RECOVERS HER LIFE

Anne's wounds had been psychic wounds, wounds that damaged her vital center, her basic trust, and her personal growth. With Anne, it was art that built the vehicle of trust between client and therapist. It was art and the art of writing, the exercise of both right- and left-brain activities that reached into Anne's wounds and restored her spirit.

Anne, a good Catholic girl from a small town had had first communion at six and was confirmed at ten. She lived in America's liberation years: civil rights, women's lib, Woodstock and Gurley Brown's *Sex and the Single Girl*. Although *Wade versus Roe* had passed, and birth control pills were available, Anne, a high school senior in transition, living in a transitional world, had no idea they existed and believed that abortion was unthinkable. She was not a foot soldier in the sexual revolution (Evans & Avis, 1998), but she did, like many other young girls before and after her, become pregnant as the result of a brief relationship, her senior prom date. As the summer wore on and her worst fears were confirmed, Anne went to her older sister, her mentor and confidant, who took her to a doctor for examination and advice. The doctor suggested, and her sister agreed, that Anne should move away and relinquish her child to adoption. Wasn't it obvious that she was not ready to care for a child? How could she care for a child if she could not care for herself?

When one is excluded when suffering, rather than taken in and comforted, to whom, after that, does one return? At age 18, Anne left her home, her basic trust and her self-esteem. For the next 20 years she lived with what is known as disenfranchised grief (Madsen, 2000), grief that is unshared, unrecognized, and unvalued by any other person.

Anne's ultimate decision to release her child went back two years earlier, when Anne, 16, and her family experienced her mother's heart attack and near death. At that time, emergency services were limited. Transplants, bypasses, and pacemaker insertions were done only in major hospitals by famous medical teams who appeared on television and in the evening news. The family celebrated the miracle that mother had lived. In addition, Anne's older sister had followed all of society's rules. Cheerleader, scholar, engaged to her college sweetheart, judgmentally, older sister was convinced that the information that Anne had not and was now pregnant and unmarried could kill their mother. The sister supported the doctor's solution. He could arrange for Anne's care and the baby's adoption.

Anne drew many of these family dynamics in a Kinetic Family Drawing (K-F-D; Appendix A-7, Figure 71). Anne showed her feeling of isolation as encapsulated, she listened behind the door to her mother and older sister gossip (gossip about whom? Surely Anne could be the topic of much gossip). In addition, the kitchen scene was drawn in the right quadrant of the paper, the area identified as the unconscious. Anne had also excluded herself from dad and younger sister in the car drawn above her, the area identified with the conscious.

The scarlet letter placed historically on unmarried, pregnant young women has often been carved in the flesh of their hearts, leaving violent and lasting scars of loss and grief. "Society," notes Stabno (1998, p. 62), "generally condemns the birthmother for being a promiscuous, irresponsible sinner, and a social outcast who forfeits her fundamental rights concerning her child. The act of relinquishment is seen as an act extinguishing all biological and genetic ties." Our young professional Anne had never married or had another child. In fact, she said, "I have chosen to see married men because then I am not pressed into a lasting relationship. Love to me is too interlaced with pain. The difference between losing a person and a pet is that you can't go to the pound to replace a person."

In her journal and in her art, Anne revealed the loss of her daughter and her years of emptiness and grief without her. The therapist, validating Anne and her feelings, wrote in Anne's journal, "Have you ever tried to find her?" Anne, who had already thought of this and felt validated by the therapist's suggestion, was motivated further.

Anne hired an investigator and his search helped Anne cope with her questions. Participating in art psychotherapy provided Anne with a way to face what Stabno (1998) calls "uncertainties, conflicting emotions, fantasies, painful memories," and fears as they related to her daughter and her family. Therapy provided a safe place to "vent, explore and emote." When the therapist led Anne through a guided imagery using the metaphor of trees, Anne was able to see that this was just one season of her life (Figure 101, *Fall Tree*, Appendix B-F). She could see that although metaphorically fall is an ending, trees are beautiful in their changing fall colors of gold, rust and red before they enter their time of dormancy and inner growth and the beginning of a

Figure 101. *Fall Tree* by Anne.

new life cycle. Using metaphors helped Anne reframe her world view and give her hope. For Anne, who had lived so isolated from her feelings for so many years, creating collages of both words and pictures (Figure 102, *A collage*) between sessions helped her identify her concerns before bringing them to therapy to discuss and clarify.

It took Anne less than two years to find and reunite with her daughter. She was aware that "a reunion would not erase history" (Stabno, 1998, p. 79). Today, the two adults are in a bittersweet position, positive in that they are together, but painfully aware of what they both missed. Anne has helped her daughter reunite with her natural father, grandparents, aunts, uncles, and cousins. Her daughter's adoptive mother has been more than supportive of her adopted daughter's reunion with Anne. Anne's daughter has filled some of the emptiness in her life. But Anne's need for an adult, loving companion still remains. Today, as an author and advocate for adoptees and birth mothers, she continues to use art secondarily both personally and professionally.

Figure 102. *Collage* by Anne.

A RETURN TO RANDY R.–HOME IS WHERE THE ART IS

Randy was 2-1/2 when Dad left the home and Mom moved back to her family home. He was four when he moved into his stepfather's home. At 4-1/2 he moved into a new family home. At five he went to live with Dad and Stepmother in his fifth home. Over the next six years his mother had the power of money on her side and Randy became her pawn. She allowed Randy to live with her and her new significant other when it suited her and then with Dad and Stepmother when it didn't. Dad loved Randy, but on his lawyer's advice Dad did not fight mother in court. Randy's interpersonal skills suffered. They became brittle and defensive. His self-worth became small, his emotions unruly. But Randy was bright. He compensated by persevering both in school and in boy scouts, visualizing his personal dream of becoming an Eagle Scout.

Delivering his Eagle Scout acceptance speech, tears rolled down the cheeks of this six-foot three-inch 17-year-old. Looking through the large audience, his gaze fixed briefly on one red-eyed face and then another: mother, father, grandparents, aunts, uncles, brother, stepsisters, cousins and friends. Randy, a child of multiple maternal divorces and co-habitations, had lived in ten homes and a boarding school, but Randy, loved by many and abandoned by a few, like many, many other children of divorce, could not remember ever having seen his family or even his parents together in one room.

Looking extremely handsome in his suit and wing tips on his most recent trip to the area to visit his Dad, Randy told his therapist that in his whole life he had never attended a single school for more than two years. He had done reasonably well in high school with only one or two bouts with authorities and therapists. He felt that he had had two pretty good years in military school, but had not liked the regimentation. He transferred out when his brother Charlie transferred in. He attended another school in the area, where he finished high school. Although he often made honor roll grades in both schools, his social competence was limited and his self-esteem was low. He didn't admit to doing much art but he proudly talked about being appointed to the coveted high school newspaper photographer position. Although he saw his mom on holidays, after ages 10 or 11 he never stayed with her again. His grandmother, on the other hand, continued to shower Randy with gifts as long as he did what she wanted. She gave him a white Corvette, an American Express card, and ongoing living expenses while he attended a prestigious school on the East Coast. Wondering how Randy was handling the crippling psychological control in his life (Soucy & LaRose, 2000), the therapist asked Randy if he would like to draw whatever comes to mind. Not surprisingly, Randy drew *It's just a house*, Figure 103.

For most of Randy's life, doing art, creating and selecting images had provided a visual account of his inner concepts. Art and image had provided him a cognitive voice to express the "flesh and blood" of his emotions, dreams, heartbreaks, and realities (Arnheim, 1969, p. 134). His most recent picture was no exception. Looking at the "form as information" (Gantt & Tabone, 1998), one may observe that on the left side of the picture, Randy has drawn a large tree growing from the water. Jung states that water is a symbol of the unconscious and links it with the shadow. Water, he claims, "is where all life floats in suspension, in the realm of the sympathetic system, the soul of everything" (1969, p. 21). Was the tree representative of Randy's life, floating in suspension? The tree has no crown or leaves, only a textured pattern on the trunk and branches. The tree is in front of three carefully divided and double-

Figure 103. *It's just a house* by Randy.

outlined green and peaceful hills. On the right side of the picture, a strange, unrealistic-looking split house, a blue triangle with a black square for a door and a red-striped rectangle, sits on the hill. The house and the hill are outlined in black. A gray pathway begins close to the water and curves up the hill to the house but not to the door. Although only one third of the lower space is used, the drawing appears to have been done with a considerable amount of energy. The drawing shows some artistic sophistication but, except for the texture on the tree and the house, it is drawn simply with little detail. As was typical of most of Randy's pictures, there are no people. This softly colored picture is more guarded and closed than prior pictures. Looking at the thick boundaries, one could assume that Randy is more comfortable when he alone controls his environment.

Today, Randy is a young adult. His anger has not disappeared, but it is no longer his center of focus or presenting persona. He is not on medication, but he is searching, searching for his own SPIRIT and ultimate concerns. There is no question that Randy was a child at risk. Research indicates that adolescents who have had protective factors in their lives, high intelligence, quality schools, interested adults, models for conventional behavior, intolerance of and high controls against deviant behavior, values on achievement, church attendance, involvement in school and clubs, and the involvement of multiple family members passed on from one generation to the next live successful lives as adults (Jessor, 1993). We hope this can be Randy's future but his art indicates that he is an adult at risk, at risk for isolation and loneliness.

Randy is not unlike many youngsters, rich or poor, throughout the world today, who are exposed in their families of origin to violence in the form of malnurturance. He is distrustful of authority. Although Randy's brain and the marvelous groupings of neurons in it have helped him successfully progress to Piaget's formal operations stage he has never found that one person that he can trust, therefore, relationships in both love and work continue to be a challenge. Randy has never held a job and has limited friendships. The big question surrounding Randy and others like him is, will he, will they, be able to move forward, to a place of domestic affection, a place where they can feel they belong, a place where their hearts can feel at home?

CONCLUSION

Families are dynamic systems of relationships. Their influences are so encompassing and powerful that they taint or flavor the past, present, and future of human existence. Researchers tell us that adult deviant attitudes and behaviors emerge from early experiences with parents and in the family. Family theorists tell us that all families evolve through stages. Those stages, identified by Duvall (1957) and combined and updated by Barnhill and Longo (1978), Carter and McGoldrick (1980), and Becvar and Becvar (1982; 1993), include:

Stage 1. Married couples (without children)
Stage 2: Childbearing families (oldest child 30 months)
Stage 3: Families with preschool children (ages 2 1/2–6)
Stage 4: Families with school children (ages 6–13)
Stage 5: Families with teenagers (oldest child 13–20)
Stage 7: Middle-aged parents (empty nest to retirement)
Stage 8: Aging family members (retirement to death)

Considering "the inherent uncertainties of life" (Seppa, 1997), and today's diverse culture, we question not just what will happen to families in the future, but what will happen to blended, extended, or broken families that do not fit our popular models. Will families still have developmental stages? What will happen to individuals like Humberto whose families are destroyed in political upheaval? What will happen to individuals like Jenny whose families are toxic and abusive (Visher & Visher, 1988)? What will happen to confused and grieving families like Anne's, or divorced and redivorced families like Randy's, or addictive and homeless families like Chad and Bethanne's? What will happen to children like Michael and Neal, who, due to illness in the family, may be left as orphans? In the future, how will family therapists treat these significant relationships?

In most cases, primary caregivers in families, i.e., mothers, fathers, grandparents, stepparents, mothering agents, aunts, uncles, or whatever else we choose to call them, will always raise children. They will leave the imprint of their core values on every aspect of their children's choices, social roles, and internal rules. These caregivers will interact and relay in word, deed, *and image,* to those entrusted to their care, ultimate concerns that they feel are life-preserving and life-enriching. Whereas the majority of their issues will be developmental, or relate to repairing broken and bruised relationships, some will relate to sick and toxic families that do not have the skills to raise children, or purposely abuse and damage them.

Because of the wide use today of art in therapy, I believe that family members will be treated with creative expression, creative expression that returns people to a sense of normality through participation in a spontaneous process that incorporates the mind in its entirety—the right and left areas of the brain; the conscious, the preconscious, and the collective unconscious (Arieti, 1976)—and the body. While it is the therapist who guides treatment, it is the experience, the process, and the materials that act as a vehicle for physiological communication, connecting neuron to neuron, awareness to insight, and sensation to the brain's tender center. It is the creative product, the image, "the treasure that is exhumed" (Arieti, 1976, p. 27) that acts and reacts as the good parent, accepting, soothing, healing, and restoring hope and SPIRIT to humankind's "wounded inner child." Family art therapy, through the use of the creative process, helps humans connect or reconnect to lost parts of themselves as well as their significant others, even if it is just done metaphorically in art and image (Alexander, 1991).

In safe and sacred spaces, the creative process, doing, seeing, and reflecting, facilitates choices, reassessment of life's roles and rules, and exploration of ways to change. Choices restore hope, and hope is indicative of healing. Hope allows family members not only to dream again, but also encourages them to live out their dreams, often in the most unpredictable or creative ways. Jung (1933/1955) citing Goethe says, "Shaping and reshaping—is the eternal spirit's eternal pastime" (p. 157).

SPECIAL NOTATION

When using any new theoretical approach, it is important to follow the ethics and clinical standards of practice that apply. Art therapy requires training in both art and therapy. Without this training, "there is a risk that the defense can be undermined due to the rapid access to inner processes that result from art therapeutic techniques" (Gunter, 2000, p. 13). Ethical standards of practice for art therapy can be obtained from the following sources:

American Art Therapy Association
1202 Allanson Road
Mundelein, IL 60600

American Association of Marital & Art Therapy
1133 15th Street, NW
Washington, DC 20005-2710

American Psychological Association
750 First Street, NE
Washington, DC 20002-4242

APPENDICES

Appendix A

FAMILY ART-BASED ASSESSMENTS

General Instructions

Formally or informally, art based assessments used with families or individuals in families create a framework for assessment, communication, diagnosis and treatment. They provide an opportunity for the therapist to directly observe family interactions and explore historical and existential perspectives for strengths as well as challenges. Please note: assessments are treatment and treatment protocols are assessment. As your skills build, you will not need to feel that they must be kept separate.

- Assessment procedures, integrating medical and mental health history, include the client(s) process and art product. This part of the evaluation is done quantitative (Table 1, Art Based Assessment Eval). The therapist observes and rates the body language, the level of interaction of the client(s), psychological insight and the developmental age of the art expression. The product and the perception, identifying, isolating and integrating art components are evaluated qualitatively. Client(s) defense mechanisms are also noted.
- Assessment includes helping the client(s) focus by teaching them to see what is in their art, verbalize descriptively, and when appropriate, frame areas of concern.
- The Family Art-Based Assessments (FABA) included in this book: Family Art Evaluation (FAE); Family Sculpts (FS), Kinetic Family Drawings (K-F-D), Non-verbal and Verbal Team Art Tasks, Family Portraits, Family Murals, Shared Self Portraits Given to Spouse, Family Landscapes Drawings (FLD) and Draw a Bird Nest (BND) are to be considered as resources, not color-book patterns. Because different tasks assess different information, the Family Art-Based Assessments are often mixed or matched to include at least three art products. As a protocol, the three

185

products give more opportunity to observe graphic patterns, gather additional information and increase reliability of findings.

• Whereas art and image patterns do present an isomorphic blueprint of the creator identifying family or individual attitudes, beliefs, behaviors or thoughts at the time they were created or selected, the process of assessment is continual in that images change over time and through experiences.

Art Supply Kit

There is no way to do a family art-based assessment or intervention without art materials. Basic art materials can be simple, inexpensive and store easily, but the "structural qualities inherent in the materials interact with expressive styles influencing either development or regression or both" (Lusebrink, 1990, p. 84). For instance, using both ends of the media continuum (See Table 9, Medium Continuum). Clay is a hands-on fluid and, often regressive experience requiring both time and skill. Blobs of clay in hands become symbols and images. Pencils, on the other hand, are more resistive, and simple. Pencils permit distance from both the media and the product. One holds a pencil and makes marks thereby building trust in his or her own abilities, in the helper, and the setting providing the experience.

Art materials can be found at crafts stores, discount warehouses, teacher supply stores and even the local drug store. Necessities include non-toxic materials such as:

• Colored markers both wide and narrow tip.
• Pencils, erasers, and colored pencils with a portable sharpener.
• Colored tempera pallets. (They come in packages of eight colors: primary, secondary, as well as black and white. Each color is 2″ x 2″ across the top, about the size of a nice southern biscuit. Because they are tempera, they produce bright and dark as well as soft and light colors. They are easily stored. They can dry out, be reactivated with water and do not become rancid.
• A variety of brush and sponge sizes to use with the tempera pallets and watercolors.
• Several boxes of crayons
• Several boxes of crapas crayons
• A box of pastels
• Several pairs of good scissors
• Multicolored oil-based clay and a plastic baggie for storage
• A couple of bottles of Elmer's® blue glue (it dries faster than white glue)
• A pack of assorted colored construction paper

TABLE 9. MEDIUM CONTINUUM (Lusebrink, 1991)

Most Controlled

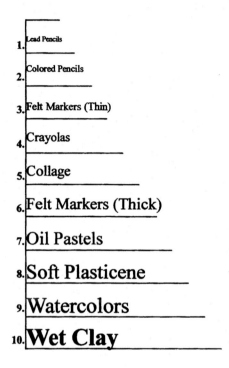

1. Lead Pencils
2. Colored Pencils
3. Felt Markers (Thin)
4. Crayolas
5. Collage
6. Felt Markers (Thick)
7. Oil Pastels
8. Soft Plasticene
9. Watercolors
10. Wet Clay

Least Controlled

- Tissue paper cut in 8″ x 12″ squares (1/4 of full sheet). Store in large plastic freezer bags then you can see the colors you want.
- A small bottle of liquid starch to attach tissue paper to paper or hard surfaces
- A tablet of white drawing paper 12″ x 18″
- A tablet of white drawing paper 18″ x 24″
- Paper towel roll and sponge for clean up
- A roll of masking tape or,
- 3M makes a large (20″ x 30″ Post it®) pad that can be mounted on the wall without tape or pins.

Recycling materials makes creating more fun. These can be almost anything including computer paper, paper bags, old socks, buttons, yarn, string, stones, feathers, ribbons, large and small boxes, pipe cleaners, and glitter. Big and little kids love glitter. Today you can buy "glitter" glue in a variety of colors. It is easy to use.

The Basics

- **Process.** Provide a safe and protected environment. Assume a positive and friendly attitude. Find a balance between conducting an assessment and joining with the client(s). Be present. Be patient. Be quietly supportive. Contain your opinion. Do not be clever. Do not pass judgment on the art, the verbal reflection, or the client. Establish a neutral perspective. Practice confidentiality and client advocacy.

   The art process includes: preparation, participation, clean up, client(s) reflection and therapist review. It also includes using therapeutic skills and intuition to help the client reflect and make sense of their expression.

- **Care and preparation.** No one wants to use dirty, old, and tired materials. Store them in clear plastic cartons, boxes or baskets but make them appealing, even seductive. When planning to use art materials, cover areas you do not want soiled with newspapers or plastic. Provide a wide-based container for fresh water to use when painting or cleaning brushes. Clean brushes after using. Encourage clients to participate at whatever level they are comfortable. But more importantly, don't ask your clients to do anything in art that you have not tried. A lot of hesitation occurs because a client does not know what to do with the materials. If you have tried the process and the materials you will be able to guide your clients through areas of concern.

- **Observation and participation.** Clients expect you to pay attention. Sit quietly and observe, taking mental or even written notes of what is happening. Clients often remind me, "You're not taking notes. Aren't you going to write it down." You are providing time, space and materials for clients to express their inner feelings and thoughts; allow that to happen. Do not leave the room, talk on the phone, straighten supplies or prepare for your next session. If you are not comfortable sitting quietly, observing the process of creation, perhaps art is the wrong media for you. Participate when participation facilitates the clients' work, whether it is encouragement or reducing stress. If, however, you do participate in a joint art product with a client or clients, as in a Winnicott Scribble drawing (1991) **do not** get lost in your own process, or overshadow your client with your artistic ability.

- **Clean up.** Cleaning up is so much easier if you clean up before paints dry and materials get sticky or chalk dust gets on your next clients. Again, wash every brush you use, particularly if you used one in starch, glue, or glitter. Brushes that are not washed thoroughly will become stiff and can be used for stirring paint but not for painting. If you share your office or space, your space partners will not appreciate your overflowing mess. Actually, neither will you. Cleaning up is part of the process. You might encourage each client to assist in cleaning the areas where he or she worked or the materials that he used. If you love the art and its results, cleaning up is not a problem.

- **Reflection.** An important piece of art in any therapy, but particularly art in family therapy is looking at it and reflecting on it. Have your clients put their art on an easel or a bulletin board and stand back 5 to 8 feet. Betensky (1975) says, "The important question is **what do our clients see**?" What is the first thing they see? What do they consider the center of their picture? Can they give the artwork a title? Perhaps it has a theme. How did they feel when they did it? What question does the artwork ask them, its creator? Berne & Savary (1991) refers to this as a **TTAQ** (Title, Theme, Affect, and Question). Encourage your clients to complete a **TTAQ** and then talk about their art from an "I position." Teach them to own their art as a way to learn more about themselves. "I am small and unfinished." "I am bright and colorful. I am confused or focused."

- **Dates and initials.** Always have your client(s) date and initial the finished art product. If they do not put their name and date on the back of the product, you do it. Identify the art-based directive. Three weeks later it is difficult to remember who did what when.

PROFESSIONAL ETHICS

Note: Like any other assessment, you are ethical when you have had training and know what you are doing. Take some classes, get supervision and a consult, then use one or two Family Art-Based Assessments consistently with the population that you work with the most. Be consistent with the art materials you provide, until you not only feel comfortable using the assessment but can be curious when someone or some family's art product deviates in either a positive or negative direction.

The American Art Therapy Association, Inc. (AATA, 1998) and the Art Therapy Credentials Board (ATCB, 1999) have ethical standards of practice that include caring for the art, confidentiality as it relates to the art; ownership of the art; valuing the art; and training in the use of the art as therapy. All professionally licensed and certified therapists require that you practice within your scope of practice. In art therapy, that requires training and a supervised practicum experience.

Table 10. FAMILY ART-BASED ASSESSMENTS (For Communication, Assessment, Diagnosis, and Treatment)

Family Art Evaluation (FAE) Kwiatkowska (1976)	Non-Verbal/Verbal Team Art (NVT) H. Landgarten (1987)	Family Portraits/Family Murals (FP/FM) J. Rubin (1978)	Couples Joint Picture/Self Self-Portrait (CJP/SP) H. Wadeson (1980)
Process	Process	Process	Process
1. Free Picture 2. Family Portrait 3. Abstract Family Portrait (arm movements) 4. Individual Scribble 5. Joint Family Scribble 6. Free Picture	1. Non-Verbal 2. Entire family on one picture–non-verbal 3. Verbal 4. Entire family on one picture–may speak	1. Picture from Scribble 2. Family Portraits 3. Joint Mural	1. Joint Picture–Non-Verbal 2. Abstract Family Portrait 3. Self-portrait given to spouse to enhance

Family Sculpt (FS) M. Keyes (1974)	Landscapes (FL) D. Arrington (1984)	Kinetic Family Drawing (KFD) J. Burns & Kaufman (1972)	Bird Nest Drawing (BND) D. Kaiser (1996)
Process	Process	Process	Process
1. Think about a time 2. Three adjectives describing each 3. Construct a shape representing the three adjectives 4. Past, present, role models 5. Change for the future	1. Think about a specific time 2. Landscapes 3. Legend 4. View from farthest person away from you 5. View from other individuals in the landscape	Draw your family doing something together	Draw a bird's nest

A-1. FAMILY ART EVALUATION (FAE)
BY HANNA KWIAKOWSKA (1978)

I. Materials: 18″ x 24″ white or manila drawing paper. Crayolas or crapas (oil pastels).

II. History: The Family Art Evaluation (FAE) originally developed for use with families with a severely disturbed hospitalized adult or adolescent member is used today as an art-based assessment with family members in both inpatient and family treatment.

III. Protocol: The instrument consists of completing six pictures in a sequence at the same session. Participants are discouraged from making elaborate drawings. At the conclusion of the assessment, participants are asked to label each family member with their names, to give general titles to their pictures and to sign and date them. (Working on an easel or on paper taped to the wall is preferred to working on tables). These pictures are:

1. Non-directive–Draw whatever comes to mind.

2. Directive–Draw the family members in the present. (Encourage participants to make whole person)

3. Directive–Draw an abstract family portrait.

4. Directive–Make an individual scribble and find a symbol in it.

5. Directive–Make an individual scribble and then as a family choose only one from which to make a joint family scribble with other members of the family.

6. Non-directive–Draw whatever comes to mind.

IV. Art Tasks:

1. Draw whatever comes to mind–used to relax participants; the non-directive is less threatening, allowing for freedom and flexibility.

2. Family Portrait encourages family members to draw the family in the present as they see them. It provides new reactions and insights.

3. Abstract Family Portrait provides information about family member's capacity for abstract thinking. It may elicit mixed feelings about family members.

At the completion of Number 3, relaxing body exercises are introduced (arm swings).

4. Individual Scribble–like word association, this art directive can be evasive or bring primary process material into the open. It is a useful instrument for observing integrative capacities of individual family members.

5. Joint Family Scribble–allows direct observation of how family members work together. Working on a single sheet of paper can identify family member's ability to tolerate closeness or individual needs for boundaries.

Comparing the individual and joint scribbles gives information about family dynamics.

6. The final free drawing–Drawing whatever comes to mind, often is the most important picture. It sums up the family's tolerance for stress and identifies whether the family members remained stable or changed over the course of the drawing assessment.

> Burak (1981) developed a Conjoint Family Drawing Rating Scale. The scale consisted of a checklist of behaviors grouped according to mode of expression (verbal, physical, drawing process and drawing content) and classified behaviors according to whether they remained stable or changed over the course of the sessions. From this checklist characteristics of each family member and of the family as a whole were identified. These characteristics were then clustered to form (systemic) behavioral patterns. (p. 95). (Arrington, 1990, p. 165)

COMMENTS: The FAE is a thorough assessment of all ages. It is however, difficult to complete in less than an hour. When a family of four or more is involved it often takes longer than one hour. Advise participants early and, in a non-forceful way keep the participants on task. For instance, you might advise them at the beginning that there are six art-based tasks that you would like to finish in approximately one hour. If one member gets overly involved, you might mention that when they finish the task they are on, they will have an opportunity to do more art as there are blank tasks still to complete. Young children may become impatient.

Notes:

A-2. NON-VERBAL AND VERBAL TEAM ART TASKS
BY HELEN LANDGARTEN (1987)

(For families of 4 or more)

I. Materials: 12″ x 18″ white or manila paper, colored markers, colored paper, glue.

II. History: Developed by Landgarten in Los Angeles with her work with family members and families.

III. Protocol: Landgarten's (1987) art psychotherapeutic family systems diagnostic procedure is presented as game-like although the therapist is reminded to be an astute observer and recorder of family behavior and artistic communication.

1. Directive–The Non-verbal Team Art Task requires that the family divide themselves into two teams and each team work on a single piece of paper. Each person on both teams is asked to select a color marker that is different from the others and to use it throughout the session. They are requested to not speak, signal, or write notes to each other while working on the art. When finished they are merely to stop. After the tasks are completed, the verbal ban is lifted, and the teams select and add a name to their product.

2. Directive–The Non-verbal Family Art Task requires that the entire family work together on a single sheet of paper. Again, they refrain from speaking until the task is complete. At that time they may speak and are requested to title their creation.

3. Directive–The Verbal Family Art Task allows the participants to speak while making a single piece of art. Each person uses one color of plasticene, colored paper, or marker.

IV. Assessment. Observing and Noting: The composition of each team indicates family alliances. The limited color rule facilitates the therapist's observation of each person's contribution. In addition, the therapist observes and records 17 issues relating to the family and individual participation. These "Points for Observation" include, "who initiated the picture and what was the process that led to this person making the first mark on the page? In what order did the rest of the members participate? Which member's suggestions were utilized and which were ignored? What was the level of involvement on the part of each person?" (For additional information see Landgarten, 1987, p. 15.)

COMMENTS: This FABA is good for observing family dynamics of inclusiveness and exclusiveness. A free drawing or a K-F-D, however, provides a good example for a third picture.

Notes:

A-3. FAMILY PORTRAITS AND MURALS
BY JUDITH RUBIN (1978)

I. Materials: 2″ x 12″ paper and butcher paper, chalks, crayolas, crapas and markers.

II. History: Inspired by the pioneering work of Hanna Kwiatkowska, working with Dr. Max Magnussen, Chief of Psychology, at the Pittsburgh Child Guidance Center, Rubin experimented with many possible tasks and sequences. She found the following procedural sequence most productive.

III. Protocol: Rubin (1978) developed three specific tasks for use with families when a child or adolescent is being seen in treatment. Presented as a collaborative undertaking, the tasks include:

1. Directive—The Individual Scribbles, in addition to their value as a powerful diagnostic tool, are introduced as a first task to put the non-artist at ease. Young children who have not developed the capacity to project an image onto a scribble are encouraged to draw whatever they wish. (For complete instructions see Rubin, 1978, p. 129.)

2. Directive—Family Portraits are introduced. They can be either realistic or abstract and either two- or three-dimensional. Since family portraits are inevitably tension producing, various choices are offered family members to minimize their stress. In addition to choosing the medium, when space allows, each person is encouraged to work wherever they wish, i.e., easel or table, alone or with others.

3. Directive—Joint Mural (Large mural paper taped to the wall)—Like the joint scribble, a task that allows for direct observation of how a family works together can be an effective diagnostic assessment. Mural paper offers a larger drawing surface than single sheets of paper and enables the art therapist to observe family interactions. "It is suggested that they first decide together what they will do and then work on the paper" (p. 130).

4. Non-Directive—Free Picture, Draw whatever you want. If a participant completes either of the first two tasks before the others, he or she is encouraged to create a free picture using any medium.

IV. Assessment. Observing and Noting:

1. Scribble Drawing—with their limited media choices are conducive to informal conversations about a topic unusual to the family.

2. Family Portraits—give the therapist an opportunity to observe family member's images of each other, i.e., size, position, placement and body parts missing, emphasized, or extended.

3. Family Mural—In addition to the projective possibilities, it encourages joint decision making and collaborative participation. It gives the therapist an opportunity to observe the family working together.

Notes:

A-4. JOINT PICTURE WITHOUT TALKING (JP) AND SELF PORTRAITS (SP) GIVEN TO SPOUSES BY HARRIET WADESON (1981)

I. Materials: 12″ x 18″ paper, thick pastels in a wide variety of colors.

II. History: Working at National Institute of Mental Health (NIMH) with Kwiatkowska and family therapists, Wadeson (1980; 1973) developed a variety of techniques for working with couples both diagnostically and therapeutically.

III. Protocol:. Three techniques were developed to highlight the interactional processes in the marital relationship and are not presented in a fixed order as indicated by a particular diagnostic question or therapeutic issue.

1. Directive–Joint Picture Without Talking–The instructions are to "develop one well-integrated picture together without verbal communication" (p. 285).

2. Directive–Abstract of Marital Relationship–Participants are instructed to "draw an abstract picture of their marital relationship simultaneously but separately" (p. 290).

3. Directive–Self-portrait Given to Spouse–Each spouse is requested to draw a realistic, full-length self-portrait on a full sheet of vertical paper. When they have finished they are requested to symbolically give themselves (their self-portraits) to one another and then are given the opportunity to do anything you want to your partner.

IV. Assessment: Observing and Noting.

1. Joint Picture Without Talking–This task provides an opportunity to observe the couple work together in close proximity (single sheet of paper). Not allowing verbal communication heightens the power of the non-verbal interactions.

2. Abstract of Marital Relationship–This is a modification of the Kwiatowska Abstract Family Portrait with the same unique features. It indicates the individual's capacity for abstract thinking and elicits strong affect.

3. Self-portrait Given to Spouse–This art-based exercise elicits intense affect and dramatizes interactions.

COMMENTS: Swapped portraits are effective with other dyads as well; i.e., couples, mothers and daughters, mothers and sons, brothers and sisters, etc.

Notes:

A-5. FAMILY SCULPTS (FS)
BY MARGARET FRINGE KEYES (1982)

I. Materials: Modeling clay, paper, and pencils.

II. History: Keyes (1974) originated the Family Sculpt Technique working with clients in clinical settings.

III. Protocol: The therapist begins by having client(s) *think about their family of origin at a time between 3 and 10 years of age.*

1. On the paper, *write three adjectives for each member in the family at that time* including the client, i.e., strange, lonely, creative.

2. Next, request the client(s) to *construct a clay sculpture of the adjectives describing each family member.*

3. The client *places the sculptures on the paper in relationship to each other.* For example, those close and those that were distant.

4. Next, the therapist has the client(s) *write a question or comment that the client may have felt (probably non-verbally) from each family member* and what his or her reply (behaviorally) may have been.

5. The therapist reviews the family sculpt with the client(s) focusing first on the *family of the past,* then who meets those same adjectives in *the current relationships.*

6. Next, the therapist has the *client gestalt each term and the sculpture,* i.e., for the words, I am strange, I am lonely, I am creative and for the sculpture, I am large, flat, prickly, complicated.

7. The client(s) is not allowed to throw any of the sculpture away but *she/he can change them anyway she wants.* For example, building one up or lowering, bending another or incorporating into one sculpture.

Notes:

A-6. FAMILY LANDSCAPES (FLD)
BY DORIS ARRINGTON (1984)

I. Materials: Any paper will do but to look like a map, rice paper or a soft paper like newsprint or tissue paper combines well with colored pencils, water colors, brushes and black pens.

II. History: Arrington, (1984) working with families and individuals in families initiated family landscapes to look at boundary issues and compassion between family members.

III. Protocol:

1. *Think of a specific time in the client(s) lives between 3 and 12 years old.* Think of the *psychological space that they grew up in.* How did it feel emotionally, i.e., crowded, quiet, cramped, or comfortable?

2. *Draw a symbolic landscape, seascape, desert scape,* of the psychological space. *Include each member of the family* that was in the family at the time, *placing those emotionally close,* close together, and those distant, distant. This always elicits intense emotions within a family setting as symbols are expressed and coalitions are identified.

3. Next, ask the client(s) *to place a legend on the landscape identifying each family member.*

4. If the client was in a family that had any *significant changes* during this period (3–12), i.e., death, divorce, remarriage, foster placement, ask the client(s) to draw a different landscape that depicts the emotional climate about that setting and put a legend on it as well. Individuals have often lived in several families as children and there may be several family landscapes.

5. Ask the client(s) *to draw, with the same intensity, a landscape from the viewpoint of the person that was the furthermost away* from him or her. This reframe of space between family members often begins an empathetic process not previously experienced. Encourage the client(s) to *draw the view from the symbol of each family member in the family landscape* and discuss what he or she experienced.

IV. Assessment:

The initial landscape is pretty straightforward. It represents how the creator consciously felt about the family space, including appropriate defense mechanisms. The second one gives dynamic insight into the view the creator believed to be held by the family member most distant from the creator.

COMMENTS: The FLD works well with a free picture at the beginning to relax the participants. It also works well with family members of latency age or above.

Notes:

A-7. KINETIC FAMILY DRAWINGS (K-F-D)
BY ROBERT BURNS AND S. KAUFMAN (1972)

I. Materials: 8-1/2" x 11" paper and pencils.

II. History: The K-F-D is the most widely used art-based family assessment. Introduced in 1970, Burns and Kaufman found that the K-F-D often reflected primary disturbances much more quickly and adequately than interviews or other probing techniques. At the time it was first introduced the authors had reviewed 10,000 KFD from individual patients.

III. Protocol: Ask the client (children or adults) to *draw a picture of everyone in your family, including you, doing something.*

1. Try to *draw whole people,* not cartoons or stick people.

2. Remember, *make everyone doing something*–some kind of action.

3. Put your initials and the date.

IV. Assessment: First look for overall affect then body perceptions of family members and self, encapsulation, compartmentalization; transparencies, missing person or self, sexualized, aggressive (with or without weapons) and fear and anxiety. For more complete assessment see Art Based Assessment Evaluation (ABA-EVAL) Arrington, 2000, Burns and Kaufman , 1972, and Peterson and Hardin, 1995.

COMMENTS: Peterson and Hardin (1997) have adapted a Qualitative and and a Quantitative Screening Inventory for the K-F-D from Burns & Kaufman (1972).

Notes:

DRAW A BIRD'S NEST (BND) BY D. KAISER (1996)

I. Materials: 8-1/2″ x 11″ white paper, a #2 pencil with eraser, thin colored markers, crapas or pastels.

II. History: "A rich body of research assessing attachment in children has evolved over the past two decades. This research has expanded to include assessment of attachment patterns and organization in older children, adolescents and adults, and provides a conceptual framework, contributing to the understanding of optimal development throughout the life span. In addition attachment relationships are being studied as they relate to other relationships through life and to the development of risk for psychopathology (1996, p. 334).

III. Protocol: The client(s) is asked to *Draw a bird's nest.*

This can be accompanied by The Attachment to Mother (ATM) scale of the inventory of Parent and Peer Attachment (Armsden, G., & Greenberg, M. (1987).

IV. Assessment: Inclusion of parent and baby birds indicated a higher attachment score on the Attachment to Mother scale than the inclusion of eggs. No eggs and no birds indicated a lower attachment score. "The results of Kaiser's study are consistent with the view that less securely attached women may be unconsciously expressing or felt lack of support from significant others when they leave out parent and or baby birds" (pp. 333–340). The BND could assist in designing strategies for reconstructing or repairing an internalized insecure working model for attachment.

Notes:

Appendix B

THE LIFE CYCLE LOG AND OTHER INTERVENTIONS USED IN FAMILY ART THERAPY

Family art therapists are trained to notice. They work with families or individuals in families, often requesting that clients draw this, or draw that, create this, or create that, make this, make that, show us this, show us that. This is done with serious intent always watching physical and emotional interactions with the process, the art product, and others in the room. The Art-Based Assessment-Eval, (ABAEval, Table 1) assists in ongoing quantitative and qualitative assessment.

The following interventions are offered as resources. With experience they are interchangeable between communication, assessment, diagnosis and treatment in the cycle of healing. The therapist is always taking their clients' attitude temperature on the attitude continuum and not just whether they are happy (Csikszentmihalyi, 1999) but whether they see any goodness in the world in which they live. Subtle changes will be evident in the art weeks before it is evident to the client(s).

ATTITUDE CONTINUUM

Positive_____ Neutral_____ Negative

Interventions include

B-A. The Life Cycle Log and Wordtapping
B-B. My Lifetime*–Our Family Time*

B-C. The Family Tree, or Forest—Genogram*
B-D. First Memory—First Shared Memories
B-E. Instant Collage (Persona and Shadow: Cultural, family and gender roles and rules).
B-F. Tissue Paper Trees (Dialoging and expanding lifelong issues)
B-G. Me Boxes and We Boxes
B-H Outside and Inside
B-I.. Shared Values*
B-J. Protectors, (Pets and Principles)
B-K. Repair! Repair! Repair! The Repair Box
B-L. Treasure Folders of Golden Dreams*

B-A. LIFE CYCLE LOG AND WORDTAPPING

As you define your SPIRIT of individuation and relationship, you may want to keep a personal journal where you can write and sketch personal questions and answers. One way to begin this process is to construct a Life Cycle Log.

Materials: Life Cycle Log pages or sketchbook, pen, pencils, colored pencils.

Preparation and process: The following Life Cycle Log is designed to complete in seven - year segments beginning with first memories as you know them. Begin with family history. Write it down. Make it as long and as detailed as you want. Go to elders with a tape recorder, video camera or just pencils and paper. Talk over family history, family personalities and childhood stories. Study genealogies of your family. Attend family reunions. The elderly change quickly. Memories and stories are forgotten. Choose an area that you are interested in, like your life, and begin.

When filling in the Life Cycle Log, start with the year before your birth and complete all the year columns and the address columns up to the present time. Now you have a chronological structure. Fill in information about prenatal years and birth stories. Sometimes as simple as these events may be, they give clues to personal choices and current behavior. As therapy progresses, the Life Cycle Log can create a time of intimacy for you to sit down with significant others and share experiences or information gained.

Goals
1. To allow free movement within inner space and time.

---

* Adapted techniques. Appropriate credits listed on descriptive sheets.

2. To open up experiences and feelings for recognition and exploration.

3. To provide a cognitive structure for moving fluidly through memories and hopes; gaining access to memories of life to which previous contact was unavailable. Progoff (1975) refers to chronological time as the objective sequence of events, as an observer perceives them. Qualitative time, on the other hand, is seen as the meaning and value of the objective experience.

4. To communicate remembered normal and intimate events with significant relationships.

5. To give value to the experience by exploring, accepting, and forgiving the affect, and behavior of the experience so that one can move on.

Wordtapping: Memories come in clusters. Wordtapping is the right hemisphere shorthand. It leads from one idea to another with its own logic. The left hemisphere may not feel the connection but goes with it, eventually a pattern and rhythm develop.

Materials: Life Cycle Log or sketchbook, pen, pencil, or colored pencils

Preparation and process: One word or phrase will bring back a lifetime of memories. We may not want to fill a category in sequentially but to follow one memory track to the next. What was mealtime or bedtime like in my life? How did my family celebrate birthdays, or successes, or failures? Under vehicles, what was the first car that I drove or owned? Did I own a motorcycle? What were my memories around that? Did I ride my bike a lot? What smells or sounds did I enjoy or were significant to me or my family? What were my heroes or heroines, in life, books, movies, or TV programs? There is no single way to record the memories included in the Log. It is a structure only. Fill it in as it works for you. Work with relatives to focus on times and events. The structure of the Life Cycle Log gives you the freedom to move in any direction and still tap into significant memories in chronological time.

Allow yourself time over several weeks or months to complete this process, and be prepared for many feelings and thoughts to surface and be reviewed. Use abbreviations or code if you want to keep your log private. You will be surprised at how much recall you do have. Many people have found that their ability to remember many things improves when they untangle mixes of feelings and thoughts with time, space, and life events. Allow some spaces to remain blank. See them as periods of discovery in your adult development.

B-B. MY LIFETIME (RHYNE, 1973)

Before you begin, Jaynie Rhyne, author of *Gestalt Art Therapy*, would have you put it in a Gestalt framework. She says, "Gestalt psychology is a theory of

Table 11. LIFE CYCLE LOG AND WORDTAPPING

Ages	Prenatal	0–7	8–14	15–22	23–30 etc.
International/National/State					
Local					
Books–Authors, Movies, TV shows Heroes, Heroines					
Science, School Work					
Music Sports Hobbies					
Holidays Vacations					
Moral/Religious/Spiritual Experiences					
Sexual Experiences					
Sights/Sounds/Smells/Tastes					
Family Relatives Friends					
Pets/Toys					
Vehicles					
Accomplishments					
Address Changes					

perception that includes the interrelationships between the form of the object and the processes of the perceiver" (p. 7). Experience, live in the present: give full attention to what is happening at the moment; do what you want to do; trust your own data; integrate your disowned parts into a total being. Identify needs and wants. . . . perceive whole configurations-to perceive your personality as a totality of many parts that together make up the reality of you. Gestalt art experience, then, is: the complex personal you making art forms; being involved in the forms you are creating as events, observing what you do, and hopefully perceiving through your graphic productions not only yourself as you are now, but as alternate ways that are available to you for creating yourself as you would like to be" (p. 9).

Materials: A roll of paper, opaque water colors, several sizes of brushes, jars of water, scotch tape, scissors, glue, construction paper, tissue paper, crapas.

Preparation: Before you begin, relax and let your fantasies wander in the spaces of your lifetime, past, present and future.

When you look at your lifetime what does it look like? What was the metaphoric temperature in your home as a child? Who were your primary caretakers? Who helped you define who you are? How did you relate to your school and your neighborhood? How were your parents involved in your learning processes? How did your family celebrate birthdays? How did those around you celebrate success? How did they handle failure? What event, or events, changed your life? When were you frightened? Did you ever question whether life was worth living? When did you question your family's belief systems? When did you decide on your own? What were your family motivators or protectors? What were yours? Have you reconciled your dark times? Have you forgiven yourself?

Process: Unroll your paper. "You are in your own lifetime! You have the privilege and the responsibility for claiming and being and doing in your own life space. Do as you will.

B-2B. OUR MARRIAGE TIME
(SUDDABY AND LANDAU, 1998)

Begin with now. How did both of you get to this space? What came before now? What came before then? Look at the positive. Name it, reflect on it, identify it, create it in image. Now, what are the negative components? What came before them? Name them, reflect on them, identify them, create them in image.

Table 12. GENOGRAM (Best drawn on 12" x 18" paper. Include birth and death dates)

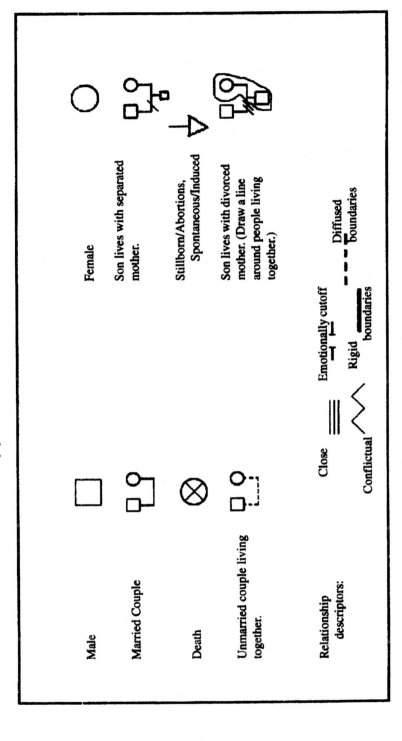

Male

Married Couple

Death

Unmarried couple living together.

Relationship descriptors:

Female

Son lives with separated mother.

Stillborn/Abortions, Spontaneous/Induced

Son lives with divorced mother. (Draw a line around people living together.)

Close

Conflictual

Emotionally cutoff

Rigid boundaries

Diffused boundaries

B-C. THE FAMILY TREE AND
THE NATIONAL FOREST–GENOGRAM

(Guerin & Pendagast, 1976; Bowen, 1978; Lewis, 1989; Hardy & Laszloff, 1995; Kuehl, 1995; McGoldrich, Giordano & Pearce, 1996)

The genogram is a diagram of three or more generations, a map of the people who make up a family. It provides a visual representation of family structure, household and relationship information, and intergenerational messages and can help family members see how current issues may be connected to issues from the past. Genograms identify:

At the minimum: Births, deaths, divorces, alliances, loyalties, splits, and emotional cutoffs.

At the maximum:

A. Expectations, family secrets, myths, suicides, triangulated relationships and gender roles.

B. Repeated patterns of certain illnesses (i.e., diabetes, heart trouble, strokes, cancer, muscular dystrophy) drug and alcohol abuse, and family violence.

C. Education, professions, skills, strengths, and talents.

D. How the family defines and shows anger and affection, acceptance and rejection, love and dislike, intimacy and isolation, nurturance, and respect.

E. Family cultural interests and ethnicities.

F. Multigenerational issues.

Questions to be pursued include: Who was close to whom? Who is currently "in" and who is currently "out" in the family? Who are family heroes? And who are the black sheep? How and where spouses met? How did different family members die? Include any significant others who lived in the home, such as cooks, caretakers, nannies, and significant animals. Include personal issues (can't keep jobs, quiet, funny).

The National Forest

Within the general symbol of landscape, forests occupy a notable place, and are often found in myths, legends, and folktales. A forest is a dense growth of trees and underbrush connected on all levels with the Great Mother. Sometime, families have so many interactions with multiple relationships they look more like a family forest than a family tree. Children, even adult children from these families, are often confused or embarrassed (because it looks different) about constructing a family tree. Encourage individuals and families to look at their relationships as a forest with a variety of specimens that live together.

B-D. FIRST MEMORY

Individuals. What was your first memory? What is the very first thing that you remember? Maybe it is only an image. Take time to draw it or write it down. It is important. Were you alone or were other people there? My first memory was before I was three, and my life has spiraled upward in seven-year cycles since that time. Perhaps your memory was two or four, or one. Emotions learned early in life relate to anger, fear, surprise, happiness, sadness, disgust, love and interest. They are on a continuum of high (hostile) to low (hopeless) intensity. This intensity affects the sympathetic nervous system releasing either adrenaline or cortisol. How did your first memory relate to these emotions?

B. Shared Memories

Couples and families. Of all the people in this world, how did the two of you get together? Working alone, draw how you met. Draw specific memories of your courtship. Draw how you got engaged. Together, draw significant events before you married. Draw your feelings about your wedding. What and how you remember and create this is important. Reflect and remember. How do these memories relate to those emotions learned early in life?

Materials: Assorted sizes and colors of papers. Simple materials like crapas, chalks, or watercolors and brushes.

Process: Spend time thinking about your first memory, or memories you share with your significant other. Try to remember the emotions and circumstances. Then sketch a picture or create an abstract of those events that express your feelings and emotions. Allow time to process these memories and feelings. Others are often able to provide insightful feedback or a different perspective.

B-E. INSTANT COLLAGE–PERSONA AND SHADOW: ROLES, RULES, AND REJECTIONS

Materials: Collections of magazine pictures collected and saved in large brown envelopes or plastic roller drawers. Topics of collections should include every age, culture, and ethnic face or body; animals; bridges, building, objects, places and words.

Preparation and Process: When I was a little girl, among other games I played paper dolls. As a therapist I revised this special time for clients by collecting magazine pictures to be used in collage. There are many ways to use collage. People often use magazines and pick out their own pictures and then paste them down. But collecting takes time and clients get lost in reading the magazines. Others provide a collection of magazine pictures and request people to choose one or many for specific tasks. Sometimes they are pasted down and other times arranged in a personal pattern but not pasted down. The process is easy. Spread the pictures on a large table to provide viewing room. Request the client to find pictures that represent one of the topics below:

1. Pick out five or six pictures that represent you and your immediate family.

2. Pick out ten pictures that represent your family culture, (busy, professional, childless, messy, kids, pets, etc.).

3. Pick out pictures that represent all members of your family of origin, focusing on roles (wife, mother, daughter, worker bee, Queen, Princess, administrator, director, assistant, cleaner, cook, chauffeur) and rules (wife cleans house and cooks, mothers stay home, daughters obey parents, etc.).

4. Pick out ten pictures of your family that relate to continuing issues (money, sex, tardiness, collecting, shopping, etc.), and perpetual problems (differences in parenting, watching football, poor communication, in-laws, etc.).

5. Pick out ten pictures that indicate how your family relaxes (sports, movies, nature, drinking, traveling, visiting with friends, creating, listening to music).

6. At some point you may use all of these topics and make up your own.

Of interest to the family art therapist is the information received in the process of selecting. Were the selections generally positive or negative? What statements were being made about family culture? What roles and rules were discovered or identified? What are the continuing issues and perpetual problems in the family? Are they perceived negatively or positively, with humor, irritability or disgust. Has the couple or family learned to live with the issue or problem? Does the family know how to relax together with non-addictive solutions? (i.e., limited drinking, eating, shopping, smoking, working). All of these topics open up discussions that can be non-threatening because they are focused on the images rather than the client.

B-F. TISSUE PAPER TREES–PUTTING LIFE IN PERSPECTIVE (ARRINGTON, 1985) DIALOGING AND EXPANDING LIFELONG ISSUES AND PERPETUAL PROBLEMS

Materials: Colored tissue paper cut in 6″ x 6″ squares and arranged by color. White paper–12″ x 18″ or 18″ x 24″. Starch, brushes, paper or plastic cups to hold the starch.

Preparation: Gather or take 20 to 50 pictures or postcards of trees, every kind, every age, every color, and the various parts of a tree, roots, trunk, bark, branches and leaves. Review the pictures.

See yourself in the metaphor of the tree growing and expanding. Your environment: is it structured, or free flowing? You started out as a seed on a forest floor that was either covered with herbs and soft ferns, or packed and trampled and strewn with fallen debris. . . . Perhaps your seed bed had been carefully prepared so that you could receive lots of warm sun. So that your roots were able to explore and stabilize as you grew and developed into a fine representative of your family and culture . . . and your roots could sink deep into the soil. . . .

Maybe life wasn't so easy, and you grew up living close to the edge. Maybe because of erosion, your root system was exposed but you hung in there and grew and grew, each year . . . at each new cycle, a new ring of bark grew to protect you from the elements and to strengthen your trunk. Maybe you felt different from those around you. . . . From a distance all trees look the same; however as we get closer, we see they vary. . . . Like human beings, trees are different from each other. How different is your tree? Is your trunk straight or crooked? Does it have a single trunk, or many? Is your bark (your outside protection) thick or thin? Does it split or crack? Perhaps your slant is different. Do your branches go up? Or out? Or maybe they go down.

What are your leaves like? How do you take in the environment? Do you feel like blooming? Like it might be spring? Are you producing the fruit you want? Maybe your leaves are turning brilliant colors and you are even more beautiful in your fall. Perhaps you feel burdened and weighted down because you have too many living off of you. You may even feel sick or dead and may need to be pruned or cut back so that each of your limbs can reach its full potential.

Maybe you have been grafted so that you produce beautiful fruit, or, instead you feel cramped, or restricted, or in a fog, or out of focus. Maybe you feel isolated or barren and dry. Maybe it is your winter, a time of dormancy and inner growth; a time to stay warm and safe inside, to make new self discoveries and new decisions. Perhaps you need to take a new path, go over a bridge, or around a mountain . . . to water, the refreshing well springs of life, and follow it as a tree down to the sea . . . where the cycle begins again . . .

from a new birth . . . expanding . . . ever . . . upward. . . . Our lives are root-
ed in memories. Tap into the root system of your sensory experiences. Create your tree.

Process: Use colored tissue paper and starch or any other materials that
you have on hand to draw or create your tree, as a whole or as a part of a tree.
The reason for selecting tissue paper is that the colors are seductively beautiful and inviting, and mixed with the adhesive starch they are, like life, not
totally controllable. Reflect on the tree you made, the season you made by the
colors selected, and any problems you had with the materials.

Clean up: Wash brushes in water.

B-G. ME BOXES–DIALOGING AND EXPANDING PERSONAL AND RELATIONSHIP ISSUES

They were called Me Boxes when we worked with teachers of Headstart
children in the early 60s. Keyes (1974) called them Self Boxes and suggested
that you begin with a cardboard box and a pile of old magazines, determining what you keep on the inside and what you choose to show to the outside.

Preparation: Call it what you like because it is your expression, as you
believe others see you and the way you feel. What parts of your external
world are you? What part belongs to your other commitments? Think of your
external world as the people and concerns that you are responsible to and for.
How do you respond to these responsibilities, positively or negatively? Who
are you loyal to? Whom do you expect loyalty from? Think of your internal,
private world as physical sensations, emotional feelings, and intuitive plans.
What are your dreams, fantasies, memories, and expectations around love
and work? Think of your activities, behavior, accomplishments, body language and culture. Your inner feelings and thoughts are private. Protect them
however you want. Others have made small inner boxes or cubbyholes to
shelter those parts. Let your Me Box illustrate what it feels like to be you.
There is no right or wrong way. You will know the way to do it.

Materials:. Use any form of a container, a box, a carton, a basket, a paper
bag, a soft sculpture; whatever you feel portrays you. Create or find graphics
that represent symbolic descriptors of you, such as powerful, playful, spiritual, creative, positive, negative, calm, anxious, hopeful, depressed, committed
and any of the other descriptors in your head.

In the past, people have found Me Boxes extremely meaningful. Some
have made them as permanent art forms to keep and display. Others, having
made them, move on to the next project. Enjoy the experience of being in
charge of you, your image and your feelings.

B-E. WE BOXES

This same project works when two people work together on their We Box. As a couple, who are you responsible to and for? Where are your loyalties? What are your expectations of others in regards to the family? Work together to illustrate how you believe the two of you are perceived by others. What is your inner and private time like? Work together to make sculpture of your descriptors, your family mission, children careers, dreams, home life, personal relationships, and relationship to the community. Is there a good fit? Or a mismatch?

B-H. OUTSIDE AND INSIDE ART TASKS–HERE AND NOW FEELINGS AND BELIEFS

I have a public me that I let you see even if I don't know you well. Jung (19) calls that public part of the personality that we present to others a persona. The Greeks refer to the persona as the Mask. We all know that there are many parts of ourselves that live under and behind the mask. I have a private me that I share with family and close friends. I have an even more private me that I feel inside but may not know well, if at all. When I get stressed or needy that part of me wants attention and, more than likely, I will be embarrassed to see the parts of me that I don't know or understand. The more I get to know the various parts of myself, the more I am able to care for their different needs. Actually, the more I know of me, the more comfortable I feel in my own skin, the more I am willing to share with you. The more I trust me, the more I trust you.

An Outside and Inside Art Task is a here and now picture. Who are you right now, both on the inside and the outside, perhaps two different feelings in the same art piece. Maybe they are drawn or made figuratively. Although art is an X-ray of the mind, its beauty is that it remains private and personal until I tell you what it means to me. Art is the behavioral approach to "getting in touch" with here and now feelings.

Materials: A large piece of paper (24″ x 35″) or a box with a lid, or a brown sack without any advertising on it, paints, oil pastels, and markers or colored construction scraps, tissue paper, glitter glue and found materials.

Preparation and process: Our inner and outer feelings or thoughts are not always congruent and sometimes, we are the last to know they are not. Before you begin to relax and breathe deeply, think about the presence that you are presenting to others right now. Is it calm, assured, confused, groovy, sexy, irate, cooperative, or something else? Now, think about how you are feeling right now. Are the two congruent? It does not matter if they are or if they are not because this is your picture, this is your life, your feelings. If you can relax and work from your gut instead of your head it is even better. This art task is similar to a Me Box but it is intended to be a resistance combatter and a spontaneous barometer of congruence. Because it is spontaneous, Your Outside and Inside art piece will not contain precious and carefully selected art objects but symbols here and now feelings, beliefs or attitudes. To combat resistance, you want to finish this art task within 20 to 30 minutes.

Take your large paper and fold both sides together until they meet in the middle. Press the outside edges flat. Using the top as one piece of paper, draw how you present yourself today. If you are using a box or bag, create your current presenting behavior on the outside of the box or bag. Now open the two sides of the paper and, inside, draw how you are feeling. If you are using a box or a bag, use magazine pictures and the found objects to identify your feelings. Finishing this task within 20 to 30 minutes will encourage spontaneity.

B-I. SHARED VALUES

I have included this twenty-five-year-old non-art task because it helps families and family members find their SPIRIT. Today, many young people have not been exposed to identifying their values and those of their significant others. Thank you, Mr. Simon. "People in general have a multitude of value indicators but few values. Having value indicators is good, but having values is better. The more we understand about values, the more likely we are to make satisfactory choices and take appropriate action" (Simon, 1974).

Simon (1974, p. xv) gives the following criteria for clarifying values:

1. Chosen freely
2. Chosen from among alternatives
3. Chosen after due reflection
4. Prized and cherished
5. Publicly affirmed
6. Acted upon
7. Part of a pattern that is a repeated action.

Today, when millionaires are made daily we all want our part of the "market." We want "all the gusto we can have." We want "our cake and want to eat it too." Occasionally, we read about people who get what they thought they wanted and it did not satisfy their inner needs. When this happens to you or me is it because we don't stop and look at what we really enjoy most. We let media madness, financial frenzies and family pressures decide how we spend our time and energy. If we were to look at what motivates us we could see what our attitudes really are and perhaps we might fill our time with things and people that are most meaningful.

How do we assess what motivates us? We could construct a VALUES CHART. Simon (1974) suggests that we begin by writing down **ten things we love to do.** Since they will be what we individually love to do they can be anything we want them to be, i.e., swimming the Shark Fest in San Francisco, hang gliding in New Zealand, skiing anywhere, listening to certain musicians, singing in the shower, talking to friends, and/or traveling. Choose your likes, your values. Don't let anyone else's values count at this point. You may want to use initials or codes so that no one else can tell what you value or really love, at least until you have decided they are your choices. Now, move to the next step.

- Rank order your choices, i.e., what would you find impossible to give up? Is there something else? And something else? Place a 1, 2, 3, 4, and 5 to place in order the things you love doing.
- Next, put an A right next to the choices that you like to do alone. Again, if it is reading, maybe you prefer doing that alone. Put an A. If you like to do something with people, i.e., extreme sports, put a P. If you like to do something with and without people put an AP. Now, do you get the picture?
- Next, put a $ sign for anything that costs over $10.00.
- Put an M if you think your mom would have liked doing it and an F if you thing father would. Put an MF if you think both would have enjoyed it. They may never have had the opportunity but you think they would have enjoyed it. In my case, I believe my Dad would have liked skiing. I know my mother would not have enjoyed any cold, outdoor sport.
- Next, put a W for the last week or M for the last month or Y for the last year that you participated in your favorite thing.

Relook at your choices, their ranks and how you identified them. Think about what you were pleased with or surprised to find. Write it down.

What did you find out about yourself? Do you like to do things alone, or with people? Are you more like Mom or Dad or neither? Do you spend lots of money keeping yourself happy so that you have to work a lot to meet your values? When was the last time you did most all of those things you love to do? If it has been a long time, no wonder that you are anxious and stressed out. Your inner self is starving. What do you really love to do best?

DO A VALUE CHART WITH YOUR SIGNIFICANT OTHER. Understanding each other's values can often clear up misunderstandings. You may find that you have different values (this doesn't necessarily mean that you have different value systems). Often, couples find that one is more verbal and likes to visit over dinner or a glass of wine while the other is more physical and prefers making love to talking. It is surprising to both to find out how easy both needs can be met in the same evening, and how rich the relationship can become when both needs are met.

REFERENCE

Simon, S.B. (1974). *Meeting Yourself Halfway.* Niles IL: Argus Communications (adapted from p. 6).

B-J. PROTECTORS: PETS, PRINCIPLES
AND PRINCIPALITIES

Materials: 12″ x 18″ paper. Drawing materials, markers, crapas, chalks, magazines, scissors, and glue.

Preparation: Today, school children drink milk from containers with pictures of children that have disappeared. They attend schools where a peer has used a gun to kill and maim other students and teachers. They watch violent television and they often live in communities where murder is a household word. Physical fear is real and more real for some children than others. As children we develop our own fears. They may be of movement, fast, high, unbalanced; strangers and not so strangers, change, noise or even light or not light. As we grow we learn to fear failure and success. How do we protect ourselves from the real dangers around us and from our own fears? Like our ancient ancestors we reach out to those with physical and emotional power to harm, or to provide and we gather our protectors around us.

What makes us fearful? This is the time to bring fear into the therapy room. Instead of acting out, act in. What are your protectors? What makes you feel safe? Do your protectors change over time? What do you do when you are threatened or frightened? Action can be as concrete as having a AAA card in your pocket, or a cell phone for calling the police, or 911; having your lucky charm or installing a security system.

Sometimes we feel safe being an American citizen, or calling the doctor and having insurance, keys, social security, or an education. Security is often ethereal as in immediate prayer; feeling close to God or our ancestors; holding or surrounding ourselves with sacred images or ritual totems like crosses, angels and sacred potions; participating in familiar rituals, or just having a sense of familiarity. Our relationships, spouses and children can help us to feel safe; our pets, our time alone, or just time for meditating in nature or in a chapel or a museum can make us feel safe. Sometime our protectors are helpful and other times they feel helpful like when we use pills, or alcohol or food. When we identify our images or rituals of protection, it is easier to dismiss them or to call on them when we need them.

Process: Reflect on your health, your home and your relationships. Create, draw or select from magazines up to ten pictures of the most important things that you do to make you feel safe. What does your family do to feel safe? Identify them and own them.

B-K. REPAIR! REPAIR! REPAIR! THE TOOLBOX

Something is always broken and needs repairing but the tools needed for repairing are dependent on what is broken. Certain tools are necessary for different purposes. If you lose the screw in your glasses, just any screwdriver will not work. It must be a tiny screwdriver. This exercise will help you gather tools you might need for your family art therapy toolbox. A personal story may explain how necessary appropriate tools and time are in repairing something that may be broken.

Five hours after arriving on sabbatical in London to write this book, I broke in five places, both the fibula and the tibia, of my left leg. Whereas all manner of tools were needed to repair my leg, it was necessary to use them in an orderly fashion. First medic personnel needed stretchers, morphine, scissors and splints to remove me from a small opening in the kitchen where I had landed after falling from a small stool. With empathy, insight, patience, skill, and powerful spirits four men and my husband carried me down a narrow winding stairwell to a waiting ambulance that had come with sirens blasting and was now going to carry me to the ER. ER personnel assessed damage to understand what tools, adhesives, and binders would be necessary to repair my leg. Personnel in ER interrogated me, poking, X-raying, and applying strong spirits. The operating team consisting of four surgeons poured over X-rays, procedures and theatre schedules. Two anesthesiologists made me more than comfortable. As the time for the cutting, arranging, screwing and sewing began, physicians, surgeons and nurses collaborated for five hours inserting 7 screws and titanium plates. Six days of hospitalization was assisted by a plethora of nurses and nurses aides with their own toolboxes. Returning to the States, recovery was well over ten months, taking additional personnel, doctors, nurses, technicians, physical therapists, as well as family and friends and pharmacists, all with different tools or homespun remedies.

What I have come to understand is that reparation is a necessary part of life, extending from miniscule to life-threatening, for people, animals, acquisitions and environments. Over time, we all repair things, even if it is by calling the plumber. But empathetic and skilled professionals, funds, tools, time and patience are all necessary to repair brokenness, whether it is consumer goods or relationships. We humans, however, often spend the least funds, tools, time and patience on family relationships. Sometimes we therapists have to be the permission givers to bring the angry, the hurt, and the hate, into the art to act out. Sometimes, like a dentist, we have to dig out the decay" before we can repair the tooth.

So, what do we need in our Relationship Reparation Toolbox? The thesaurus (Chapman, 1977) lists two pages of mechanical tools, two pages of joining functions, and a half page of adhesives, binders, and cohesives used to build or repair consumer goods. Let us use some of those as metaphors for relationship reparation.

Materials: Examples only, and not in order of need or importance.

Adhesives	Apologizing, calls, cards	Exercise
Binders	Creating, dancing, singing	Friends
Cohesives	Helping others	Humor
Funds	Nourishing or nurturing foods	Pets
Professionals	Shoulders to rest on	Play
Spirits	Religious literature	Prayer
Letting go of past hurts	Listening, understanding	Rest

Preparation and Process: Sit quietly with your eyes closed, feet flat on the floor, hands resting lightly on your thighs while you breathe in and out, getting in touch with your normal breathing rhythm. Then let your inner guide take you to a recent time when you felt a slight or even serious break in a significant relationship. Picture the event. Picture your hurt. What color is it? How large is it? Is it stabilized or floating? Bring it into focus. Reach out for it, look at it clearly and assess what it needs. Is it miniscule or major? Do you have the necessary tools and skills to fix it? Do you know where to go if you don't? Look through your toolbox. What skills do you have? What tools are in the box? Adhesives? Binders? Cohesives? Empathy? Spirits? Funds? Professionals? Picture what you need. Watch it appear in your toolbox. Repair your break or wound. Using the art materials draw your repair project. Spend time sharing your process with another.

B-L. TREASURE FOLDERS OF GOLDEN DREAMS AND SOUVENIR COLLECTING

Materials: A file folder and collage material.
Preparation: Everyone has something they want to change. Art Therapist J. Priestly asks her clients to keep a *treasurer folder* of things they want to

change. For example, attitudes, behaviors, body concerns, career focus, or money issues, people they want to meet, how they want to look, or where they want to be.

Process: Place the pictures in a file folder and file it. The process will help you identify and focus on changes and goals. Pull your treasure folder out every three months and update it. It will surprise you how quickly some of your wishes become reality. Place serene and exciting pictures or even knick-knacks around where you work or live to remind you of your own inner peace or what excites you. Souvenirs are not necessarily just souvenirs. Expand your symbol repertoire: A friend and I were in the Everglades of Florida watching alligators rise and submerge in the water. This became an important shared symbol in our lives. Today, we exchange alligator cards or alligator items small enough to sit on our computers. The meaning of this symbol is expanded in our daily exposure to it.

My husband and I spent a vacation in Israel and having water was very important. By accident I brought an Israeli water bottle back in my purse. I used it all winter refilling and refilling it. It reminded me of the trip, the friends we met and the importance of some of the places I had heard about all my life. It was also fun to drink from it in small lunch settings where colleagues would question whether I had really brought a case of Israeli spring water home with me.

When editors of *Prevention Magazine Health Book* interviewed art therapists for their *New Choices in Natural Healing for Women* (1997), I suggested keeping a calendar of art work or a glossy art book near your desk as a minigallery for minivacations because simply looking at art and beautiful scenes can relieve stress. Sometimes one needs to express feeling to relieve tension. At other times one can relax and release tension by enjoying the senses, sight, sound, smell and touch. A private journal that includes both writing and drawings provides a way to sketch thoughts and feelings and write your own captions for the sketches.

Appendix C

KEY ASSUMPTIONS, CONCEPTS, AND
TERMS OF FAMILY SYSTEMS THEORY

Family systems theories are congruent with an art therapy approach. Many of the concepts are interchangeable when working with individuals in families or with families. Family theorists and a brief overview of their approaches include but are not limited to: Appendix D-1, Experiential Communication Model (Satir, 1967; 1972); Appendix D-2, Family of Origin Model (Bowen, 1978) with the integration of feminist developmental concepts by Knudson-Martin (1994); Appendix D-3, Structural Model (Minuchin, 1974); Appendix D-4, Strategic Model (Haley, 1973; 1976); and Appendix D-5, Cognitive Behavioral Model (Gottman, 1998). For an in-depth study of individual theorists and theory refer to primary references or compilations by Becvar & Becvar (1998) or Goldenberg & Goldenberg (1999) or Gottman (1998). Family therapy begins with:

- **Engagement.** This requires an understanding of basic goals and fundamental assumptions of systems theory as they apply to problems in the family. In all cases, engagement requires a safe therapeutic environment that includes empathy, warmth, and genuineness. Maintaining engagement requires congruence, positive regard and status recognition while encouraging varied and possible new ways of communicating. Engagement is followed by:
- **Problem Identification.** Family members are encouraged to communicate their knowledge and perspective of the problem, using whatever means, verbal or graphic work. This broad perspective enables the therapist to acquire a precise description and detailed sequence of the issues as seen by the family members.
- **Change.** Occurs when family members recognize their contributions to the problem and commit to alternative ways of responding. Positive

change requires a commitment to repairing the relationship between self and others. Therapeutic support during this stage facilitates change.

• **Closure.** Procedures recognize all constructive efforts to problem solving; provide back-up support and resources to call at times of stress; and leaves the family with an open invitation to return if crises should recur.

C-1. EXPERIENTIAL COMMUNICATION FAMILY THERAPY MODEL

Known as the mother of family therapy for her pioneer work with families, Virginia Satir (1964) approached therapy as a process model "in which the therapist and the family (unit) joined forces to promote wellness" (p. 12). A warm and interactive woman, her dynamic ideas, her focus on feelings, and her here and now approach continue to be researched and adopted by prominent clinicians, and researchers in family therapy. Satir's communication model is timeless in that it is considered cultural and gender sensitive, including both verbal and non-verbal intervention tools and techniques.

A fundamental assumption of family therapy is that families behave as if they are one unit, therefore, when an *Identified Patient (IP)*, the one the family calls the sick one, displays a symptom, it is like an SOS signal and serves both the IP and a family function. Symptoms are often the results of: (a) traumas outside of the nuclear family; (b) changes in the two families of origin; someone entering; or leaving the family of origin; or (c) physical or developmental changes in members of the nuclear family.

Satir's Four Fundamental Assumptions

1. All behavior, body language, autonomic body functions, coping mechanisms, values, expectations, senses, words, tone, and thought processes are communication.

2. When families or individuals access all of their human potential, they can increase the possibility of self-nourishment.

3. In a family "everyone and everything is impacted by, and impacts everyone and everything else" (Satir, 1982, p. 13).

4. Whereas Satir believed that the therapist was there as a consultant to provide support and choices for the family as a unit, as well as individually, she also believed that each and every member of the family was responsible in their response to therapy or to becoming healthy. Choices allow clients to move from linear either/or content positions, to a process level where one can see and hear what is actually present; say what one feels and thinks; feel what

Table 13. A COMPARISON OF FAMILY SYSTEMS THEORIES.. Understanding how to solve problems requires understanding of how problems are created and maintained. Therapy is brief, direct, action-oriented, problem focused.

Experiential Communication (Satir, 1964)	Family of Origin (Bowen, 1976)	Structural (Minuchin, 1974)	Strategic (Haley, 1976)
Focus on feelings, understanding and trust	Differentiation of self from undifferentiated family ego mass	Establish effective hierarchy and appropriate boundaries	Each family has assumptions about the world
Goals: To look at how the couple came together and learned: self-worth, communication style, rules for being, links to society.	**Goals:** Separate thoughts from feelings; reduce emotion reactivity to issues and concerns. Reduce emotional cutoff and repetition of dysfunctional patterns.	**Goals:** Strengthen parental coalition and spousal subsystem.	**Goals:** To identify and interrupt problematic feedback loops. Identify solvable problems. Set goals and design intervention that achieves these present problems
Fundamental Assumptions	**Fundamental Assumptions**	**Fundamental Assumptions**	**Fundamental Assumptions**
The therapeutic process is an interaction involving client and therapist. Individuals possess all the resources necessary for their own development. Natural movement is toward positive growth and development. Symptomatic behaviors a reflection of family pain.	Emotional triangles evolve when an emotional overflow causes a twosome to reach out to another. Nuclear family emotional processes occur when there is emotional distance between spouses, unresolved marital conflict, or psychological impairment in a child. Family projective focus on most vulnerable child. There may be emotional cutoff. Sibling position may affect the family and a multi-generational transmission.	Action precedes understanding. Tasks are utilized to change patterns. Therapist observes how the family achieves balance and homeostasis. **Three Axioms** Psychic life is not entirely an internal process. Changes in a family structure contribute to changes in the behavior and the inner psychic process of members of that system. When a therapist works with a client or a client's family, his or her behavior becomes part of that context.	Each family has a world view and assumptions about the world. Action precedes understanding.

Treatment	Treatment	Treatment	Treatment
Teaches and leads experiential game. Interventions change indirect communication. Stresses action over insight. Therapist creates a safe setting, where clients may risk.	Discusses facts and cognitive insight about going home. Coaches reestablishing family contact through calls, visits and letters. Diagram family scripts. Encourages "I stand" positioning.	Present focus. Joins the family. Accommodates to family style. Reframes meaning of behavior. Creates a family transactional map. Works to break up patterns of triangulation.	Active–Sees the whole family. Explore in what is being done to maintain the problem. Social engagement with family. Purposeful interventions. Therapist takes responsibility for the therapy but not for change.
Key Terms	**Key Terms**	**Key Terms**	**Key Terms**
Conjoint Congruent Incongruent Identified patient (IP) Sculpturing Reframing Homeostatis	Emotional reactivity Dysfunctional reciprocal relationships Coach Nodal events Solid self Pseudo self Fusion Triangle	Enmeshed Boundaries Enactment Coalitions Mimesis Spontaneous Parentified child Disengaged Hierarchy Alliances Joins Behavior sequence	Prescribing the symptom Paradoxical injunctions Metaphoric tasks Circular questioning Positive connotations Hypothesizing Neutrality

one feels, ask for what one wants and risk in one's own behalf. Satir *reframed* or relabeled behavior and family issues in a more positive perspective so that the family and its members could look at them in new ways (Becvar & Becvar, 1993). The following is an example of a non-verbal process of communicating

Individuals, according to Satir (1972) are raised in family systems with characteristic behavior patterns that are repetitive. Over time these repeated stances, or roles and rules form both verbal and non-verbal communication patterns. These patterns establish the notion of *homeostasis* (family existence and balance within this family system).

THERAPEUTIC GOALS. The therapist's goal is to look for the context in which symptoms and characteristic intergenerational patterns emerge. The therapist reveals and corrects discrepancies in family communication. By having each family member speak for him or herself, she recognizes differences and different perceptions of the same situation.

ACTION-ORIENTED TREATMENT. Satir's workshops were often works of art themselves. She stressed action over insight, focusing on feelings, understanding and trust. Through the drama of sculpting family relationships, Satir changed indirect communication to direct communication. With dramatic experiences and humor she created settings and *sculpted* relationships (had family members take static positions) where clients could see, know and understand life at another time or by another person. She used touch when invited (even on a subliminal level) to non-verbally support and to connect with family members. Satir, like family and art therapist that have come after her, used many expressive arts tools and techniques for learning contracts, interventions, and awareness enhancement.

KEY TERMS AND CONCEPTS. Satir used terms like *congruent* or *incongruent* to describe behavior and communication. She initiated the term *conjoint therapy,* therapy with the spouses, and she talked about dysfunctional games played in families. In addition, Satir often presented metaphors, such as a seed and bulbs as models for promoting health and growth, "insisting that given the proper conditions of nurturance, children, like seedlings can develop into healthy adults." (Goldenberg and Goldenberg, 1997, p. 158).

C-2. THE FAMILY OF ORIGIN THERAPY MODEL

Murray Bowen, a key figure in the early development of family therapy was an initial link between psychodynamic theory and family system theory. His seminal work with families in the 1950s and 1960s began with the unusual arrangement of having the mother of a psychotic child live with that child at the hospital. In the hospital, the staff observed the mother-child relationship (Bowen, 1976). Bowen came to believe that the family was the focus regardless of who was in the room. A peer of Bowen, Lyman, and Wynne, working at the National Institute of Mental Health with an intermodal team that included art therapist Hanna Kwiatkowska, repeated this methodology.

BOWEN'S SIX FUNDAMENTAL ASSUMPTIONS. Originally (1963), Bowen formulated six interlocking theoretical concepts that provided a theoretical base for family systems theory. Briefly these six interlocking concepts are:

1. Differentiation of self refers to an individual's ability to separate his/her intellectual and emotional functioning. For example, the lower the individual's level of differentiation, the greater the likelihood that the individual will be fused with the emotions that dominate other family members. "Fusion represents the inability of some family members to distinguish between the subjective feeling process, and the more objective intellectual process" (Bowen, 1976, p. 59).

Bowen's term "undifferentiated family ego mass" conveys the idea of a family fusion or a family emotionally stuck together, e.g., a family member believing he or she knows another family member's thoughts and feelings.

2. Emotional triangle. The family forms as a dyad, a two-person system. When that dyad experiences anxiety or vulnerability, then a third and often vulnerable person is pulled into the system forming an emotionally riddled triangle. A triangle provides an accomplice or a sounding board for either or both of the dyad. The function of the triangle is to maintain family equilibrium.

3. Nuclear family emotional process. The nuclear family emotional process includes the use of defense mechanisms used to deal with the family tension and instability. These are expressed as (a) distancing spouses; (b) physical or emotional dysfunction in a spouse; (c) chronic marital conflict; and/or (d) psychological impairment in a child.

4. Family projective process. The family projective process refers to the manner in which the parental conflicts are transmitted (projected) on to, usually, one child, as in a *scapegoat*. This child is usually the one who exhibits the most immaturity and the lowest level of differentiation.

5. Emotional cutoff. Emotional cutoff refers to methods by which children (often adult children) attempt to free themselves from emotional ties to their families and to avoid emotional involvement. A distant move may reduce or eliminate communication, it does not, however, free their inner thoughts of family members and influence behaviors.

6. Multigenerational transmission process. This process represents the severe dysfunction of a family's emotional system (lack of differentiation) transmitted through several generations.

Later, Bowen included two additional theoretical concepts:

Table 14. EXPERIMENTAL COMMUNICATION APPROACH (Satir, 1964)

Change is possible. The therapist and the family, in the "here and now," join to promote wellness. Using family life chronology therapy focuses on feelings, understanding and trust.

Family Life Chronology and Life Cycle Log.
Past _____ High School _____ Marriage _____ First Child _____ Present

Goals: Recognizing individual differences. To do this the therapist begins by looking at how the couple came together and how, in their families they learned:

1. **SELF-WORTH** - Building self-esteem in all members.
2. **COMMUNICATION STYLES** - Four universal styles - blaming, placating, distracting, and computing for revealing and correcting discrepancies in family communication.
3. **RULES FOR BEING** - Each person speaks for self. They say what they see, think or feel. Accept disagreements and different perceptions of the same situation.
4. **LINKS TO SOCIETY** - Understanding and addressing how the family and its members interact with society.

Key Terms and Concepts

Conjoint
Congruent
Incongruent
Identified patient (IP)
Sculpturing
Reframing
Homeostatis

Fundamental Assumptions

1. The therapeutic process is an interaction involving client and therapist.
2. Individuals possess all resources necessary for their own growth and development.
3. Natural movement in all individuals is toward positive growth and development.
4. Symptoms indicate an impasse in the growth process.
5. Symptomatic behavior is a reflection of family pain.

Blamer
Placater
OK
Super Reasonable
Distracter

All placate at expense of personal needs.

Lethal

Coalition

One
Agrees
Disagrees

SRD

Rescue Game

P ——— B

P=Placater
B=Blamer
SRD=Super Reasonable
D=Distracter

Action-Oriented Treatment

Teaches and leads experiential games.
Direct interventions change indirect communication.
Joins with family to facilitate growth.
Stresses action over insight.
Therapist creates a safe setting where clients feel comfortable to risk.

7. The sibling position. A child's functional position in a family is often related to his/her birth order, and how the child is treated in the family, as in a parentified child.

8. Societal regression. Bowen recognized how emotional factors in society affect the emotional functioning of families. (Bowen, 1978.)

THERAPEUTIC GOALS. Briefly, the goals of Family of Origin therapy center on Bowen's fundamental assumptions that include helping clients separate their thoughts from their feelings, differentiating of self from others, and reducing emotional reactivity, family emotional cutoffs, and repetition of dysfunctional multigenerational patterns.

ACTION-ORIENTED TREATMENT. Bowen emphasized the role of the therapist *as coach,* an active expert who discusses facts and cognitive insights, instructs and supports individual and team players to perform at the best of their ability. The therapist focuses on adults, even if the *Identified Patient* is a symptomatic child. The therapist incorporates tasks that are aimed at reducing fusion by encouraging one of the adults in the dyad to learn when and how to take *I stand* positions. An *I stand* position helps individuals become aware of their own dreams, needs, and aspirations and their evolvement. With coaching the therapist helps the couple establish those needs within their significant relationships. This position can help family members fill their emptiness and establish a solid sense of self. The therapist encourages the client to go home through calls, letters and visits and to observe family patterns of roles and rules. Often it is easier with new insight for the client to take an *I stance,* and differentiate, because for a variety of reasons, *going home* is no longer possible than *going home* is metaphorical and played out through psychodrama and letters not sent. Bowen helped couples look at how their families played out repeatable scripts from one generation to the next.

KEY TERMS AND CONCEPTS. Key terms in Family of Origin theory include *parentified child,* used to identify the child that takes the parent's hierarchical place regularly or on occasion. *Solid self as opposed to a pseudo- or false self.* The person with the *solid-self* has clearly defined beliefs, opinions, and convictions regarding life's ultimate concerns. The person with the *pseudo-self* is emotionally fused originally to the Family of Origin and later to significant others in his or her life. A person with a *pseudo-self* is drawn to others to whom they can also become fused. When there is too much emotional energy between two people, a third person is drawn in to make a *triangle.* A *nodal event* refers to an occasion that has significant psychological impact on an individual (i.e., anniversary death of a parent could equal depression).

Genograms is a three or more generational map of the people who make up one family (see Appendix B). It provides a visual concept of family structure, relationships and intergenerational messages. In some ways, a genogram is like a family tree but it is a psychological family tree. It is presented in a specific format and generally includes more personal details than one sees in a family tree. A genogram helps the person making it to understand the family he or she was born into as well as the generations before. It has been known throughout history that what happens in a family in any particular generation, can echo through the generations that follow. Genograms assist in discovering repeated patterns of physical, psychological, and physiological behavior.

Genograms, in addition, can increase cultural, and gender sensitivity. In keeping with art as therapy, family therapists, Hardy and Laszloffy (1995) suggest that the genogram should include:

> symbols designed by the (creator) to depict graphically the prevalence of pride/shame issues and to highlight their impact on family function. The use of symbols is a form of anagogic communication that allows the presenter to express the intuitive and affective aspects of cultural (and gender) issues which are sometimes difficult to capture with words. Essentially, using symbols provides (participants) means for communicating the irrational, emotional dimensions of cultural and gender issues which often defy verbal expression. (p. 230)

Female Developmental Theory in the Differentiation Process

Bowen's stellar theoretical model was developed within the traditional patriarchal culture of the 1960s and 1970s. However, as Western culture has become more ethnic and gender sensitive, family systems theory has expanded to include additional models and address potential biases. Because male and female development is different, it is important to take into account their recognized differences as healthy, rather than pathological. As noted earlier, Bowen's first interlocking concept for family systems theory is based on the concept of differentiation of the self and anxiety due to emotional fusion. Knudson-Martin (1994) notes that "female developmental studies consistently find that women develop . . . and define themselves through attachments to others" (p. 36). Arrington's (1986) study confirmed that women select images that positively identify with relationships (marriage, motherhood and companionship, p. 140). Knudson- Martin notes that feminine identity is not a matter of whether or not women define themselves in the context of relationships but how those relationships are used in the process of identity. Relationships are often used for security, self-validation, support and for self-awareness. Thus, in identity development, it is important for women to choose to whom they are attached. This behavior, like other behaviors, is modeled, and learned in the relationship between mother and her adolescent daughter who struggle to "maintain connection while evolving a unique self" (1994, p. 36).

The affect or the feeling system refers to experiencing, or sensing a feeling, i.e., depression, desire, or well-being. The behavioral system refers to acts, activities, responses, reactions, and movements. The cognitive system includes the capacity to think, conceive, reason, observe, to know, to understand and problem solve.

> Bowen's theory is based on the idea of two competing life forces: individuality and togetherness. According to the theory, the need for other people heightens emotional reactivity to others and decreases the ability to think and respond independently. Yet for many persons, especially women, the feeling system may be their primary source of self-awareness. (p. 39)

When individuation is defined as maturity, and togetherness and individuality are seen as competing forces, then those that become self-aware through their feeling systems are seen as immature. Women develop in the context of their relationships. They differentiate, learning to hear and trust their own voices, as they listen to the voices of others. They often hear themselves and others through observing their feelings. When women are told they are immature because they feel rather than think, they lose their ability to hear their inner voice and trust themselves.

Affect and cognition are parallel systems and mutually reinforcing (Knudson-Martin, 1994). Anxiety rises from tension between the two needs of togetherness and individuality. "Higher levels of differentiation . . . include an integration of these functions" (p. 40). Therapeutic techniques, like art, which increase the capacity to utilize subjective and emotional experiences through intellectual choices, facilitate integration. Lower levels of differentiation could interfere with either need (togetherness or individuality) developing. Therefore, therapy can be more effective if both needs (togetherness and individuality) are addressed concurrently. As one increases so does the other. Knudson-Martin concludes that, "Highly differentiated individuals recognize their needs for responsibility to one another at the same time that they have the capacity for autonomous functioning" (p. 42).

C-3. STRUCTURAL FAMILY THERAPY MODEL

Structural Therapy became popular in the 1970s through the influences of Salvador Minuchin and Braulio Montalvo. A clearly articulated theory, it "provides a useful tool for helping people see the patterns, processes and transactions of the family as system" (Becvar and Becvar, 1988, p. 172).

Emphasis is on the wholeness of the family system. Three essential components of structural family theory include family structure, subsystems and boundaries.

FAMILY STRUCTURE. The family's interactional patterns regulate the behavior of its members. Behavior is maintained by the universal rule of *hierarchy,* a family's hierarchical organization. Hierarchy refers to order of power in the family, i.e., who has the authority to make the decision and who has the power to carry those decisions out. For example, the parent is more powerful than the child. Strengthening the executive or parental subsystem and strengthening the marital dyad (spousal subsystem) are key elements in this theoretical model.

SUBSYSTEMS. Families organize into *subsystems* to carry out their roles and rules (spousal, parental, and sibling subsystems). Subsystems are important because of the flexible or permeability of the **boundaries** between them. The therapist works to break up patterns of triangles and coalitions in the subsystems thereby shifting hierarchical power as needed.

Minuchin's (1974) Fundamental Assumptions

1. "An individuals psychic life is not entirely an internal process.

2. Changes in a family structure contribute to changes in the behavior and the inner psychic processes of members of that system.

3. When a therapist works with a client or a client's family, his/her behavior becomes part of that context" (1974, p. 9).

THERAPEUTIC GOALS. The goals of structural therapy are "somewhat idiosyncratic to the family" (Becvar and Becvar, 1988, p. 186). They strengthen the spousal and parental systems, establish boundaries and restore the family hierarchical structure. Restoration facilitates the ultimate growth of each of its members and encourages each family member to become mutually supportive of every other member in their personal development of talents and interests. Goals include the therapist joining with the family to help the family repair or modify their family organization.

Families negotiate and accommodate to rules and roles around boundaries. The key is to achieve homeostasis through balance and flexibility of boundaries over time. Boundaries, as well as roles and rules work to the degree that each partner is not overly tied to roles and rules of its family of origin. Boundaries are as easily defined through symbols as well as words. The following symbolic descriptions define the terms of boundaries and relationships used in structural family therapy.

ACTION-ORIENTED TREATMENT. Structural family therapy is action-oriented and present focused beginning with the initial interview where the therapist acting as the family's host *joins* with all family members. Next, the

Table 15. FAMILY OF ORIGIN THERAPY APPROACH (FOO). The therapist is a coach, working with clients as they observe, practice and learn how to move outside of their family scripts often seen in the family genogram (Bowen, 1976).

Goals: Differentiation of self from undifferentiated family ego-mass

1. Separating thoughts from feelings
2. Reducing emotional reactivity to issues and concerns
3. Reducing emotional cutoff from family of origin
5. Reducing repetition of dysfunctional multigenerational patterns

Key Terms and Concepts

Emotional reactivity
Dysfunctional reciprocal relationships
Coach   Nodal events
Solid self   Pseudo self
Fusion   Triangle

Action-Oriented Treatment

Discusses facts and cognitive insight about going home.
Coaches in re-establishing contact through calls, visits, and letters.
Family scripts
Family sculpts
Encourages "I stand" positioning

Fundamental Assumptions

1. Emotional triangles evolve when an emotional overflow causes a twosome to reach out to a pre-programmed vulnerable person.
3. Nuclear family emotional processes occur when:
   There is an increased emotional distance between the spouses,
   Physical or emotional dysfunction in a spouse,
   Overt, chronic, unresolved marital conflict,
   Psychological impairment in a child.
4. Family projective processes usually occur with the:
   Oldest child,
   Child born during a time of family stress,
   Child perceived as special or (most) immature.
5. Child emotionally cuts off from families.
6. Multigenerational transmission process occurs in families.
7. Sibling position is important.
8. Societal regression occurs in the community.

Gender Consideration   *(Knudson-Martin, 1994)*

Affect and cognition are parallel systems and mutually reinforcing. Higher levels of differentiation...include an integration of these functions (p. 40).

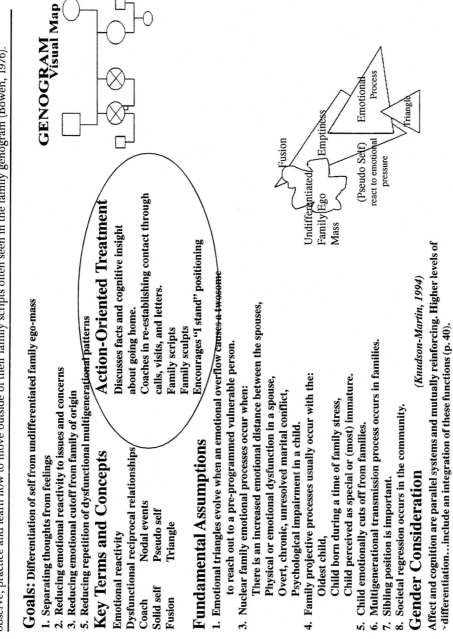

GENOGRAM
Visual Map

Fusion
Undifferentiated Family Ego Mass
Emptiness
Emotional Process
(Pseudo Self) react to emotional pressure
Triangle

therapist observes and questions the family to *map* the family structure of boundaries and behaviors within the family. The therapist accommodates to the family style to build a therapeutic alliance so that s/he can broaden the focus from the individual to include the family system. *Mimicing* and *tracking* facilitates the therapist's work with the family to develop an interim contract.

Broadening the focus often includes *reframing* the meaning of behavior. Reframing changes the original meaning of an event or situation for something equally plausible. Reframing helps to change the way an event or situation is viewed, i.e., instead of Johnny being bad, he might be sick (Goldberg & Goldberg, 1996, pp. 202–204). At subsequent sessions, the therapist may provide the opportunity for a spontaneous family *enactment*. In an enactment, the family brings an outside family conflict into the session and the therapist allows the space for family members to interact so that s/he can observe the sequence and introduce a plan for structural changes.

Additional Key Terms and Concepts

Interactional patterns refer to how the family interacts. Often the actual reason for the family's interactional patterns are lost in the history of the family and may be out of sync with the developmental stages of family members.

Mimesis is Greek for copy. The therapist imitates the manner, style, affect or content of the family's communication style in order to make the family feel more relaxed and to join with the family (crossing her legs, taking off her jacket, talking slowly).

The therapist *tracks,* or adopts symbols of the family's life gathered from their' communication (such as events, life-styles, and values) and intersperses them in conversation with family.

Spouses have *complementary* functions. Spouses operate as a team and complement each other. One may provide resources for the family whereas the other may provide services for the family. Today, spouses trade off these roles. Both may provide resources and services.

Coalitions are those subsystems that align themselves with the powerful movers and shakers in the family. Emotional triangles are formed within the family by either spouse, as they engage a child to ally with him or her against the other parent. A dysfunctional family fails to meet the needs that provide relief and nurture the growth of individuals within the family.

Enmeshment and *disengaged* refer to emotional distance between family members. Enmeshed family members are too close and often thinking for the other. Disengaged family members are too distant providing little emotional support.

Triangulation is "a process in which a parent demands that a child ally with him or her against the other parent during parental conflict" (Goldenberg & Goldenberg, 1996, p. 432).

C-4. STRATEGIC THERAPY MODEL

Strategic therapy, building on earlier family systems models, became popular in the 1980s through the influences of Milton Erickson, Jay Haley, Cloe Madannes and Peggy Papp. In strategic therapy, the therapist takes responsibility for directly influencing clients by strategizing ways to identify and interrupt the cycles of problematic feedback loops. Strategies are used to relieve the family stuckness; identify solvable problems; set goals; design intervention to achieve those goals; examine family responses to interventions and correct the approach; and reexamine the outcome of therapy to determine if it has been effective. The therapist is active; sees the whole family and whereas interested in what is being done to maintain the problem, is not interested in why the problem exists.

FUNDAMENTAL ASSUMPTIONS. The strategic therapist is interested in the family's world view; i.e., how the family sees the world. Is it safe, unsafe, trustworthy, etc? What are the family's assumptions about the world? Is the world sick, dangerous, crazy, etc? This can be determined through an in-depth interview or through family drawings.

TREATMENT GOALS. Include identifying and interrupting the cycles of problematic feedback loops. Identifying solvable problems; setting goals always including the present problem; and designing, assessing and correcting therapeutic interventions.

ACTION-ORIENTED TREATMENT. Stages of strategic therapy, according to Jay Haley (audio tape 1998) include:

1. Social engagement. Social engagement with the family allows the therapist to observe family interaction, their moods, metaphors and constructs.

2. Purposeful intervention. Purposeful intervention refers to asking specific questions, such as: What do you want from counseling? What changes do you want? If you could change your family, how would you change it? What has been tried to correct the problem and failed. The therapist may give cognitive information or event paradoxical and non-paradoxical directives during this period. The therapist may use metaphorical tasks. The therapist will respect the family's current pattern of interaction at all times regardless how dysfunctional (i.e., Haley's famous example of the husband chasing his wife with an ax).

Table 16. STRUCTURAL FAMILY THERAPY APPROACH. Therapist is brief, direct, action-oriented, problem focused (Minuchin, Montalvo, 1974).

Goals:

1. Reestablish effective hierarchical structures and establish appropriate boundaries.
2. Strengthen parental coalition and spousal subsystem.

Key Terms and Concepts

Alliances	Boundaries
Coalitions	Complementary
Disengaged	Enactment
Hierarchy	Joins
Mimesis	Parentified child
Tracking	Triangulation

Action-Oriented Treatments

Joins the family and accommodates to family style
Reframes meaning of behavior
Creates a family transactional map
Works to break up patterns of triangulation

Fundamental Assumptions

1. Action precedes understanding.
2. Tasks are utilized to change patterns
3. Therapist observes how the family achieves balance and homeostasis.

Family Transactional Mapping

M _____ F

C   (Minuchin, 1974, p. 53)

IP

Three Axioms

1. An individual psychic life is not entirely an internal process.
2. Changes in a family structure contribute to changes in the behavior and the inner psychic process of members of that system.
3. When a therapist works with a client or a client's family, his/her behavior become part of that context.

Nuclear Family Focus

Executive/Parental Subsystem
Spousal Subsystem

Disengaged   VS   Enmeshed

Stuck in old roles and rules.

3. Ending stage. During the ending stage, the therapists may restrain the family from getting better too quickly or the therapist may predict a relapse. The therapist takes responsibility for the therapy but not for change within the family.

Key Terms and Concepts

Prescribing the symptom "is a paradoxical technique in which the client is directed to voluntarily engage in the symptomatic behavior; as a result, the client is put in the position of rebelling and abandoning the symptom or obeying, thereby admitting it is under voluntary control" (Goldenberg & Goldenberg, 1996, p. 428).

Restraining is a paradoxical technique used to restrain the client from getting better too quickly.

Paradoxical injunction means taking a resistant position.

Circular questioning–"An interviewing technique, first formulated by the Milan therapists, aimed at eliciting differences in perception about events or relationships from different family members, particularly regarding points in the family life cycle which significant coalition shifts and adaptations occurred" (Goldenberg & Goldenberg, 1996, p. 420).

Positive connotations–"a reframing technique used primarily by systemic therapists whereby positive motives are ascribed to family behavior patterns because these patterns help maintain family balance and cohesion; as a result, the family is helped to view each other's motives more positively" (Goldenberg & Goldenberg, p. 428).

Hypothesizing–"The process by which a therapist or a team of therapists form suppositions, open to revision, regarding how and why a family's problem have developed and persisted; in advance of meeting the family, in order to facilitate asking relevant questions and organizing incoming information" (Goldenberg & Goldenberg, p. 425).

Neutrality–"a non-judgmental position intended to enable the therapist to avoid being caught up in family *games* through coalitions or alliances" (Goldenberg & Goldenberg, p. 427).

C-5. COGNITIVE BEHAVIORAL FAMILY MODEL

Because of the epidemic proportions of divorce in the United States, serious questions have continued to arise about what couples divorce and why. Gottman, at the Seattle Marital & Family Institute, and associates, Levenson, (1992) and Buehlman, and Katz (1992) and James Murray (1998) have been researching these questions for the past 20 years. Using physiological tests, interviews, and video, Gottman and his team predict, with 90% accuracy, which couples will divorce in the first seven years of marriage, or between 16 and 20 years of marriage and why (1998, p. 15). The research team has discovered two reasons couples divorce early and later. Couples divorce in the early years because they engage in negative interaction when they fight, i.e., which results in the couple distancing and isolating. Couples that divorce in the later years have had a "general absence of positive affect" in their early years of marriage. "Both aspects appear to be somewhat independent and both seem to be essential" (1998, p. 15). According to Gottman (1998, p. 17), "Family therapists have found that identifying communication patterns in marriages that work can help therapists "individualize therapy to fit the needs of couples" in marriages that aren't working.

FUNDAMENTAL ASSUMPTIONS. Gottman (1998) identifies seven predictors of divorce and marital misery. They include:

1. More negative affect than positive affect in the family.

2. Criticism, Defensiveness, Contempt and Stonewalling (referred to the Four Horsemen of the Apocalypse) with gender specific behaviors, i.e., criticism by women, and stonewalling by men.

3. Unsuccessful repair attempts.

4. Negative perception, sentiments, and attributions with males internalizing more negativity physically resulting in pain and,

5. Physical flooding (heart pounding, changes in breathing, sweating, trembling, anger, sadness, sighs, whining, attempts to hold the floor) followed by a cascade of distancing and isolation.

6. Chronic physiological arousal and immuno suppression.

7. Failure of males to accept influence from significant female, particularly when they are complaining, is manifested in either male emotional distancing (stonewalling and resolution) or escalation (belligerence, contempt, defensiveness).

Lasting effects in marital therapy are most likely when interventions are designed with two prongs: one to increase everyday positive affect (not just in the resolution of conflict), and one to reduce negative affect during conflict resolution (Gottman, 1998, p. 15).

Reviewing evidence of gender sensitive reaction to "negative affect in marriage and close relationships," Gottman & Levenson (1988, p. 33) found that "predictions of marital outcome involved the physiological soothing of the male by either the male or the female." These events included "de-escalation by the husband, humor by the wife, validation by the husband, and affection by the husband." When these events occurred, the heart rate of the husband was significantly decreased. This physiological decrease was significantly higher in couples who wound up stable and happy compared to other

Table 17. STRATEGIC FAMILY THERAPY APPROACH. Each family has assumptions about the world. Therapist takes responsibility for directly influencing clients (Haley, 1973).

Goals:

1. To identify and interrupt the cycles of problematic feedback loops.
2. Identify solvable problems.
3. Set goals always including the present problem.
4. Design interventions to achieve those goals.
5. Examine family responses to interventions and correct the approach.
6. Reexamine the outcome of therapy to determine if it has been effective.

Key Terms and Concepts

Prescribing the symptom
Restraining
Paradoxical injunctions
Positioning
Prescribing rituals
Neutrality
Circular questioning
Positive connotations
Hypothesizing

Action-Oriented Treatment

Active - See the whole family.
Interested in what is being done to maintain the problem, not why it is a problem.
Social engagement with family includes observing mood, metaphors, constructs and interactions.
Purposeful interventions ask specific questions, i.e., what do you want from counseling, what changes do you want? If your family could be whatever they wanted, what would it be?

Fundamental Assumptions

1. Each family has a world view that is safe or unsafe, trustworthy, or untrustworthy.
2. Each family has assumptions about the world. Is it sick, dangerous or what?
3. Actions precede understanding.

World View

groups of couples in the study. When de-escalation does not occur, the family member feels physically uncomfortable. He or she notes the problem (maybe internally), as severe and begins to work it out alone. At this point the couple begin to live parallel lives, which result in loneliness, an affectless relationship, and in the final decision to part.

Therapeutic Goals

1. Regulate conflict to diffuse autonomic arousal in both males and females.
2. Recognize when emotional flooding is occurring.
3. Encourage de-escalation by the male by helping him accept influence from the female.
4. Encourage a softer start-up in communication and increased humor in the female.
5. Rebuild friendship in the relationship in non-conflict situations.
6. Establish a dialogue with what Gottman refers to as the perpetual problem.
7. Acquire a variety of ways to repair the relationship on a consistent basis.
8. Assist each person in the relationship to live out his or her life dreams and aspirations.

ACTION-ORIENTED TREATMENT. Gottman's action-oriented treatment based on 20 years of solid research, integrates behavior, cognition, and physiology. His Sound Marital House metaphor includes interventions based on research as to why marriages fail and what constitutes a stable happy marriage. It both validates and supports ideas used by pioneers (Satir, 1972; Bowen, 1976) in the field, using the initial interview to ascertain the true love relationship between the couple; caring days, metacommunication styles, the incorporation of positive feelings throughout therapy, and empowering the family to self-sooth, relax, and get well.

In addition, Gottman and associates use a wide variety of assessments and interventions to investigate different areas that are related to his Sound Marital House theory. The areas include where is the couple in the marriage? What is the nature of the marital friendship? Is the nature of sentiment in the marriage positive or negative? What is the nature of conflict? What is the nature of life dreams and shared meaning? What potential resistances exist?

Interventions target seven components (Gottman, 1998, pp. 50, 51) that make up the Solid Marital House Theory. A good outcome for the couple is predicted, only to the extent that they can soothe self and partner (p. 32), and repair the relationship. Self-soothing is based on baseline physiology and the ability to reduce emotional flooding.

KEY TERMS AND CONCEPTS. Gottman (1998), building on earlier communication models identifies three different marital communicating styles. They are *avoiders, validators,* and *volatiles.* In his research, communicating mismatches predict divorce.

Gottman's (1988) most important finding was that on a physiological level, males respond to emotional material more dramatically and longer than do women resulting in emotional flooding and actual physical discomfort. Therefore, the more positive the affect, whether verbally, or non-verbally communicated, the less physical discomfort was experienced by the male, and the happier and more stable the relationship.

Gottman's (1998, pp. 50, 51) Sound Marital House Theory integrates both earlier techniques that were effective in therapy as well as new perspectives and approaches that address areas of his stellar research. These include:

Foundation or first floor–Love Map–involves the couple knowing one another and periodically updating this knowledge (p. 50). (Supportive of early family therapy ideas by Satir.)

Second floor–the Fondness and Admiration System, which is the antidote for contempt (p. 50). (Supportive of early family therapy ideas by Satir.)

Third floor–is identified by Gottman as the Emotional Bank Account–Turning toward versus turning away from each other (p. 51). (Caring events and days.)

Fourth floor–Bob Weiss's idea of Positive Sentiment Override or presence of positive affect in problem-solving discussions and the success of repair attempts during conflict resolution. (p. 51)

Fifth floor–Relates to 1. "Four parts of effective problem solving: Soften start-up, repair and de-escalation, accepting influence, compromising, or use of positive affect in the service of de-escalation. 2. Dialoguing with perpetual problem (p. 51).

Sixth floor–Recognizing and making dreams and aspirations come true (p. 51). Unlocking gridlock and exploring symbolic values of each person's position. (Supportive of Jung ideas.)

Seventh floor or attic–Includes dreams, narratives, myths, and metaphors, as well as "the active creation of a new culture" (p. 51). Gottman's theory includes structured interviews and techniques as couples address different floors in the Sound Marital House and different marital issues. These interviews and techniques include questions about philosophy, basic attachment topics and emotions as well as the meanings and history of everyday rituals, roles, and rules looking for similarities, differences and ultimate concerns.

The floors in the house are interconnected. Affectlessness and emotional disengagement, the killer of relationships, is created when the relationships have dealt inadequately with the bottom three and top two floors of the Sound Marital House. (p. 52)

TABLE 18. COGNITIVE BEHAVIORAL FAMILY THERAPY APPROACH (Gottman, 1990–1998). Couples divorce early because they engage in negative interactions when they fight. Couples divorce later because they have lived with a general absence of positive affect.

Goals:

1. Diffuse emotional flooding and autonomic arousal in both males and females by helping to regulate conflict.
2. Recognize when emotional flooding is occurring.
3. Encourage de-escalation in the male by helping him accept influence from the female.
4. Encourage a softer start-up in communication and increased humor in the female.
5. Rebuild couple friendship in non-conflict exchanges.
6. Establish a dialogue with perpetual problems.
7. Acquire a repertoire of repairing behaviors.
8. Encourage family members to live out their dreams and aspirations.

Key Terms and Concepts

Avoiders
Validators
Volatiles
Positive and negative affect
Sound Marital House
Four Horsemen of the Apocalypse

Fundamental Assumptions

1. More negative affect than positive in the family.
2. Negative sentiment results in physical pain.
3. Gender specific behaviors. Women more critical. Men stonewall.
4. Unsuccessful repair attempts.
5. Chronic physiological arousal and immuno suppression.
6. Physical flooding results in a cascade of distancing and isolation.

Action Oriented Treatment
Sound Marital House

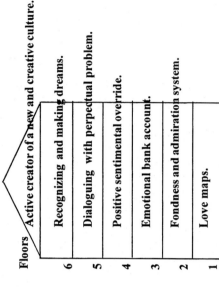

Floors	Active creator of a new and creative culture.
6	Recognizing and making dreams.
5	Dialoguing with perpetual problem.
4	Positive sentimental override.
3	Emotional bank account.
2	Fondness and admiration system.
1	Love maps.

REFERENCES

Acton, D. (1998). *Retablos: The tradition of painting the tragic, the miraculous and the wish: Art therapy applications with Latino Adolescents.* Unpublished master's thesis, College of Notre Dame, Belmont, CA.

Alder, J., Underwood, A., & Kolb, C. (1999, June 14). How stress attacks you. What works to bust it. *Newsweek,* 56–63.

Alexander, K. (1991). Artmaking: Bridge to metaphorical thinking. *The Arts in Psychotherapy, 18,* 105–11.

Allan, J. (1988). *Inscapes of a child's world.* Dallas: Spring.

Allan, J., & Bertoia, J. (1992). *Written paths to healing: Education and Jungian child counseling.* Dallas: Spring.

Allen, C. (1949). *Healing words.* Westwood, NJ: Fleming H. Revell Classic Books.

Allen, P. (1995). Coyote comes in from the cold: The evolution of the open studio concept. *Art Therapy: Journal of the American Art Therapy Association, 12*(3), 161–166.

Altschuler, R., & Hattwick, L. (1947/1967). *Painting and personality.* Chicago: University of Chicago.

American Journal of Art Therapy. (1979). Obituary: Hanna Yaxa Kwiatkowska. *American Journal of Art Therapy, 18,* 118.

American Psychiatric Association. (1994). *Diagnostic and Statistical Manual of Mental Disorders* (4th ed.). Washington, DC: American Psychiatric Association.

Anderson, F. (1992). *Art for all the children* (2nd ed.). Springfield, IL: Charles C Thomas.

Anderson, H. (1999). Reimaging family therapy: Reflection's on Minuchin's invisible family. *Journal of Marital & Family Therapy, 25*(1), 1–8.

Appleton, V. (1989). Transition from trauma: Art therapy with adolescent and young adult burn patients. Doctoral dissertation, University of San Francisco. *University Micofilm International,* Ann Arbor, MI. No. 9027812.

Appleton, V. (1993). An Art Therapy Protocol for the Medical Trauma Setting. *Art Therapy: Journal of the American Art Therapy Association, 10*(2), 71–77.

Appleyard, D., & Carrol, H. (1998, January 26). Revealed: The truth about our '90s marriages 1997 poll. London: *Daily Mail.*

Arieti, S. (1976). *Creativity: The magic synthesis.* New York: Basic Books.

Armsden, G., & Greenberg, M. (1987). The inventory of parent and peer attachment: Individual differences and their relationship of psychological well-being in adolescence. *Journal of Youth and Adolescence, 16*(5), 427–453.

Arnheim, R. (1954/1974). *Art and visual perception.* Berkeley: University of California.

Arnheim, R. (1969). *Visual thinking.* Los Angeles: University of California.

Arnheim, R. (1997). Foreword. *The Arts in Psychopathology: An International Journal, 24* (2).

Anthony, E.J. (1994). The phenomenon of anxiousness. In E.J. Anthony & D.C. Gilpin (Eds.), *Clinical faces of childhood* (pp. 127–133). New Jersey: Jason Aronson.

Arrien, A. (1992). *Signs of life: The five universal shapes.* New York: Harper Collins.

Arrien, A. (1993). *The four-fold way: Walking the paths of the warrior, teacher, healer, and visionary.* New York: Harper Collins.

Arrington, D. (1985). *Gardening in the great forest.* Belmont, CA: At the Studio.

Arrington, D. (1986). A Jungian-based study of selected visual constructs preferred by women (Doctoral dissertation, University of San Francisco, 1986). *University Microfilm International,* Ann Arbor, MI. No. 87-13, 271.

Arrington, D. (1990). Art-based assessment procedures and instruments used in research. In H. Wadeson (Ed.), *A guide to conducting art therapy research* (pp. 157–158). Mundelein, IL: The American Art Therapy Association, Inc.

Arrington, D. (1991). Thinking systems: Seeing systems. Systemically oriented art therapy: An integrative model. *The Arts in Psychotherapy, 18,* 201–211.

Arrington, D. (1992). Art therapy with a public school child. In *Art for all the children: Approaches to art therapy for children with disabilities* (pp. 232–270). Springfield, IL: Charles C Thomas.

Arrington, D. (1997). *Home is where the art is.* Keynote address, Florida Art Therapy Association.

Arrington, D. (1998). *In search of soul.* Keynote address, South Carolina Art Therapy Association, Charleston.

Arrington, D., Eslinger, S., & Virshup, E. (1975). *In touch through art.* Fresno, CA: Fresno Art Museum.

Ault, R. (1989). *The healing vision.* Topeka, KS: Menninger Clinic. Video recording.

Ault, R. (1996). *Drawing on the contours of the mind.* Unpublished paper. Topeka, KS.

Baker, C. (1986). *Developing written language and reading skills through art: A program for children with learning disabilities.* Unpublished master's thesis, College of Notre Dame, Belmont, CA.

Barnhill, L., & Longo, D. (1978). Fixation and regression in the family life cycle. *Family Process, 17,* 469–478.

Bateson, M.C. (1991, March). Giving survival skills to our children. *McCall's,* 14–16.

Begley, S. (1997, Spring–Summer). How to build a baby's brain. [Special issue: Your Child]. *Newsweek,* 28–32.

Becvar, R.J., & Becvar, D.S. (1988). *Family therapy: A systemic integration.* New York: Allyn and Bacon.

Becvar, R.J., & Becvar, D.S. (1989). *Family therapy: a systemic integration* (2nd ed.). New York: Allyn and Bacon.

Bender, L. (1938). *A visual motor gestalt test and its clinical use.* New York: The American Orthopsychiatric Association.

Beres, D. (1965). Symbol and Object. *Bulletin of the Menninger Clinic, 29,* 3–23.

Berne, P., & Savary, P. (1991). *Dream symbol work: Unlocking the energy from dreams and spiritual experiences.* New York: Paulist.

Betensky, M. (1973). Patterns of visual expression in art psychotherapy. *Art Psychotherapy, 1,* 121–129.

Blaisure, K., & Geasler, M. (2000, March). Divorce interventions. *Clinical Update, 2*(2), 1–8.

Bloomgarten, J. (1998). Inside art: Cave images in France. *Art Therapy: Journal of the American Art Therapy Association, 15*(3), 203–206.

Bowen, M. (1976). Theory in the practice of psychotherapy. In P. J. Guerin, Jr. (Ed.), *Family therapy theory and practice.* New York: Gardner.

Bowen, M. (1978). *Family therapy in clinical practice.* New York: Jason Aronson.

Bowlby, J. (1969/1982). *Attachment and loss* (Vol. 1) (2nd ed.). New York: Basic Books.

Bowlby, J. (1970). *Child care and the growth of love*. Harmondsworth: Pelican.

Bradley, E. (1989). Growing up in LA. *60 minutes*. National Broadcasting Co.

Brazelton, B. (1990). *The earliest relationships: Parents, infants and the drama of early attachment*. Reading, MA: Addison-Wesley.

Bridges, W. (1980). *Transitions: Making sense of life's changes*. Menlo Park, CA: Addison Wesley.

Bronfenbrenner, U. (1979). *The ecology of human development*. Cambridge, MA: Harvard University.

Brown, L., & Politt, E. (1996, February). Malnutrition, poverty and intellectual development. *Scientific American*, 38–43.

Brown, P.C., & Smith, T.W. (1992). Social influence, marriage and the heart: Cardiovascular consequences of interpersonal control in husbands and wives. *Health Psychology*, *1*(2), 88–96.

Brudenell, T. (1989), *Art representations as functions of depressive state: Longitudinal studies in chronic childhood and adolescent depression*. Unpublished master's thesis, College of Notre Dame, Belmont, CA.

Buck, J. (1948). The House-Tree-Person technique: A qualitative and quantitative scoring manual. *Journal of Clinical Psychology*, *10*, 315–396.

Buck, J. (1966/1978). The house-tree-person technique: Revised manual. Los Angeles, CA.: Western Psychological Services.

Buehlman, K., Gottman, J.M., & Katz, L. (1992). How a couple views their past predicts their future: Predicting divorce from an oral history interview. *Journal of Family Psychology*, *5*, 295–318.

Burns, R. (1987). Kinetic-House-Tree-Person Drawings (K-H-T-P). New York: Brunner/Mazel.

Burns, R., & Kaufman, H.S. (1972). *Actions, styles and symbols in kinetic family drawings (K-F-D)*. New York: Brunner/Mazel.

Byng-Hall, J. (1990). Attachment theory and family therapy: A clinical view. *Infant Mental Health Journal*, *11*, 228–236.

Byng-Hall, J. (1999). Family and couple therapy: Toward greater security. In J. Cassidy & P.R. Shafer (Eds.), *Handbook of attachment: Theory research and clinical applications* (pp. 625–645). New York: Guilford.

Callagan, G., & Rawls, M. (1993). From entrapment to empowerment: Family art therapy. In E. Virshup (Ed.), *California art therapy trends* (pp. 189–202). Chicago: Magnolia Street.

Campbell, J. (1972). *Myths to live by*. New York: Bantam Books.

Cane, F. (1951). *The artist in each of us*. New York: Pantheon Books.

Carter, E.A., & McGoldrich M. (Eds). (1980). *The family life cycle: A framework for family therapy*. New York: Gardner.

Chapman, L. (1998). Current research. Presentation at the Research Round Table, Twenty-Ninth Annual Conference of the American Art Therapy Association, Portland, OR.

Chapman , R. (1977). *Roget's international thesaurus* (4th ed.). New York: Thomas Y. Crowell.

Children's Defense Fund. (1994). *The state of America's children: Yearbook, 1994*. Washington, DC: Author.

Chira, S. (1995). Struggling to find stability when divorce is a pattern. *The New York Times*, *1*, 17.

Christensen, L., Russell, C., Miller, R., & Peterson, C. (1998). The process of change in couples therapy: A qualitative investigation. *Journal of Marital and Family Therapy*, *24*(2) 177–188.

Cirlot, J.E. (1962). *A dictionary of symbols*. New York: Philosophical Library.

Cline, F. W. (1991). *Hope for high risk and rage filled children: Attachment theory and therapy*. Evergreen, CO: Author.

Cohen, A. (1994). *An exploration of the soothing effects of the mandala on an adolescent population.* Unpublished master's thesis, College of Notre Dame, Belmont, CA.

Connell, G., Mitten, T., & Whitaker, C. (1993). Reshaping family symbols: A symbolic-experiential perspective. *Journal of Marital and Family Therapy, 19*(3), 243–251.

Cooper, J.C. (1978). *An illustrated encyclopaedia of traditional symbols.* London: Thames and Hudson.

Corn, W.M. (1973). *The art of Andrew Wyeth.* Greenwich, NY: Graphics Society, Ltd.

Cornell, J. (1994). *Mandala: Luminous symbols for healing.* Wheaton, IL: Quest Books.

Crick, F. (1994). *The astonishing hypothesis: The scientific search for the soul.* New York: Simon & Schuster.

Csikszentmihalyi, M. (1999). If we are so rich, why aren't we happy? *American Psychologist, 54*(10), 821–827.

Csikszentmihalyi, M. (1990). *Creativity: Flow and the psychology of discovery and invention.* New York: Harper Collins

Damasio, A.R. (1994). *Descartes' error: Emotion, reason, and the human brain.* New York: Avon.

DeLue, C. (1994). *The physiological related effects of children creating mandalas.* Unpublished master's thesis, College of Notre Dame, Belmont, CA.

Detre, K., Frank, T., Kniazzeh, C.R., Robinson, M., Rubin, J., & Ulman, E. (1983). Roots of art therapy: Margaret Naumburg (1890–1983) and Florence Cane (1882–1952)–A family portrait. *American Journal of Art Therapy, 22*(4), 113.

DiLeo, J.H. (1970). *Young children and their drawings.* New York: Brunner/Mazel.

DiLeo, J.H. (1983). *Interpreting children's drawings.* New York: Brunner Mazel.

Dissanayhe, E. (1992). Art for life's sake. *Art Therapy: Journal of American Art Therapy Association, 9*(4), 169–175.

Dorsey, S., Chance M., Forehand R., Morse, E., & Morse P. (1999).Children whose mothers are HIV infected: Who resides in the home and is there a relationship to child psychosocial adjustment? *Journal of Family Psychology, 13*(1), 103–107.

Dougherty, D. (1993). Adolescent health: Reflections on a report to the U.S. Congress. *American Psychologist, 48*(2), 193–201.

Drachnik, C. (1995). *Interpreting metaphors of children.* Burlingame, CA: Abbeygate.

Drachnik, C. (1975). *An historical study of art therapy.* Unpublished master's thesis, California State University, Sacramento, CA.

Duvall, E. (1957). *Family development.* New York: Harper & Row.

Edinger, E. (1973). *Ego and archetype.* Baltimore, MD: Penguin Books.

Edwards, M. (1987). Jungian analytic art therapy. In J. Rubin (Ed.). *Approaches to art therapy* (pp. 92–113). New York: Brunner/Mazel.

Erdman, P., & Caffery, T. (1997/1998, December/January). Systemic treatment of attachment issues in parent-child relationships. *Family Therapy News,* 12–13.

Erickson, M., Rossi E., & Rossi S. (1976). *The induction of clinical hypnosis and forms of indirect suggestion.* New York: Irvington Publications.

Erikson, E. (1963). *Childhood and society.* New York: Basic Books.

Evans, S., & Avis, J. (1998). *The women who broke all the rules: How the choices of a generation changed our lives.* Napierville, IL: Source Books.

Fairbairn, W.R. (1954). *An object relations theory of the personality.* New York: Basic Books.

Falicov, __. (1995, December). Training to think culturally: A multidimensional comparative framework. *Family Process, 34,* 373–388.

Feldman, D. (1980). *Beyond universals in cognitive development.* Norwood, NJ: Ablex.

Figley, C. (2000, September). Post-Traumatic Stress Disorder. *Clinical Update, 2,* 5.

Figley, C. (Ed.). (1997). *Burnout in families: The systemic costs of caring.* New York: CRC Press.

Foa, E., Friedman, M., & Keane, T. (Eds). (2000). *Effective treatments for PTSD: Practice guidelines from the International Society for Traumatic Stress Studies.* New York: Guildford.

Folken, A. (1998). *Drawing mandalas: Its physiological effects on children with severe emotional disturbance.* Unpublished master's thesis, College of Notre Dame, Belmont, CA.

Fontana, D. (1993). *The secret language of symbols: A visual key to symbols and their meanings.* San Francisco: Chronicle Books.

Forward, S., & Buch, C. (1989). *Toxic parents: Overcoming their hurtful legacy and reclaiming your life.* New York: Bantam.

Frankl, V.E. (1984). *Man's search for meaning.* New York: Washington Square.

Freud, S. (1900/1958). *The interpretation of dreams.* London: Hogarth.

Freud, S. (1905). *General introduction to psychoanalysis.* New York: Liveright.

Frugel, J.C. (1948). *The psychological study of the family.* London: Hogarth.

Furth, G.W. (1988). *The secret world of drawings: Healing through art.* Boston, MA: Sigo.

Gadon, E.W. (1989). *The once and future goddess: A sweeping visual chronicle of the sacred female and her reemergence in the cultural mythology of our time.* New York: Harper Collins.

Gardner, H. (1973). *Art through the ages.* New York: Harcourt Brace, Jovanovich.

Gardner, H. (1985). *Frames of mind.* New York: Basic Books.

Gantt, L., & Tabone, C. (1998). *Forms elements art therapy scale.* Morgantown, WV: Gargoyle.

Geller, J.D. (1978). The body, expressive movement, and physical contact in psychotherapy. In J.L. Singer & K.S. Pope (Eds.), *The power of human imagination.* New York and London: Plenum.

Gerber, W., & Lyons, S. (1980). A developmental approach to assessment in adult art psychotherapy. *The Arts in Psychotherapy, 7,* 105–112.

Gilligan, S. (1995). *Sponsorship of the soul.* (Cassette Recording No. J241-W11A and B.) The Brief Therapy Conference: Cornerstone Principles, Cornerstone Practices. San Francisco, CA: The Milton H. Erickson Foundation.

Gleick, E. (1995, February 27). Should this marriage be saved? *Time,* 48–56.

Glick, P. (1989). Remarried families, stepfamilies and stepchildren: A brief demographic profile. *Family Relations, 38,* 24–27.

Goldberg, S., Grusec, J., & Jenkins, J. (1999). Confidence in protection: Arguments for a narrow definition of attachment. *Journal of Family Psychology, 13*(4), 475–483.

Goldenberg, I., & Goldenberg, H. (1996). *Family therapy: An overview* (3rd ed.). Pacific Grove: Brooks/Cole.

Goldenberg, I., & Goldenberg, H. (1998). *Family therapy: An overview* (4th ed.). Pacific Grove: Brooks/Cole.

Goleman, D. (1995). *Emotional intelligence: Why it can matter more than IQ.* New York: Bantam.

Goodenough, F.L. (1926). *Measurement of intelligence by drawings.* New York: Harcourt, Brace, & World.

Gottman, J. (1993). A theory of marital dissolution and stability. *Journal of Family Psychology, 7,* 57–75.

Gottman, J. (1994). *Why marriages succeed or fail.* New York: Simon & Schuster.

Gottman, J. (Ed.). (1996). *What predicts divorce? The measures.* Hillsdale, NJ: Lawrence Erlbaum Associates.

Gottman J. (1998). *Clinical manual for marital therapy: A scientific based marital therapy.* Seattle: The Seattle Marital and Family Institute.

Gottman, J., & Katz, L. (1989). The effects of marital discord on young children's peer interaction and health. *Developmental Psychology, 25,* 373–381.

Gottman, J., & Levenson, R. (1985). A valid procedure for obtaining self-report of affect in marital interaction. *Journal of Consulting and Clinical Psychology, 53,* 151–160.

Gottman, J., & Levenson, R. (1992). Marital processes predictive of later dissolution: Behavior, physiology, and health. *Journal of Personality and Social Psychology, 63,* 221–233.

Guerin, P., & Pendagast, E. (1976). Evaluation of the family system and the genogram. In P. Guerin (Ed.), *Family therapy: Theory and practice.* New York: Gardner.

Guilligan, S. (1995). *Sponsorship of the soul.* (Cassette Recording No J241-W11A and B.) The Brief Therapy Conference: Cornerstone Principles, Cornerstone Practices. San Francisco, CA: The Milton H. Erickson Foundation.

Gunter, M. (2000). Art therapy as an intervention to stabilize the defenses of children undergoing bone marrow transplants. *The Arts in Psychotherapy, 27*(1), 3–14.

Haley, J. (1973). *Uncommon therapy.* New York: W.W. Norton.

Haley, J. (1976). *Problem solving therapy.* New York: Harper Collins.

Haley, J. (1984). *Ordeal therapy.* San Francisco: Jossey-Bass.

Haley, J. (1998). Keynote address. The Brief Brief Therapy of Milton Erickson. (Cassette Recording. No. J241-K2.) The Brief Therapy Conference: Cornerstone Principles, Cornerstone Practices. San Francisco, CA: The Milton H. Erickson Foundation.

Hammer, E.F. (1958/1967). *The clinical application of projective drawings.* Springfield, IL: Charles C Thomas.

Hampden-Turner, C. (1981). *Maps of the mind.* New York: Collier Books.

Hampson, R., Beavers, R., & Hulgus, Y. (1990). Cross-ethnic family differences: Interactional assessment of white, black, and Mexican-American families. *Journal of Marital and Family Therapy, 16*(3), 307–319.

Hardy K., & Laszloffy, T. (1995). The cultural genogram: Key to training culturally competent family therapists. *Journal of Marital & Family Therapy, 21*(3), 227–237.

Harris, D.B. (1963). *Children's drawings as measures of intellectual maturity.* New York: Harcourt, Brace and World.

Hays, R., & Lyons, S. (1981). The bridge drawing: A projective technique for assessment in art therapy. *The Arts in Psychotherapy, 8,* 207–217.

Heller, K. (1996). Coming of age of prevention science. *American Psychologist, 51*(11), 1123–1127.

Heller, P., & Woods, B. (1998). The process of intimacy: Similarity, understanding and gender. *Journal of Marital and Family Therapy, 24*(3), 273–288.

Hetherington, E., Bridges, M., & Insbella, G. (1998). What matters? What does not? *American Psychologist, 53*(2), 167–184.

Hillman, J. (1996). *The soul's code: In search of character and calling.* New York: Warner.

Hong, Y., Morris, M., Chiu, C., & Benet-Martinez, V. (2000). *Multicultural* minds. *American Psychologist, 55*(7), 709–720.

Howowitz, M. (1970). *Image formation and recognition.* New York: Appleton-Century-Crofts.

Jennings, P. (1998, February 26). The Columbine killings: An American tragedy. *Dateline,* National Broadcasting Company.

Jessor, R. (1991). Behavioral science: An emerging paradigm for social inquiry? In R. Jessor (Ed.), *Perspectives on behavioral science: The Colorado lectures* (pp. 309–316). Boulder, CO: Westview.

Jessor, R. (1993). Successful adolescent development among youth in high-risk settings. *American Psychologist, 48*(2), 117–16.

Johnson, R. (1974). *He: Understanding masculine psychology.* King of Prussia, PA: Religious Publishing.

Jolles, I. (1964/1992). *A catalogue for the qualitative interpretation of the House-Tree-Person (H-T-P).* Los Angeles, CA: Western Psychological Services.

Jung, C. (1933/1955). *Modern man in search of a soul.* San Diego: Harcourt Brace Jovanovich.

Jung, C. (1938/1983). *Psychology and religion*. In A. Storr (Ed.), *The Essential Jung* (pp. 239–249). New York: MJF Books.

Jung, C. (1954/1974). *The development of the personality*. (R.F.C. Hull, Trans.). Princeton, NJ: Princeton University.

Jung, C. (1960/1978). *The structure and dynamics of the psyche*. Bollingen Series XX (Vol. 8). New York: Pantheon.

Jung, C. (1964). Approaching the unconscious. In J. Freeman (Ed.), *Man and his symbols* (pp. 18–103). Garden City, New York: Doubleday.

Jung, C. (1965). *Memories, dreams, reflections*. (Aniela Jaffe, Ed.; Richard and Clara Winston, Trans.). New York: Vintage Books.

Jung C. (1966/1972). *Mandala symbolism*. Princeton, NJ: Princeton University.

Kaiser, D. (1996). Indications of attachment security in a drawing task. *The Arts in Psychotherapy, 23*(4), 333–340.

Kaplan, G. (1997). Scientific art therapy: An integrative and research-based approach. *Art Therapy: Journal of the American Art Therapy Association, 15*(2), 93–98.

Kaufman, B., & Wohl, A. (1991). *Casualties of childhood. A developmental perspective on sexual abuse using projective drawings*. New York: Brunner Mazel.

Kellogg, J. (1978). *Mandala: Path of beauty*. Towson, MD: Mandala Assessment and Research Institute.

Kellogg, R. (1969–1970). *Analyzing children's art*. Palo Alto, CA: Mayfield.

Kellogg, R., & O'Dell, S. (1967). *The psychology of children's art*. New York: CRM-Random House.

Keyes, M.F. (1983). *The inward journey: Art as therapy*. La Salle, IL: Open Court.

Kirn. (1997, August 18). The ties that bind: CNN poll 1997. *Time*, 48–50.

Knudson-Martin, C. (1994). The female voice: Applications to Bowen's family systems theory. *Journal of Marital and Family Therapy, 20*(1), 35–46.

Kohut, H. (1971). *The analysis of the self*. New York: International University.

Koplewicz, H., & Goodman R. (1999). *Childhood revealed: Art expressing pain, discovery and hope*. New York: Abrams.

Koppitz, E.M. (1968). *Psychological evaluation of children's drawing's human figure drawings*. New York: Grune & Stratton.

Kramer, E. (1958). *Art therapy in a children's community*. Springfield, IL: Charles C Thomas.

Kramer, E. (1974). Art therapy and childhood. *American Journal of Art Therapy, 14*(1), 15–16.

Kramer, E. (1987). Sublimation and art therapy. In J. Rubin (Ed.), *Approaches to art therapy: Theory and technique* (pp. 26–43). New York: Brunner/Mazel.

Kris, E. (1964). *Psychoanalytic explorations in art*. New York: Schoken Books,

Kris, E., & Kurz, O. (1979). *Legend, myth, and magic in the image of the artist: A historical experiment*. New Haven: Yale University.

Kroger, W. (1963/1977). *Clinical & Experimental Hypnosis* (2nd ed.). Philadelphia: J.B. Lippicott.

Kuehl, B.P. (1995). The solution-oriented genogram: A collaborative approach. *Journal of Marital and Family Therapy, 21*(3), 239–250.

Kwiatkowska, H. (1975). Family art therapy: Experiments with a new technique. In E. Ulman & P. Dachinger (Eds.), *Art therapy in theory and practice* (pp 112–125). New York: Schocken.

Kwiatkowska, H. (1978). *Family therapy and evaluation through art*. Springfield, IL: Charles C Thomas.

Lachman-Chapin, M. (1983). Making verbal the nonverbal. *The American Journal of Art Therapy, 1*(1), 47–49.

Lambert, D., Bramwell, M., & Lawther, G. (1982*). The brain: A user's manual*. New York: Perigee Books.

Landgarten, H.B. (1981). *Clinical art therapy: A comprehensive guide.* New York: Brunner/Mazel.

Landgarten, H.B. (1987). *Family art psychotherapy: A clinical guide and casebook.* New York: Brunner/Mazel.

Lankton, C., & Lankton, S. (1989). *Tales of enchantment: Goal oriented metaphors for adults and children in therapy.* New York: Brunner/Mazel.

LeDoux, J. (1996). *The emotional brain: The mysterious underpinnings of emotional life.* New York: Simon & Schuster.

Levick, M. (1983). *They could not talk and so they drew: Children's styles of coping and thinking.* Springfield, IL: Charles C Thomas.

Levy, T., & Orlans, M. (1998). *Attachment, trauma and healing: Understanding and treating attachment disorder in children and families.* Washington, DC: CWLA.

Lewis, K. (1989). The use of color-coded genograms in family therapy. *Journal of Marital and Family Therapy, 15*(2), 169–176.

Liddle, H. (1982). On the problems of eclecticism: A call for epistemologic clarification and human-scale theories. *Family Process, 21*(2), 243–249.

Liddle, H. (1982). Diagnosis and assessment in family therapy: A comparative analysis of six schools of thought. In B. Keenry (Ed.), *Diagnosis & assessment in family therapy* (pp. 3–33). Rockville, MD: Aspen .

Lowenfeld, V. (1957). *Creative and mental growth* (3rd ed.). New York: MacMillan.

Lusebrink, V. (1990). *Imagery and visual expression in therapy.* New York: Plenum.

Machover, K. (1958). *Personality projection.* Springfield, IL: Charles C Thomas.

Madsen, A. (2000). *The disenfranchised grief of single mothers.* Unpublished master's thesis, College of Notre Dame, Belmont, CA.

Mahler, M., Pine, F., & Bergman, A. (1975). *The psychological birth of the human infant: Symbiosis and individuation.* New York: Basic Books.

Mailloux, S. (1998). *Graphic indicators of sexual abuse in children using the human figure drawing.* Unpublished master's thesis, College of Notre Dame, Belmont, CA.

Malmquist, C. (1994). Theoretical status of depressions in childhood. In E.J. Anthony & D.C. Gilpin (Eds.), *Clinical cases of childhood* (vol. 1) (pp. 173–204). New York: NYU International University.

Mandelbaum, P. (1994). The inhibited child: A family therapy approach. In E.J. Anthony & D.C. Gilpen, Eds., *Clinical cases of childhood* (vol. 1) (pp. 121–130). New York: NYU International University.

Marks, J. (1992). *Bring us a dream.* Menlo Park, CA: Tangler.

McGoldrick, M., Giordano, J., & Pearce, J. (1996). *Ethnicity and family therapy* (2nd ed.). New York: Guildford.

McMurray, M. (1988). *Illuminations: The healing image.* Berkeley: Wingvow.

McKim, R.H. (1980). *Experiences in visual thinking* (2nd ed.). Monterey: Brooks/Cole.

McNiff, S. (1992). *Art as medicine: Creating a therapy of the imagination.* Boston: Shambhala.

McNiff, S. (1998*). Trust the process: An artist's guide to letting go.* Boston: Shambhala.

Miller, A. (1990). *Banished knowledge: Facing childhood injuries.* New York: Doubleday.

Miller, J. (1997). *Graphic communications: A case study of a dissociative identity disorder.* Unpublished master's thesis, College of Notre Dame, Belmont, CA.

Minuchin, S. (1974). *Families and family therapy.* Cambridge, MA: Harvard University.

Minuchin, S. (1998). Where is the family in narrative family therapy? *Journal of Marital and Family Therapy, 24*(4), 397–403.

Moon, B. (1994). *Existential art therapy.* Springfield, IL: Charles C Thomas.

Moon, B. (Ed.). (1991). *Archive for research in archetypal symbolism: An encyclopedia of archetypal symbolism.* Boston: Shambhala.

Moore, T. (1992). *Care of the soul: A guide for cultivating depth and sacredness in everyday life*. New York: Harper Collins.

Naumburg, M. (1950). *Schizophrenic art: Its meaning in art therapy*. New York: Grune & Stratton.

Naumburg, M. (1966). *Dynamically oriented art therapy: Its principles and practice*. New York: Grune & Stratton.

Neumann, E. (1976). *The child*. New York: Harper Collins.

Neumann, E. (1956). *Psyche and amour*. New York: Bollingen Foundation, Princeton University.

Newcomb, M., & Loeb, T. (1999), Poor parenting as an adult problem behavior: General deviance, deviant attitudes, inadequate family support and bonding, or just bad parenting? *Journal of Family Psychology, 13*(2), 175–193.

Nichols, W. C., & Everett, C. (1986). *Systematic family therapy: An integrative approach*. New York: Guilford.

Olser, G., & Gould, P. (1987). *Using drawings in assessment and therapy*. New York: Brunner/Mazel.

Palazzoli, M., Boscolo, L., Cecchin, G., & Prata, G. (1978) *Paradox and counter paradox*. New York: Jason Aronson.

Papp, P. (1983). *The process of change*. New York: Guilford.

Parson, T., & Bales, R. (1955). *The family, socialization and interaction process*. Glencoe, IL: Free Press.

Pasto, T. (1968). *The space frame experience in art*. London: Thomas Yoseloff Ltd.

Perls, F. (1973). *The Gestalt approach: An eye witness to therapy*. Ben Lomond, CA: Science & Behavior Books.

Perry, B. (1997). Incubated in terror: Neurodevelopmental factors in the cycle of violence. In J. Osofsky (Ed.), *Children in a violent society* (pp. 124–145). New York: Guilford.

Peterson, L., & Hardin, M. (1997). *Children in distress: A guide for screening children's art*. New York: W. W. Norton & Co.

Phillips, S. (1999, April 23). The Columbine killings: An American tragedy. *Dateline*. National Broadcasting Company.

Piaget, J. (1971). The theory of stages in cognitive development. In D.R. Green (Ed.), *Measurement and Piaget*. New York: McGrawHill.

Piaget, J., & Inhelder, B. (1969). *The psychology of the child*. (Helen Weaver, Trans.). New York: Basic Books.

Pipher, M.B. (1995). *Reviving Ophelia: Saving the selves of adolescent girls*. New York: Ballantine Books.

Pipher, M. (1996). *The shelter of each other: Rebuilding our families*. New York: G.P. Putnam & Sons.

Politsky, R. (1994). Penetrating our personal symbols: Discovering our guiding myths. *The Arts in Psychotherapy, 22*(1), 9–20.

Powell, C. (1997). *Sexual abuse indicators in kinetic family drawing*. Unpublished master's thesis, College of Notre Dame, Belmont, CA.

Prinzhorn, H. (1972). *Artistry of the mentally ill*. New York: Springer-Verlag.

Progroff, I. (1980). *The practice of process meditation: The intensive journal way to spiritual experience*. New York: Dialogue House Library.

Pynoos, R. (1985). *Post-traumatic stress disorder in children*. Washington, DC: American Psychiatric.

Pynoos, R.W. (1993). Traumatic stress and developmental psychopathology in children and adolescents. In J.M. Oldham, M. Riba, & A. Tasman (Eds.), *American Psychiatric Press Review of Psychiatry, (12)*. Washington, DC: American Psychiatric.

Ratcliffe, E. (1977). The old masters art collage: An art therapy technique for heuristic self-discovery. *Art Psychotherapy, 4,* 29–32.

Read, H. (1958). *Education through art.* New York: Pantheon.

Rhyne, J. (1973). *The Gestalt art experience.* Belmont, CA: Wadsworth.

Rhyne, J. (1979). Drawing as personal constructs: A study in visual dynamics. (Doctoral dissertation, University of Santa Cruz, 1978). *Dissertation Abstracts International, 79,* 10569.

Rice, F.P. (1997). *Human development* (3rd. ed.). Upper Saddle River, NJ: Prentice Hall.

Riley, S. (1993). Illustrating the family story: Art therapy, a lens for viewing the family's reality. *The Arts in Psychotherapy, 20,* 253–265.

Riley, S., & Malchodi, C. (1994). *Integrated approaches to family art therapy.* Chicago, IL: Magnolia Street.

Rosal, M. (1992). Approaches to art therapy with children. In F. Anderson (Ed.), *Art for all the children* (2nd ed.) (pp. 142–183). Springfield, IL: Charles C Thomas.

Rosal, M. (1996). *Approaches to art therapy with children.* Burlingame, CA: Abbeygate.

Rosenblatt, N., & Horwitz, J. (1996). *Wrestling with angels: What Genesis teaches us about our spiritual identity, sexuality, and personal relationships.* New York: Delta.

Rubin, J. (1978). *Child art therapy: Understanding and helping children grow through art.* New York: Van Nostrand Reinhold.

Rubin, J. (1986). From psychopathology to psychotherapy through art expression: A focus on Hans Prinzhorn and others. *Journal of the American Art Therapy Association, 3,* 27–33.

Rubin, J. (Ed.). (1987). *Approaches to art therapy: Theory and technique.* New York: Brunner Mazel.

Rubin, J. (1998). *Art therapy: An introduction.* New York: Brunner/Mazel.

Rychlak, J.F. (1981). *Introduction to personality and psychotherapy* (2nd ed.). Boston: Houghton Mifflin.

Samuels, A. (1983). The theory of archetypes in Jungian and post-Jungian analytical psychology. *International Review of Psychoanalysis, 10*(4), 429–444.

Sapolsky, M. (1998). *Why zebras don't get ulcers: An updated guide to stress, stress-related disease, and coping.* New York: W.H. Freeman.

Satir, V. (1964/1967). *Conjoint family therapy.* Palo Alto, CA: Science and Behavior Books.

Satir, V. (1972). *Peoplemaking.* Palo Alto, CA: Science and Behavior Books.

Satir, V., & Baldwin, M. (1983). *Satir step by step.* Palo Alto, CA: Science and Behavior Books.

Savery, L., Berne, P., & Williams, S. (1984). *Dreams and spiritual growth: A Judeo Christian way of dreamwork.* New York: Paulist.

Scarre, C. (1993). *Smithsonian timelines of the ancient world: A visual chronology from the origins of life to AD 1500.* New York: Dorling Kindersley.

Schaeffer-Simmern, H. (1948). *The unfolding of artistic activity.* Los Angeles and Berkeley: University of California Press.

Schifflett, K., & Cummings, E.M. (1999). A program for educating parents about the effects of divorce and conflict on children: An initial evaluation. *Family Relations, 48,* 79–89.

Schmidt, S. (1998). *Art and poetry for stress reduction: An outcome study with an acutely depressed, partially hospitalized, adult population.* Unpublished master's thesis, College of Notre Dame, Belmont, CA.

Schneider, S., Ostroff, S., & Ligow, N. (1990). Enhancement of body image: A structured art therapy group with adolescents. *Art Therapy Journal of the American Art Therapy Association, 7*(3), 126–138.

Seppa, N. (1997). Wisdom: a quality that may defy age. *The APA Monitor, (28)*2, 1.

Shagman, H. (1996). *The diagnostic drawing series: A comparison of psychiatric inpatient adolescents in crisis with non hospitalized youth.* Unpublished master's thesis, College of Notre Dame, Belmont, CA.

Shank, D. (1998, April 12). Data smog. *60 Minutes*. National Broadcasting Co.

Shlain, L. (1998*)*. *The alphabet vs the goddess: The conflict between word and image*. New York: Viking Penguin.

Silverstein, L., & Auerbach, C. (1999). Deconstructing the essential father. *American Psychologist, 54*(6), 397–407.

Simon, S., Howe, L., & Kirschenbaum, H. (1972). *Values clarification: A handbook of practical strategies for teachers and students*. New York: Hart Publishing.

Simpkinson, C., & Simpkinson, A. (1993). *Sacred stories*. New York: Harper Collins.

Simpkinson, A., Simpkinson, C., & Solari, R. (1995). *Nourishing the soul*. San Francisco: Harper Collins.

Sluzki, C. (1998). In search of the lost family: A footnote to Minuchin's essay. *Journal of Marital and Family Therapy, 24*(4), 415–417.

Smitherman-Brown, V., & Church, C. (1996). Mandala drawing: Facilitating creative growth in children with ADD or ADHD. *Art Therapy: Journal of the American Art Therapy Association, 13*(4), 252–262.

Snyder, H. (1996, Winter). The juvenile court and delinquency cases. *Future of Children, 6*(3), 53–63.

Snyder, D., & Heim, S. (1992). Marriage depression and cognition: Unraveling the Gordian knot—Reply to E. Hinger et al. *Journal of Marital & Family Therapy, 18*(3), 303–307.

Soucy, N.E., & LaRose, S. (2000). Attachment and control in family and mentoring contexts as determinants of adolescent adjustment to college. *Journal of Family Psychology, 1*, 125–143.

Sowers, L. (1999, March 1). Therapy for the soul. *Houston Chronicle*, C1.

Stabno, C. (1998). *Finally found: A reunion survival handbook for all members of the adoption triad*. Unpublished doctoral dissertation, Western Graduate School of Psychology, Palo Alto, CA.

Stevens, R. (1983), *Erikson: An introduction*. New York: St. Martin Press.

Suddaby, K., & Landau, J. (1998). Positive and negative timelines: A technique for storying. *Family Process, 37*(3), 287–298.

Terr, L. (1990). *Too scared to cry*. New York: Harper & Row.

Tolin, N. (1994). *The Japanese art form koinabasi*. Unpublished master's thesis, College of Notre Dame, Belmont, CA.

Tomm, K. (1984). One perspective on the Milan systemic approach: Part II. Overview of development, theory and practice. *Journal of Marital and Family Therapy, 10*(2), 113–125.

Torassa, U. (1999, January 22). Resilient children seem to share a common trait. *San Francisco Examiner*, A-9.

Troeger, B. (1992). Application of child art theories to the interpretation of children's art. *Art Therapy Journal of the American Art Therapy Association, 9*(1), 30–35.

Ulhin, D. (1972). *Art for exceptional children* (2nd ed.). Dubuque, IA: Wm. C. Brown.

Ulhin, D. (1981). *Healing without words*. San Francisco, CA: Public Broadcasting Systems, Channel 9.

Ulman, E. (1974). Innovation and aberration. *American Journal of Art Therapy, 14*(1), 14.

Ulman, E. (1975). Art therapy: Problems of definition. In Ulman, E. & Dachinger (Eds.), *Art Therapy* (pp 3–13). New York: Schocken.

U.S. Congress, Office of Technology Assessment. (1991). *Adolescent health*. (OTA-H-468.) Washington, DC: U.S. Government Printing Office.

U.S. Department of Justice. (1995). *Juvenile offenders and victims: A national report*. Washington, DC: Office of Juvenile Justice and Delinquency Prevention.

U.S. Select Committee on Children, Youth and Families. (1989). *No place to call home: Discarded children in America*. Washington, DC: U.S. House of Representatives.

Vachss, A. (1994, August 28). EmotionaL Abuse: A plea for the wounded. *San Francisco Examiner & Chronicle,* Parade.

Vachss, A. (1998, March 29). Hard look at how we treat children. *San Francisco Examiner & Chronicle,* Parade.

Visher, E.F., & Visher, J.S. (1988). *Old loyalities, new ties: Therapeutic strategies with step families.* New York: Brunner Mazel.

Vo, K. (1999, February 16). Typical American Family is more atypical every year. *San Mateo Times, 1,* 4.

Wadeson, H. (1980). *Art psychotherapy.* New York: John Wiley.

Walker, B.G. (1988). *The woman's dictionary of symbols and sacred objects.* San Francisco: Harper Collins.

Watzlawick, P., Beavin, J.H., & Jackson, D.D. (1967*). Pragmatics of human communication. A study of interactional patterns.* New York: W.W. Norton.

Webster's new world dictionary, college edition. (1966). Cleveland: World.

Wench, L.S. (1980). *House-Tree-Person: An illustrated diagnostic handbook.* Los Angeles: Western Psychological Services.

Wilson, C. (1996). *The atlas of holy places and sacred sites: An illustrated guide to the location, history and significance of the world's most revered holy sites.* New York: ADK Publishing Book.

Wilson, L. (1987). Symbolism and art therapy. In J.A. Rubin (Ed.), *Approaches to art therapy* (pp. 44–62). New York: Brunner/Mazel.

Wilcoxon, S. (1987). *Perspective in intergenerational concepts. Families of origin therapy.* Rockville, MD: Aspen.

Winnecott, D. (1971). *Playing and reality.* New York: Basic Books.

Zaslow, R. (1975). *The psychology of z process: Attachment and activation.* San Jose, CA: San Jose State University Spartan Bookstore.

Zilbach, J. (1986). *Young children in family therapy.* New York: Brunner/Mazel.

NAME INDEX

251

SUBJECT INDEX

application, instructions, materials, 212–14

criteria, 212

Vase symbolism, 145

Violence, ix

  Cycle of Violence, ix, 75–116

    brain development influences via images, 76–77

    demographics of violence, 75–76

    disappearance of role model hero figure, 77

    epidemic of violence in U.S., 75–78

  domestic, ix, 132–39

  malnourishment/malnurturement, 78–80, 180

  malnourishment and violence, 78–80

    physiologic impact, 78–80

  malnurturement and violence, 78–80, 131

    physiologic impact, 78–80, 131

  neurophysiologic responses, 76–77, 131

  response or relaxation, 77, 131

    physiologic impact, 78–80

  youth offender demographics, 117–19

Visual art, xii

Visual construct development, 71–74

  familial impact on expressive development, 71–72

  patterns and continuum themes, 73

Visual imagery and personality development, 63 (see also Archetypal symbols)

W

Water symbolism, 178

Wisdom and anima, 62

Women

  feminist approach to differential process, 226–27

  identity formation, 226

Word (the) and animus, 62